Sand St

Surprising truths about the global sand crisis and the quest for sustainable solutions

Kiran Pereira

First published in 2020 by Rhetority Media
86–90 Paul Street, London, EC2A 4NE, UK

ISBN   paperback 978-1-8381252-0-2
          ebook 978-1-8381252-1-9
          hardback 978-1-8381252-2-6
          audiobook 978-1-8381252-3-3

www.sandstories.org

Cover illustration Michelle Bauer and Laura Neocleous

Typesetting and design www.ShakspeareEditorial.org

Publisher's Cataloging-in-Publication Data
Names: Pereira, Kiran, author.
Title: Sand stories : surprising truths about the global sand crisis and the quest for sustainable solutions / Kiran Pereira.
Description: London, UK: Rhetority Media, 2020.
Identifiers: ISBN 978-1-8381252-2-6 (Hardcover) | 978-1-8381252-0-2 (pbk.) | 978-1-8381252-1-9 (ebook) | 978-1-8381252-3-3 (audio)
Subjects: LCSH Sand. | Technology and civilization. | Sustainable development. | Natural resources--Management. | BISAC BUSINESS & ECONOMICS / Development / Sustainable Development | BUSINESS & ECONOMICS / Industries / Natural Resource Extraction | SCIENCE / Environmental Science | NATURE / Environmental Conservation & Protection | NATURE / Natural Resources
Classification: LCC TA455.S3 P47 2020 | DDC 620.1/91--dc23

Dedication

For my parents who supported my dreams all through the years. I love you both and owe you everything.

For my husband Paolo. Without your support, this book would be just a pipe dream.

Contents

Illustrations

Abbreviations

ACT	Accelerated carbonation technology
AEC	Architecture engineering and construction
AI	Artificial intelligence
ALSF	Aggregate Levy Sustainability Fund
ALT UK	Andrew Lees Trust UK
AMD	Atomic Minerals Directorate for Exploration & Research, India
APCr	Air pollution control residues
ASTM	American Society for Testing and Material
AV	Autonomous vehicles
BAMB	Buildings as material banks
BBC	British Broadcasting Corporation
BFS	Blast furnace slag
BREEAM	Building Research Establishment Environmental Assessment Method
BS	British Standards
C&DW	Construction and demolition waste
C2C	Cradle to cradle certification
CAG	Comptroller and Auditor General of India
CBD	Central business district
CBI	Central Bureau of Investigation, India
CCDI	Community conservation and development initiatives
CCTV	Closed-circuit television
CCU	Carbon capture and utilisation
CEFAS	Centre for Environment, Fisheries and Aquaculture Science, UK
CEM	CEM I is 100% OPC (Ordinary Portland Cement) CEM II is a mixture of OPC and additives such as fly ash, slag or limestone, up to a maximum additive content of 35% CEM III is a mixture of OPC and BFS. There are 3 types: A contains least slag, 40%; C contains most, 90%
CGIAR	Consultative Group for International Agricultural Research
CHF	Swiss franc
CIC	Community interest company
CLT	Cross laminated timber

CO_2	Carbon dioxide
COP23	UN Climate Conference in Bonn
CPSE	Central public sector enterprise
CSN	Civil Society Network
CSTB	French Institute for Standardisation
DAE	Department of Atomic Energy, India
DC	District collector
DEFRA	Department for Environment, Food and Rural Affairs, UK
DIN	German Institute for Standardisation
DMG	Directorate of Mining and Geology, India
ECHA	European Chemicals Agency
EEB	European Environmental Bureau
EfW	Energy from waste
EIA	Environmental impact assessment
EITI	Extractive Industries Transparency Initiative
ELRI	Environmental Law Research Institute
EU	European Union
EuDA	European Dredging Association
FDA	Food and Drug Administration
FSC	Forest Stewardship Council
GDP	Gross domestic product
GFRP	Glass fibre reinforced plastic
GPS	Global positioning system
GRP	Glass reinforced plastic
HBS	Heinrich Böll Stiftung
HQE	Haute Qualité Environnementale
IADC	International Association of Dredging Companies
IARC	International Agency for Research on Cancer
IBAA	Incinerator bottom ash aggregate
ICBM	Intercontinental ballistic missiles
IGY	International Geophysical Year
IIED	International Institute for Environment and Development
IIT	Indian Institutes of Technology
INR	Indian rupee
IoT	Internet of Things
IPBES	The Intergovernmental Science-Policy Platform on Biodiversity and Ecosystem Services
IPCC	Intergovernmental Panel on Climate Change
IREL	Indian Rare Earths Ltd.
IT	Information technology
IUCN	International Union for Conservation of Nature
JIS	Japanese industrial standards
KEMCO	Kotobuki Engineering & Manufacturing Co., Ltd.

LCD	Liquid crystal displays
LILAC	Low impact living affordable community
LNG	Liquefied natural gas
MAB	Movimento dos Atingidos por Barragens
MALSF	Marine Aggregates Levy Sustainability Fund
MCZ	Marine conservation zone
MDE	Marine data exchange
MDF	Medium-density fibreboard
MRI	Magnetic resonance imaging
MSFD	Marine Strategy Framework Directive
MW	Megawatt
MYR	Malaysian ringgit
NASA	National Aeronautics and Space Administration, USA
NDMA	National Disaster Management Authority
NGO	Non-governmental organisation
NIOSH	National Institute for Occupational Safety and Health
NNDC	North Norfolk District Council
NPI	Net positive impact
NSAG	North Sea Action Group
ONE	Office National pour l'Environnement, Madagascar
PAKSBAB	Pakistan Straw Bale and Appropriate Building
PBS	Public Broadcasting Service
PCQVP	Publiez Ce Que Vous Payez, Madagascar
PFA	Pulverised fuel ash
PM	Particulate matter
PR	Public relations
PV	Photovoltaics
PW6	Pigment white 6
PWD	Public Works Department
PWYP	Publish What You Pay
QMM	QIT Madagascar Minerals
RBINS	Royal Belgian Institute of Natural Sciences
REACH	Registration, Evaluation, Authorisation and Restriction of Chemicals
REE	Rare earth elements
RHA	Rice hull ash/rice husk ash
RIKILT	Wageningen University & Research Centre
RIVM	National Institute for Public Health and the Environment, the Netherlands
ROI	Return on investment
RSMP	Regional seabed monitoring programme
RT	Rio Tinto
RTI	Right to information

SB	Senate Bill
SCCS	Scientific Committee on Consumer Safety
SDG	Sustainable development goal; SDG5 is goal 5 for gender equality
SGBV	Sexual and gender-based violence
SiO2	Silicon dioxide
SPF	Sun protection factor
TILES	Transnational and integrated long-term marine exploitation strategies
TiO2	Titanium dioxide
UK	United Kingdom
UN	United Nations
UNCLOS	United Nations Convention on the Law of the Sea
UNEP	United Nations Environment Programme
UNESCO	United Nations Educational, Scientific and Cultural Organisation
US	United States
USA	United States of America
USGS	United States Geological Survey
UV	Ultraviolet light
VAT	Value-added tax
WEF	World Economic Forum
WLE	Water, land and ecosystems
WRM	World Rainforest Movement
WSRW	Western Sahara Resource Watch
WWF	World Wide Fund for Nature

Foreword

On that morning of January 2009, the thermometer hit a record minus 28° Celsius. From the small window of the editing room, all I could see was the grey concrete wall of the building across the street. A monochrome Montreal, which I wanted to leave behind as fast as I could.

I had left home two winters before to direct my first theatrical documentary in partnership with a Quebec-based production company. It had been a wonderful adventure at first. Now I was feeling trapped, struggling to wrap up an endless edit and go back to Barcelona. In times of melancholy, the snow outside became a white canvas on which I projected my Mediterranean dreams of salty water and warm sand. I missed the beach.

Relieved and satisfied to have finally wrapped up the film, I got on the plane with a smile. The first thing I would do when I got home was go to the beach, take my shoes off and take the energising walk on the sand I had dreamt of for so long.

Barceloneta, one of the city's most popular beaches, was a thick and beautiful 100 metres, the perfect illustration of what geologists call a 'healthy' beach. After a 15-minute bike ride from home I found an atrophied landscape.

'My' beach had vanished.

For the first time in my life I asked a very simple question: 'Where does sand come from?' Which led to, 'Where did the beach go?'

I thought it could be a geological phenomenon or, maybe worse, an effect of climate change. I decided to look into it. But I was tired of investigative documentary filmmaking – it was too long, too hard, too time consuming. At least that's what I thought, but on a lazy day at the office I randomly googled 'what is sand'. The first link led to a quote by Rachel Carson:

> In every outthrust headland, in every curving beach, in every grain of sand there is the story of the earth.

The story of the earth?

I spent the next year reading, researching, interviewing and travelling in an effort to understand what the marine biologist – mother of the ecologist movement – had meant 70 years ago. But nothing had prepared me for the discovery of yet another instance of humans profiteering from Nature.

Like grains of sand, each new element of data, each new bit of information began to aggregate to form a global, rather alarming, picture. I learnt that the beach in Barcelona had died at the hands of unscrupulous land developers who'd used the sand to build an artificial island and a five-star hotel – and this was not an isolated case. Three-quarters of the world's beaches are disappearing; it takes 25,000 years to create a grain of sand; our society – progress, as we call it – depends on sand more than on any other natural resource; sand mafias emerge …

'If I'm ever going to make another investigative film, it will be about sand.'

Sand Wars was released in 2013. It was wildly successful. It reached an audience of over a 100 million in cinemas and on broadcast television. It gathered awards at festivals around the world. And it inspired the international community – including the United Nations Environment Programme – to put sand at the top of the list of our global endangered natural resources.

When I made the film only a handful of scientists, activists and academics knew about the issue and could help me scaffold the story. Kiran, whom I met while I was editing the film, was one of them. Her expertise was key to understanding how sand is a key ingredient in our society, fundamental to all its strata, from infrastructure to technology, and in an endless list of consumer goods – all literally built on sand.

A decade has passed since that day on the beach. *Sand Wars* built up awareness, thanks to scattered media coverage, reports, talks and articles. Sand is now on our radar, but the truth is that sand and gravel consumption has gone up several-fold. Beaches keep disappearing. Cities keep expanding, using stolen sand. People get killed for sand. Yet masterfully, this whole industry is kept hidden. The mining happens in the middle of oceans, away from all eyes. The sand is concealed in products or transformed before it is sold to unsuspecting customers. Maybe one day it will be as common to boycott sand-based products as it is to boycott products that use palm oil or animal testing; or that sand will be as regulated as FSC for forests or Fairtrade for producers. So far, this isn't a reality.

Are we prepared to bury this mineral world heritage in tonnes of concrete? In miles of highways? In countless glass bottles? And in many other products in which sand is less apparent? Like the colour white. What if I told you that gorgeous white walls, whitening toothpaste or even a white beauty cream, all come from sand?

The world is facing unprecedented challenges as I write this. People hoard what's free, regardless of the consequences. We see it with oil fracking and overfishing, and now with sand. It's the tragedy of the commons, that public resources are depleted for the profit of the few. Are these people short-sighted, arrogant, or simply unaware that they are sawing off the branch they are sitting on? Nature will slowly and irrevocably react to these depletions and we'll all pay the price.

The beach of our first kiss, this fragile strip from which our thoughts can deviate to the horizon, is also an engine that supports economies in countless coastal regions. We are endangering thousands of species in the name of urban expansion. International law and policy-making is still far from properly regulating these ecological violations.

This book provides clear and compelling reasons for us to act now, while there is still time. There is a lot we cannot control, but there are some things we can control and change for the better.

Since *Sand Wars*, I have worked on many different projects, but this book took me straight back to the days when I discovered how precious sand is. I'm thankful for the relentless activists, non-governmental organisations, businesses and politicians around the world who heard the warning and are struggling to find solutions. I'm flattered that my work inspired Kiran to reveal the issue in more complexity. Solutions are very much what makes this essential book different from others.

It gives me great pleasure to introduce Kiran's debut book, which is a crucial and admirable step in the right direction. Kiran unveils so many more uses of sand and so many more industries involved in sand extraction. She goes deep into why dams and dredging are seriously damaging our ecosystems. She clarifies why floods occur more often and why climate change is only one part of this problem, and how the sand that forms natural millennia-old barriers in riverbeds and seabeds is stolen away for profit.

Kiran shares the stories of how people, companies, even cities, are beginning to take a stand and are now recycling sand or using alternate materials, particularly renewable resources in construction. Illustrations and figures help clarify the issues, and the narrative provides a comprehensive overview of the whole system.

If you care about environmental justice, respecting Nature, or simply having a viable planet, this book is for you. I hope you will find it as necessary and timely as I do. I hope you can take action, however small.

I hope our children and grandchildren will be able to feel sand tickling their feet as their eyes sparkle at the sight of an open horizon.

Denis Delestrac – award-winning filmmaker and director of the classic eco-documentary *Sand Wars*

Barcelona, 4 October 2020
www.denisdelestrac.com

SECTION 1

HOW SAND IS DEEPLY EMBEDDED IN OUR LIVES

•1•

The Making of an Oxymoron

Sand, the stuff that makes childhood so special and dreamy, is woven into the very fabric of our lives and touches every aspect of our modern lifestyles. Contrary to popular belief, sand is essentially a non-renewable resource.

Nature forms sand mostly through the weathering of rocks and land over thousands, and even millions, of years. In many places, living organisms also contribute to its formation. I don't want to ruin it for you, but some prized tropical beaches are made thanks to the poop of parrot fish. Corals and shellfish break down to form sand deposits. Microorganisms such as Foraminifera or forams also contribute to its formation. But in the larger scheme of things the majority of sand deposits that we've been using commercially as a 'resource' were laid down by glaciers in previous ice ages. Each year, humans extract far more sediment than the rivers and glaciers of the world deposit – some estimates say three times more than nature transports.[1]

Not all sand is equal. Sand crafted by water is much more in demand than that shaped by wind, as in the deserts. Since the natural availability of the right types varies considerably, we're quickly running out of what is easily available.[2] There is an ever-growing list of uses because sand is 'cheap' and 'abundant'. But unlike other non-renewable resources such as oil, sand provides crucial ecosystem services that aren't yet widely recognised.

Sand mining is the extraction of sand, which sounds boring until you delve deeper. In this book, we examine why the United Nations Environment Programme (UNEP) has called it 'one of the major sustainability challenges of the 21st century'.[3] The UNEP mentions that this is the largest mining industry in the world, yet it remains largely unregulated and unknown. If we think in terms of a bank account, we have been living on the savings by ploughing our way through the easily available deposits. There is still plenty of sand in the world, but as far as industry is concerned it is the wrong type of sand or it is in the wrong place, such as under a city or in a nature reserve or in an inhospitable ocean bottom, or perhaps competing uses preclude its extraction. As our hunger for sand increases, we're developing extreme ways to get to it; while the climate crisis is exposing newer deposits of sand as glaciers melt. But fundamentally, we are focused on a linear model of taking, making and disposing.

Unlike nature's way of working, very little focus has gone into putting back what we've taken so that we've come up against a self-created scarcity. We've locked up much of the easily available sand in everything you see around us. Skyscrapers, multistorey buildings and houses, airports, roads, parking lots, bridges, flyovers, dams, underpasses and tunnels, are all a hallmark of modernity. All of them, and more, are based on this fundamental resource. Sand has formed the critical basis of concrete since Roman times. Sand is indispensable to the construction industry. In this book, the term 'construction' is merely a convenient placeholder because it includes so much more than making buildings. I use it to mean any activity that involves the creation of place, whether it is an island, a nuclear power plant or infrastructure such as highways or airport runways, or a lifestyle and leisure space such as a golf resort or beach.

Certain sectors use specific terminology for sand. For instance, sand and gravel used in the construction industry are called 'aggregates'.[4] Other terms such as proppants, ores, placer deposits, dredge spoil, alluvial or fluvial sediments, borrow material, fill material and more are all used to refer to sand within specific contexts or as catch-all phrases within industries. While these terms are necessary within these sectors, they can alienate the general reader. The diversity of terms has also contributed to a lack of awareness about this issue. Within this book, for the most part, I have used the terms sand and gravel to keep the focus on the big picture. Where it is necessary to use an industry term, it is accompanied by a brief explanation.

I also talk about humanity as a whole society. Although we have unique cultural heritages, this is being diluted by a globalisation that is homogenising not only our food and language, but also our approach to building, whatever the surrounding environment. As a result, it appears that we now have much more in common than we did a few generations ago, at least in the way we build our cities.

Although sand is classified into various types – aggregate and mineral sand – there is no compiled data on sand across all categories. We need to revisit this data and policy divide if we want to get a true overview. There are no discrete boundaries in nature. The sand in the river is the same sand that feeds the oceans and the beaches. Yet we seem to have created distinct policy worlds that operate in silos. Concrete use is often quoted to demonstrate that most sand extraction is happening in developing economies because they are building up their infrastructure, which is true. However, it is a partial truth. Another dimension to this truth is that while developing economies are extracting the most aggregate to develop their infrastructure – sometimes basic and sometimes wasteful, but no different from the pattern laid out 50 to 60 years ago – they are also facing a double whammy because, while mineral sand extraction does happen largely in developing economies it is mostly for the benefit of developed economies.

Sand used for energy production techniques, such as fracking, is simply recorded as industrial sand. However, I have created a separate chapter on it in this book because not only is there a huge market in energy production and storage but there is also a prolific policy ecosystem around it. Energy policies often receive the lion's share of attention. This intense focus can be counterproductive, which is something I'd like to draw attention to.

We humans have perfected the art of finding new applications for sand. From glass to urban infrastructure, from silicon chips to food and pharmaceutical products, sand has been used in mind-numbing volumes. In summary, sand has become a victim of its versatility, as you can see in Figures 1.1 and 1.2. Despite its egregious use in our daily lives, the general person on the street is unaware of how important sand is to their daily life. But, as the saying goes, there is no such thing as a free lunch. As this trend of viewing sand as a cheap and inexhaustible commodity continues, we are certainly paying a price, whether we choose to accept it or not.

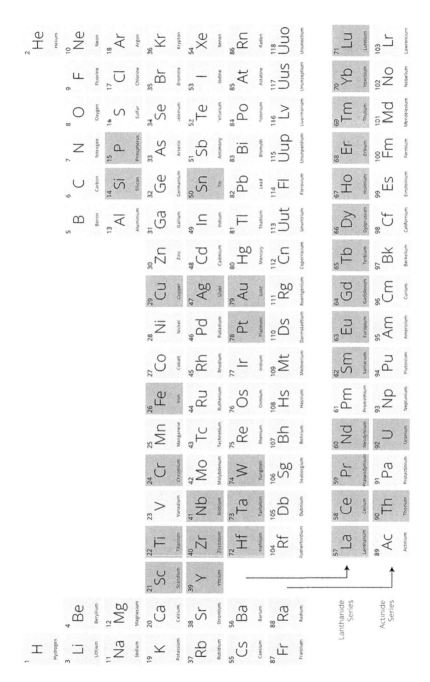

1.1   Minerals mined from sand and gravel (where economically convenient)

©SandStories.org

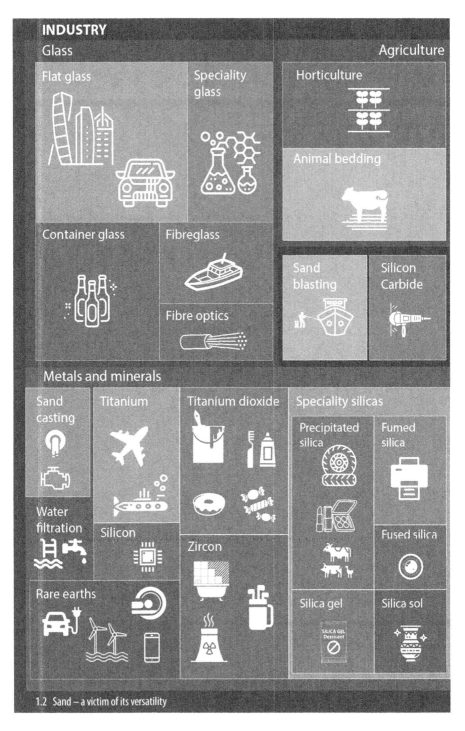

INDUSTRY

Glass

Agriculture

Flat glass

Speciality glass

Horticulture

Animal bedding

Container glass

Fibreglass

Fibre optics

Sand blasting

Silicon Carbide

Metals and minerals

Sand casting

Titanium

Titanium dioxide

Speciality silicas

Precipitated silica

Fumed silica

Water filtration

Silicon

Zircon

Fused silica

Rare earths

Silica gel

SILICA GEL
Dessicant

Silica sol

1.2 Sand – a victim of its versatility

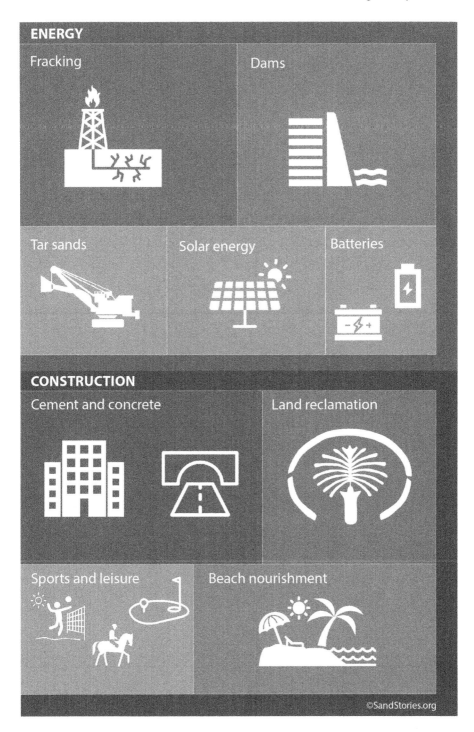

ENERGY

Fracking

Dams

Tar sands

Solar energy

Batteries

CONSTRUCTION

Cement and concrete

Land reclamation

Sports and leisure

Beach nourishment

©SandStories.org

In the following chapters, I hope to elaborate on some of the costs that have been reported in the media and in academic literature. Most importantly though, the key focus is on potential solutions, both immediate and long term. The book is divided into three distinct sections. The first examines how deeply sand is embedded in our lives. The second explores some impacts from a big picture perspective and the third looks at solutions using stories on inspiring people and places and about interesting practices. I have examined solutions for before, during and after the process of sand mining, as well as alternatives that eliminate the need for sand altogether.

This book is not a definitive guide, but it is an invitation to anyone interested in the topic to re-examine the way our society engages with sand and deals with it as a resource. The hope is that it will shed light on something we are taking for granted, something that seems mundane yet is mystical and precious.

•2•

Hiding in Plain Sight

2.1 Lilly, Lilly White Sand Ho! from The Cries of London

Source: 'The Cries of London, as they are daily exhibited in the streets', London, J. Harris, (Successor to E. Newberry), 1804[1]

Sand Ho!

In winter time, when dirty shoes
Are apt to daub the floor,
Ne'er let the honest Sandman pass
Unheeded by the door.

For whoso does assistance lend
To forward cleanliness,
All housewives surely will befriend
With bounties, more or less.

The cleanly child will be belov'd
By all the wise and good,
While sluts and slovens justly dread
Chastisement with the rod.[2]

This was written at a time when the Thames was an open sewer and, while we now work to get sand out of carpets, then sand was used *as* a carpet. London's sewerage system would not be in place until the latter part of the nineteenth century. Sand was employed in the western world for many reasons, including decorating royal dining tables and common homes, for cleaning knives and for lining bird cages.[3]

This was also when artificial cement was invented and Portland cement was patented. As natural stone became more expensive and the technology of the day enabled the creation of artificial stone, concrete began its ascent to becoming the most popular building material. The terms cement and concrete are often used interchangeably but cement is the fine powder that glues the sand and gravel in concrete. Concrete is an excellent building material but the exponential growth in its use only happened after World War II. Renowned historian Vaclav Smil says that concrete is the most important man-made material in terms of both the amount we produce each year and the total mass we have laid down; and that concrete has not only facilitated a massive urban expansion but it has also been a huge factor in reducing extreme poverty by half since 1990.[4] However, the scale and pace with which it has been embraced has meant that this growth has a steep price. *The Guardian* has called concrete 'the most destructive material on Earth'.[5] We will learn more about that in later chapters, but first, let's examine how sand comes into the picture.

2.2 Sandpainted kitchen floor, black and white photography, about 1900–1920, Drenthe, Netherlands
Public Domain[6]

The construction industry is believed to be the biggest consumer of sand. The industry term for sand and gravel used in construction is 'aggregate' – sand is referred to as fine aggregate, gravel as coarse aggregate. The United Nations Environment Programme (UNEP) estimates that every single year we extract 50 billion tonnes of sand overall, which equates to about 18 kg per person per day. With the exception of water, no other resource is used in such volumes, not even fossil fuels or biomass, which includes food, timber and other bio-based resources.[7] Despite the fact that sand is the most consumed commodity on Earth, no one knows the precise amount that is extracted. It could well be more than 50 billion tonnes a year. I'm sure we will get better at analysing our requirements but precise global data on the extraction of construction minerals such as sand did not exist in 2019.

There are many reasons for this. For instance, in India, where demand seems insatiable, sand has been classified as a 'low-value, high-volume' resource and a 'minor' mineral. As a result, monitoring its extraction is not high on the agenda and may be impeded by resource constraints.[8] Even industrialised economies only have reliable data for more recent years. Sometimes the data that is available cannot be trusted. In the case of Singapore and Cambodia there is conflicting import/export data for the same period. UN data shows 72.7 million tonnes of Cambodian sand entering Singapore between 2007 and 2015, but only 2.8 million tonnes appear to have left Cambodia for Singapore.[9]

Scientists have resorted to using the cement industry as a proxy to derive an estimate, as it is crucial to the production of concrete.[10] Aggregates (fine and coarse) generally occupy 60%-75% of the concrete by volume (70%-85% by mass).[11] For every tonne of cement used to produce concrete, six to ten tonnes of gravel are required.[12] The size of aggregate used varies with the thickness and purpose of the final concrete product. There are many types of concrete. Much like variations in recipes, each country has their own definition of concrete and proportions of raw materials that go into it. For comparison, the US and UK definitions are presented in Table 2.4.

The words cement and concrete are often used interchangeably.
But cement is only the glue that holds together concrete.

How is cement manufactured?

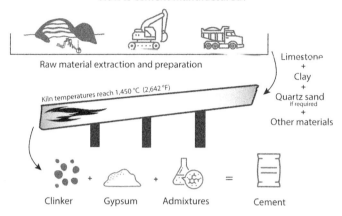

Raw material extraction and preparation

Kiln temperatures reach 1,450 °C (2,642 °F)

Limestone
+
Clay
+
Quartz sand
if required
+
Other materials

Clinker + Gypsum + Admixtures = Cement

Cement manufacture accounts for up to 8 per cent of global carbon emissions.
Sustainable cement initatives are usually focused on the use of alternative fuels, raw materials
and the development of carbon capture storage technologies.

Concrete = Cement + Sand + Gravel + Water + Air

Aggregates

'Aggregates account for the largest volume of solid material extracted globally.'
Even when sourced responsibly, they are not renewable resources.

'The 20th century saw a 23-fold increase in natural resources used for building'
The cumulative impacts of mining them cannot be ignored any longer.

Fine aggregate (sand)

Water

Coarse aggregate (gravel)

Cement

Cement   Sand and Gravel

Air

For every tonne of cement used to produce concrete,
six to seven tonnes of sand and gravel are required   Composition of concrete in the UK

2.3 Cement and concrete

*Sources: UNEP, 2014; Portland Cement Association; Cement Association of Canada; Chatham House, 2018;
UNEP, 2019; Torres et al., 2017; Krausmann et al., 2017; Bendixen et al., 2019 © SandStories.org*

Composition by volume	UK	USA
Coarse aggregate (gravel/crushed rock)	45%	30%–50%
Fine aggregate (sand)	25%	25%–30%
Water	18.5%	15%–20%
Cement	10%	7%–15%
Air	1.5%	0.5%–8%

2.4 Composition of concrete in the UK and the USA

Sources: UNEP, 2019; Kosmatka et al., 2003

If we look into the supply chain, we see that the production of cement itself uses sand, especially when the clay content does not contain enough silica.[13] Cement is manufactured by heating a carefully controlled mixture of finely ground limestone, clay, sand and other materials in a rotating kiln to temperatures up to 1,450°C (2,642°F).[14] About 85 per cent of cement is lime and silica. Other elements include alumina and iron oxide.[15]

In 2013, 70 per cent of the world's cement came from five countries – China, India, the USA, Brazil, and Turkey.[16] In 2019, China, India and the USA still dominated the list. China produced more than half of the world's cement.[17] The demand for cement in China has increased by 437.5 per cent in 20 years, in the rest of the world it increased by 59.8 per cent.[18] *The Washington Post* summed it up with the headline: 'How China used more cement in 3 years than the USA did in the entire 20th Century'.

Enormous though these figures are, China is not alone in having a ravenous appetite for sand. What is driving demand? The coveted title of World's Tallest Building has drawn in increasing competitors.[19] It started with the Chrysler building in 1930, followed by the Empire State Building in 1931, then the Willis Tower (formerly the Sears Tower) in 1974, which was overtaken by the Petronas Towers in Malaysia in 1998. Taiwan's Taipei 101 in 2004 was followed in 2010 by the current titleholder, the Burj Khalifa in Dubai. Saudi Arabia plans to oust Dubai with the Jeddah tower (formerly known as the Kingdom Tower). The Jeddah tower is planned at 3,280 feet (1,000 m) and is scheduled for completion in 2020. But Azerbaijan plans to top that feat with its own 3,445 ft (1,051 m) Azerbaijan tower. Where will it end?

The pace of construction has grown exponentially and the industry is expected to display a few megatrends. PricewaterhouseCoopers, one of the big four multinational accounting firms, predicts that the worldwide volume of construction output will grow by 85 per cent to $15.5 trillion by 2030.[20] China, India and the USA will account for 57 per cent of all global growth between them. A growth so rapid that it will outpace global gross domestic product (GDP) growth by over one percentage point.[21] Many factors are driving this growth, including: the increase in India's urban population; and China's transition to a consumer- and service-driven economy, which requires a new infrastructure, and its abolition of the one-child policy, which means more people will require housing and infrastructure.[22] Rapid construction growth is expected in other economies; Mexico will overtake Brazil, Indonesia will overtake Japan by 2030, while the UK will overtake Germany to become the largest construction market in Europe and the sixth-largest in the world.[23]

It is a popular belief that sand is only traded locally and not over large distances because it is a high volume, heavy resource of little value. A general rule of thumb is that it cannot be traded economically beyond 30 miles.[24] But this rule no longer holds true for all transactions. Sand now travels distances that were inconceivable only 50 years ago. Sand might be a relatively low-value, heavy commodity but when it is destined for use in an extremely profitable product, there is ample incentive to transport it across continents.

Today's architecture, engineering and construction (AEC) industry is a highly globalised sector. Large firms routinely work where the right type of sand is in short supply, for physical or socio-environmental reasons, and it is quite common to import sand from elsewhere. The documentary *Sand Wars* highlighted how the construction boom in Dubai was fuelled by sand imported all the way from Australia. But another trend may be much more common, yet hidden from view.

Sand imports usually happen via ocean freight. But when time is of the essence and deadlines and contractual penalties loom large, this humblest of commodities has received star treatment. For instance, when sand was required in four days and transport via the Suez Canal was not feasible, a German company air freighted 26 tons of sand from Frankfurt to Dubai. As the cargo centre admits, 'At 1.5 tons in weight per cubic meter, sand is a challenge for air freight.' First, it was packed into 25 kg sacks to be hauled by truck. The sacks were packed on pallets, which were carefully distributed throughout the aircraft to maintain balance.[25] A mere 36 hours after the call, the sand was on its way.

In 2014, the United Arab Emirates is said to have imported $456 million worth of sand, stone and gravel, not just to construct skyscrapers but also specialised race tracks for expensive thoroughbreds.[26] That same year, Dubai imported 1,500 cubic metres of sand from a German company for the Meydan racecourse, host to the world's richest horse race, the $10 million Dubai World Cup.[27] Dubai had previously imported sand for horse racing. In 2003, a British firm won a £550,000 contract to export 3,000 tonnes of sand from Lancashire in the UK for new surfaces in two horse riding arenas for the sheik of Dubai. The Crown Prince of Dubai is one of the biggest names in horse racing and he deemed Dubai's sand unsuitable for his thoroughbreds.[28]

But Dubai and its sheik cannot be singled out for their extravagance. Where there's money to be made, it is quite commonplace to import sand. Golf courses in Hawaii are constructed with Australian, Polynesian and Chinese sands.[29] Then there's the latest rage, urban beaches. 'Who says the coast has to have all the summer fun? Cities are getting in on the act too' claims *The Independent* in an article about the best urban beaches around the world.[30] Paris, London, Amsterdam, Brussels, Toronto, Vienna, Berlin, Prague, all boast of hosting several urban beaches each summer.

Each 'beach' offers not just sand but also deck chairs, colourful umbrellas, beach huts, palm trees, pop-up restaurants, cocktail bars and performance spaces to entertain weary beachgoers. Some even provide free Wi-Fi and phone chargers for those who are addicted to their smartphones. Beach-rugby is no longer restricted to the coast. Tournaments are hosted on imported beaches right in the heart of the city. Each venue imports thousands of tonnes of sand from neighbouring and distant beaches and seas and they're inspiring cities across the world to do the same.[31] Singapore's first urban beach, with the mandatory deck chairs and beach bar, opened to the public in 2015 and it is certainly not going to be the last.[32]

It is not just the places and entertainment spaces that we need to consider, but also how we travel between them. Roads are a major consumer of sand and gravel, which is in the asphalt and in the base and sub-base layers for stability and load bearing. 'Some 700,000km of roads are built every year around the world.'[33] The road infrastructure market is worth approximately $550 billion worldwide.[34]

Let's examine what this means in a broader context. Scientists have found a 23-fold increase in natural resources used in buildings and transport infrastructure in the twentieth century.[35] This change is unprecedented in all of human history and the environmental pressure from the extraction and disposal of these materials threatens global sustainability. The twenty-first century appears to have made things worse. 'Roughly one-third of all materials that have been extracted or discarded since 1900 have been mobilized between 2002 and 2015 only.'[36] Let that sink in. In just 13 years, humanity consumed one-third of all the resources used since the previous century. They also point out that industrialised countries, directly and indirectly, still lay claim to the largest share of materials extracted globally. 'In spite of the recent catch up of emerging economies it is important to keep in mind that high income countries still appropriate a disproportionately high share of all materials.'[37] In later chapters, we examine some of the costs and impacts of sand extraction in particular and also some potential solutions.

•3•

The Gorilla in the Room

'How did your great grandfathers avoid tax?' asks a cheerful tour guide in the Hague, pointing to a boarded-up window in an old building with multiple hand-painted advertisements over the bricks. Tax was levied based on the number of servants you employed and the number of horses in your stables. But falling revenues meant that monarchies and governments had to come up with innovative ways to raise money. A window tax was one such example.

A VISION OF THE REPEAL OF THE WINDOW-TAX.
"HOLLO! OLD FELLOW; WE'RE GLAD TO SEE YOU HERE."

3.1 'A Vision of the Repeal of the Window Tax'

Source: Wellcome Collection, CC BY 4.0 https://wellcomecollection.org/works/fk6abmxw

It allowed authorities to assess taxes due without having to enter a premises. Of course, this meant that people responded in equally innovative ways. New builds were commissioned with entire floors without any windows, while the owners of older houses hurriedly employed carpenters or masons to cover up windows, especially after the tax was tripled. Window taxes lasted for a good 155 years in England, until it was viewed as a tax on health and well-being, a tax that was especially unfavourable to the poor who often lived in the less salubrious parts of their employer's houses and were forced into dark, dingy, damp tenements.

Once the law changed, buildings changed and windows once again reclaimed their rightful place, as did glass. In today's world, glass is everywhere. It infiltrates every home, from windowpanes to light bulbs and glassware, from spectacles and camera lenses to the screens on our phones and laptops. Let's not forget all the glass you see or, more accurately, don't see on your chosen means of transport (unless you travel by horse or camel, in which case it's very unlikely you'd be reading this book. But I digress.). Travel to any city across the world and you'll see glass facades everywhere. So how did this material, once reserved for stained-glass windows in cathedrals, come to be so common?

It was a slow process that exploded not very long ago. It's hard to say who invented it but glass objects have been found in Egyptian tombs, which shows that humans have used glass for at least 5,000 years.[1] Many things have to come together to form this magic material, chiefly high-quality silica sand and extremely high temperatures. In fact, silica sand makes up over 70 per cent of the raw material used in glass manufacture.[2] The craft evolved over time and was a closely guarded secret. Notably, glass makers were treated like royalty in Italy but they were isolated on the island of Murano and were not allowed to fraternise with outsiders – an offence punishable by death. Glass has been pivotal to progress. It changed science forever by enabling us to see organisms too small and stars and planets too distant for the naked eye. But when glass was first used in windowpanes, it was still a luxury. At the height of its imperial self-confidence, Britain invited the world to London in 1851, to participate in the Great Exhibition housed in an ultra-modern palace of glass – the famous Crystal Palace. It was a radical choice for the time.

3.2 The Crystal Palace by J. McNeven

Source: collections.vam.ac.uk, Public Domain, https://commons.wikimedia.org/w/index.php?curid=665739

Michael Leapman, author of *The World for a Shilling*, explains:

> Until the nineteenth century, working-class aspirations had been encapsulated in the image

> of an urchin in a flat cap, pressing his nose against
> the window of a great house, where his betters
> were engaged in their social rituals of dining well
> or dancing in accordance with the current fashion.
> Now the urchin was to be invited to the party,
> though strictly on the host's terms. The Crystal
> Palace was an apt if unconscious symbol of this
> new state of affairs: the walls were all of glass but
> the lower orders were now inside, joining in the
> fun. (p. 18)

After World War II, the building and automotive industries really took off. But the supply of flat glass just couldn't keep up. There were two main processes to create flat glass at the time. One produced cheap but poor-quality sheet glass by 'drawing a sheet of glass vertically out of a ribbon of molten glass'.[3] It was hard to avoid distortions and imperfections. The other process produced plate glass that was 'optically good but expensive' because the production process was very laborious. Heavy metal rollers pressed the cooling liquid into shape over a large table. Once cooled, the glass had to be ground and polished to make it as smooth as possible.[4] It was such a slow and expensive process that many wondered if it was possible to produce clear, unblemished glass for the masses.

Then Sir Alaister Pilkington found a way to make smooth flat glass in St. Helens, England in 1952. He pioneered the method of pouring molten glass into a shallow bath of liquid tin. Legend has it that the idea came to him when he was washing up.[5] It was a stroke of genius. Tin does not react with the glass but allows it to cool. As the glass floats gently on the liquid metal, gravity and surface tension automatically create a smooth surface. Neither grinding nor polishing were necessary for the mass production of uniform, high-quality, flat glass with a smooth surface, which came to be known as float glass.[6]

It was not an easy journey for Sir Pilkington though. All through seven years of expensive hard work, people often asked him when he would succeed. In his single-minded determination, he often responded with, "We will know the answer to that only when we have succeeded."[7] Succeed he did, and how! This is now the default method across the world for producing float glass. A 6 metre by 3.2 metre ribbon of glass is the precursor to most of the construction and automotive glass you see around you.[8] Each float glass plant can produce 60,000–90,000 km (roughly 37,000–55,000 miles) of flat glass over 10 to 15 years, which is significant as we will see in Chapter 15, 'The Circle of Life in the Anthropocene'. The glass is then cut into giant pieces called 'jumbos' and sent for further processing to produce many other types of glass, such as safety glass, double- and triple-glazed glass and toughened glass.

Although float glass was very good, it was not good enough for the Computer Age. The American Corning Glass Works had been quietly working on its own method of creating flat glass and had succeeded in making thinner glass for optical quality lenses. But the process couldn't compete with the float glass technique. However Corning had an ingrained culture of innovation and they had helped Thomas Edison develop the glass envelope of the light bulb. In the 1980s, when electronics began to be mass manufactured, glass made for this purpose had to be thin, lightweight and free from any blemish on both sides – the company had found the perfect use for its fusion draw process. As the Corning Museum of Glass states:

Without glass, laptop computer LCDs wouldn't be possible. Glass is the only economical, transparent substrate that can survive the high heat and harsh chemicals needed to lay down the display's electronics.

When smartphones became all the rage, two types of glass took centre stage: sapphire glass and Corning's Gorilla® glass. The former is scratchproof but shatters when dropped and is much more expensive. As smartphones became an integral part of modern lives, Gorilla glass became, more or less, the standard glass for many phones, laptops, tablets and wearables. It is highly likely that this Gorilla is living in your home. It has been designed into 'more than 6 billion devices worldwide by more than 45 major brands'.[9] As wireless charging increases in popularity, the metal cases of phones are being replaced with glass to make it easier to go cable-free.

Despite all their mastery, the glass makers of yore could not have imagined the breathtaking range of applications for glass. It has gone well beyond being a simple connection between indoors and outdoors or decorative artefact.[10] Today, glass offers fire resistance, sound proofing, insulation and more. We take it for granted now but if you stop to consider each application, it is truly a remarkable feat of engineering. Smart cities, cloud computing and big data are commonplace today. But glass made it all possible thanks to some pioneering research with optical fibres in the 1960s at Standard Telecommunication Laboratories in Harlow, England. It proved to be so pivotal that the researcher, Sir Charles Kao, was eventually awarded the Nobel prize in Physics in 2009. The use of optical fibres has had a wide-ranging impact. For instance, it changed medicine by making it possible to conduct minimally invasive surgery thanks to the imaging technique of endoscopy.[11] The benefits for patients were enormous – less pain, shorter hospital stays and far fewer complications than with normal surgery.

Fibre-optics also revolutionised the Internet, broadband and cable television. Fibre-optic cables contain several optical fibres in a protective, insulated jacket.[12] At the heart of the Internet, are transoceanic fibre-optic cables that have mostly replaced copper wire cables. Each optical fibre is about the size of a strand of hair and is made of ultra-high-purity glass.[13] Fibre-optic cables permit higher bandwidths, that is, the transfer of a large amount of data over longer distances with less loss. Unlike metal wires, these fibres are also immune to electromagnetic interference. By 2020, over 2 billion kilometres of fibre had been installed around the globe.[14] It would be no overstatement to say that fibre-optics is the backbone of the most advanced global telecommunications network.

So, to sum up this chapter, considering how fundamental glass is to our modern lives, sand really is the forgotten foundation of modernity. In 2019 the value of the flat glass market was simply enormous. Just to give you a sense of its scale, according to one market research report, the global flat glass market size was estimated at $145.13 billion in 2018 and is predicted to reach $288.56 billion by 2025.[15]

There are several smaller glass markets too. For instance, the worldwide market for specialty glass – such as that used to make telescopic mirrors or chemical reagent bottles or cookware, bakeware and cooktops and more – is expected to cross $35 billion in 2025.[16] The global fibre-optics market size was valued at $6.5 billion in 2018 and is predicted to grow to $9.1 billion by 2025.[17]

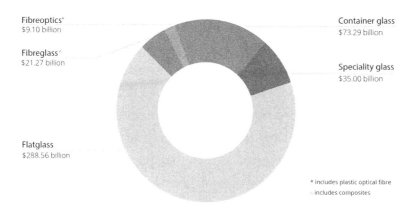

Fibreoptics*
$9.10 billion

Fibreglass^
$21.27 billion

Flatglass
$288.56 billion

Container glass
$73.29 billion

Speciality glass
$35.00 billion

* includes plastic optical fibre
^ includes composites

3.3 Estimated value of global glass markets in 2025

Sources: Grand View Research, 2017; Mordor Intelligence, 2019; Market Research Future, 2019; Research and Markets, 2019; Grand View Research, 2020

It is incredible to think that sand underpins all these markets and yet there is little attention given to where this sand is sourced from or to the cumulative impact of extracting this non-renewable resource.

•4•

Fashion for Food

The most striking use of sand is in food products. Doesn't that feel weird? But it is common, even normal – and completely understandable from the standpoint of industrial efficiency, process improvement and consumer preferences. It is used widely in products such as chewing gum, sweets and candy, fine bakery wares, lemon curd, mayonnaise, horseradish cream, sauces, and dairy products such as skimmed milk, cottage cheese, mozzarella cheese and more. If you look for traces of sand though, you're unlikely to find them because it is used in a different avatar, a derivative called titanium dioxide (TiO_2), a white pigment.[1] Its use as a food additive was approved by the FDA in the USA in 1966.[2] It is indicated on the label as E171 in the EU.

Why is it added? There is a pretty solid reason. Titanium dioxide is used extensively in industry for its high refractive index, which influences the brightness and reflective properties of the end product. Put simply, it is used to whiten products, as a barrier between different colours and sometimes to add texture. For instance, in the USA, titanium dioxide is added to skimmed milk to make it brighter, opaquer and more palatable and therefore more appealing to the end consumer.[3] In other words, titanium dioxide is make-up for milk. Consumers don't want a watery greyish liquid. We want skimmed milk to look as full-bodied as whole milk and so producers very kindly give us what we want. But the food industry is only the most recent to lay claim to titanium dioxide. Many others have been using it for a long time.

Titanium dioxide is the most important pigment in a wide variety of industries, ranging from textiles and plastics to big pharma and construction. It accounts for almost two-thirds of the pigments produced globally and in 2018 the market for titanium dioxide was valued at a whopping $15.76 billion.[4] Titanium dioxide goes into nearly everything white around you: the ceramic tiles and sanitary ware in your bathroom; the traffic lines on the road; the paints on your walls and cars and furniture; your toothpaste; the cards you write on and the paper you print on; your fashionable white trainers, keyboards or earphones; the white frosting on cupcakes; or the coffee creamer you stir into your morning cup.

Titanium dioxide is not just used because it turn things white and bright but because in relatively small amounts it can also make things opaque.[5] This is an important property because it hides whatever is underneath. Think of how convenient this is. When you paint a wall or a car or a piece of furniture, you don't want to see whatever is below that fresh coat of paint. Unsurprisingly, titanium dioxide is a critical ingredient in paints, lacquers and varnishes, coatings, glazes and enamels, plastics, paper, paperboard, fibres, inks, plastics, cements, floor coverings and roofing granules.[6] Adding titanium dioxide to plastics and textiles intended for outdoor apparel prevents discolouration in sunlight due to its UV resistance.[7] The cosmetics industry uses it routinely in lipsticks, creams, ointments, powders and toothpastes. The pharmaceutical industry incorporates it into products such as gelatin capsules, tablet coatings and syrups. If it's not listed on the label as titanium dioxide, then it will be listed as either Pigment White 6 (PW6) or CI77891 in the EU.

But you may be most familiar with it in sunscreens. Titanium dioxide has excellent ultraviolet (UV) resistant qualities and acts as a UV absorbent. Many sunscreen products contain titanium dioxide, especially those with a higher SPF. Titanium dioxide acts as a physical blocker for UV light.

You'd be hard pressed to live a single day without using a product that contains titanium dioxide. Although marketing has made them seem commonplace, many of today's commercial products would have been in the realm of science fiction only two or three generations ago. For example, smog-eating cement and self-cleaning products. An Italian firm, Italcementi, developed the smog-eating cement, called TX Active™. It was featured by TIME Magazine as one of the top innovations in 2008. It makes use of the photocatalytic property of titanium dioxide to speed up the natural process that breaks down smog into its component parts. There is a similar application in the aluminium cladding industry, where a titanium dioxide-based coating called EcoClean™ cleans the air around a structure. The manufacturer, Alcoa, claims that a building with 1,000 m²/10,000 ft² of their coated aluminium will offset the smog caused by four cars every day, which is equivalent to the air cleansing power of 80 trees.[8]

Titanium dioxide is used in an array of 'self-cleaning' products, such as self-cleaning glass, self-cleaning kitchen and bathroom tiles, and self-cleaning fabrics.[9] Self-cleaning glass uses the photocatalytic property of titanium dioxide to break down organic dirt; then it uses the hydrophilic (water-loving) property of titanium dioxide so that a flow of water, such as rainwater, spreads evenly instead of forming droplets. As the sheet of water runs off, it takes the dirt with it and dries off quickly without leaving any streaks. This glass has a wide range of applications, including conservatories, skylights and windows.[10]

In 2008, a research team at a UK university unveiled a titanium dioxide-based paint that kills the *E. coli* bacteria on its surface under the fluorescent lights that are frequently used in hospitals.[11] In another study, the application of a coat of titanium dioxide on tiles in a hospital environment reduced surface bacteria on the wall surfaces to zero and reduced airborne bacteria counts.[12] Such a disinfecting property has applications not only in medical devices and hospitals but also in food preparation surfaces, air conditioning filters and sanitary ware surfaces.[13] It works because, in the presence of water, titanium dioxide particles produce hydroxyl radicals that convert organic molecules to carbon dioxide (CO_2) and water, thus destroying microorganisms.[14]

Titanium dioxide is also being used increasingly in the manufacture of light-emitting diodes, liquid crystal displays (LCDs), electrodes of plasma displays and dye-sensitised solar cells and perovskite cells for solar energy applications. It is also being used to neutralise persistent pesticides in wastewater.[15] In 2017, NASA commissioned a test of 3D-printed titanium dioxide foams aboard the International Space Station because these foams have great potential for space applications ranging from 'efficient solar cells to batteries and radiation shielding'.[16] There's another application taking the automotive sector by storm as regulators push for greater emission controls and higher fuel efficiency. Automakers are switching from steel to lightweight polycarbonates. But polycarbonates scratch easily and that is a big drawback on vehicles. Coating the polycarbonates with titanium dioxide solves that problem. So, they can reduce the weight of the vehicle and, in turn, enhance fuel efficiency.[17] Win-win all round. Or is it?

There is an ever-growing list of applications for this wonder material. But, to cut a long story short, demand is outstripping supply.[18] The major consumers of titanium dioxide are the paints, coatings, paper and plastics sectors in the Global North.[19] But as India and China develop and adopt similar lifestyles, demand for titanium dioxide will go through the roof. We examine the impacts of this unbridled demand in later chapters.

•5•

The Backbone of Nearly Everything

What ingredient is common in all of the following? Sugar and salt substitutes, cocoa powder, dried eggs, instant coffee and tea, ground herbs and spices, non-dairy creamer, pancake and cake mixes, powdered drink mixes, powdered milk and grated cheese. The answer is, a derivative of quartz sand, silicon dioxide (SiO_2) also known as silica or, more accurately in this context, precipitated silica or synthetic amorphous silica. In the EU, it is listed on food labels as E551. Like titanium dioxide (see Chapter 4), silica is used extensively in familiar, everyday products.

For example, pharmaceutical products (such as toothpastes and pills) and cosmetics (such as eye shadows and face powders) either use silica in the production process or contain silica in the end product for its specific properties. For instance, in toothpaste its abrasiveness gets rid of plaque. In cosmetics, it not only offers light-diffusing properties and a natural absorbency, but also acts as a flow or anti-caking agent to stop products from clumping. It is this flow property that means it is also used in food products.

Another flow agent is sodium silicate, listed on labels in the EU as E550 and also known as water glass. In the days before refrigeration became common, and especially during World

War II, this product was popularly used to preserve eggs. The eggs were either painted with or kept immersed in a solution of water glass, which sealed the pores of the eggshell and meant they kept for many months.[1]

In today's world, sodium silicate is available in a wide range of concentrations and forms and is used in a huge variety of industries:

- the construction industry uses sodium silicate as as an additive to make concrete more dense and to increase its strength
- the paper and pulp industry uses it as a glue to make cardboard tubes, fibre drums and the adhesive on labels – in fact, its adhesive property is also used to bond wood, metal foil, glass, glass fibre insulation and more
- the waste water treatment industry uses sodium silicate as a coagulant to purify the water
- the cosmetics and personal care industry uses sodium silicate in skin care, hair colouring, shaving, bath, eye make-up, anti-wrinkle cream and oral hygiene products[2]
- the detergent industry uses it as a key ingredient to produce liquid and powder detergents for domestic and industrial applications.[3]

The full list of this product's uses is well beyond the scope of this chapter.

All these industries depend on this product because it is 'inexpensive and abundantly available'.[4] Sodium silicate is produced via two commercial processes: one involves heating sand and soda ash to around 1,400°C (2,552°F) in special furnaces; in the other, sand is dissolved in concentrated caustic soda liquor at high temperature and pressure.[5]

Coming back to the food industry, additives such as E550 and E551 are routinely used to make commercial products more viable. Think of it this way. Vending machines would not be practical if powdered chocolate, soup or milk did not flow properly because clumps were blocking the tubes. The taste would vary from one drink to the next if the powder was not dispensed consistently.[6]

Precipitated silica is routinely used as a flow and carrier agent in animal feed and agricultural and industrial applications because process efficiency, quality control, packaging, storage and transportation are all made easier.

The paints and coatings industry adds significant amounts of precipitated silica to flatten, thicken and for anti-corrosion. It is also used as a microporous filler for battery separators and as a performance-enhancing filler for silicone rubber applications.

Silica sand itself is extraordinarily useful in other industries. You've already read that it is the main component of glass. It is also a primary raw material for many ceramics, including earthenware, stoneware and porcelain, and it is an abrasive in a sand-blasting technique that is used to produce distressed denim for a worn look that fetches a handsome price, although some countries have banned its use.[7] The same technique is used on a larger scale to remove paint and to prepare surfaces for painting on ships and old steel bridges.[8]

Silica is crucial to the production of glass wool or glass fibre, which has excellent thermal insulation properties and, therefore, is used widely as a residential and commercial thermal insulator.[9] As an insulator, it increases energy efficiency by keeping rooms cool in summer and warm in winter.

Silica sand is a fundamental component in the manufacture of fibreglass, a composite material that is used extensively in our modern world. It is also called glass reinforced plastic (GRP), glass fibre reinforced plastic (GFRP), or fibre reinforced plastic.

This composite material was developed during World War II by British and American scientists. It was first used in the production of radomes for Lancaster bombers as the perfect strong, lightweight, non-metallic substance that was transparent to radar/radiowaves.[10] Fibreglass is highly resistant to corrosion (i.e. it won't rust) and is stronger than sheet metal (pound for pound). It is relatively easy to mould and therefore offers design freedom and unlimited possibilities to engineers seeking to create aesthetic products that are structurally strong and durable. It is easily assembled and low maintenance. It has lower shipping and storage costs because of its much lighter weight compared to metal or wood products. Fibreglass also absorbs more sound waves than bounce off it and therefore has numerous applications in acoustic engineering (e.g. by lowering machinery volumes to achieve acceptable and/or required sound levels, in music studios).[11]

Thanks to all these properties, fibreglass is used to create an infinite array of products, such as aircraft fuselages, car bodies, lightweight vehicles, boats, yachts, canoes, waterpark slides, furniture (especially outdoor), water drums, bath tubs, swimming pools, hot tubs, septic tanks, roofing, cladding, pipes, surfboards, helmets and other sports equipment.[12] Customised fibreglass is used in the manufacture of military equipment (e.g. missile motor casings) and for medical applications, such as bio-compatible glass fibre for long-term medical implants (e.g. orthodontal and dental implants, orthopaedic implants[13]), electrical insulation tape, textiles and reinforcement.[14]

SiO_2 or silica is also used in a fundamental industrial process called sand casting, where coated sand forms the mould into which molten metal is poured.[15] Even if you've never heard of the term, you've benefited from products manufactured with this process, at home and/or at work and in your travels. Around 70 per cent of all metal castings are produced using sand casting processes.[16] They can be used to produce things that weigh as little as a few grams (e.g. a watch case) to several hundred tonnes (e.g marine diesel engine); objects with a simple shape (e.g. a manhole cover) or complex ones (e.g. six-cylinder engine block); it can cater to one-off orders (e.g. paper mill crusher) or large-scale production runs (e.g. automobile pistons).[17]

This is all possible because of sand's specific properties, including:

1. **Refractoriness** – The ability to withstand extreme heat without melting. Pure silica has a very high melting/ fusion point $(1,760^0C/3,200^0F)$.[18] Just to put that in context, lava from a volcano is generally between $700^0C–1200^0C$ $(1,300^0F–2,200^0F)$.[19] However, natural sand usually has a much lower melting point due to impurities.[20] Therefore, a minimum 98 per cent pure silica sand is needed to produce steel objects, whereas objects made of cast iron or other non-ferrous metals (such as aluminium, copper, magnesium, and nickel

alloys) can make do with a lower purity of 94–98 per cent.[21] I think it would be fair to say that silica sand is used to produce most of the metal objects we use on a daily basis. Now, coming back to the other properties that make it so popular …

2. **Permeability** – This is its porosity or the ability to permit air to flow through. This ensures that the finished product is free from defects. Without the appropriate permeability, gases would get trapped within the liquid metal and would form gas holes and pores after solidification.[22]

3. **Strength or cohesiveness** – This quality ensures that the sand retains its shape after the pattern is removed and that the mould doesn't collapse when it is moved. The strength is determined by the density, clay content and particle size and it can be tailored to requirements by using specific additives.[23]

4. **Adhesiveness** – This means that the sand mixture holds its shape and clings to the sides of the mould so that it does not fall out when it is lifted or turned over. Usually, special binders (such as sodium silicate, itself a derivative of high-quality quartz) are added to bond the particles.[24].

5. **Plasticity or flowability** – This is the ability of sand to fill the nooks and crannies and intricate design without the need for special processes or equipment.[25]

6. **Availability and cost** – This is a determining factor because for every tonne of metal poured, three to six tonnesof sand are required.[26]

Sand casting is the most economical means of production compared to other methods primarily because sand is believed to be abundant and inexpensive.[27] Typically, the composition of the casting mixture ranges from 89–90 per cent sand, 3–4 per cent water, and 7 per cent clay or binder.[28] It therefore facilitates the lowest tooling cost.[29] Sand casting makes it quick and easy to modify designs, which means that engineers can save a great deal of money when testing prototypes and making alterations so that their product performs properly.[30] Castings are used in multiple industries, including industrial equipment and machine tools, hardware and household appliances, defence and transport, which includes automobiles, railways, shipping and aerospace.[31]

Over half of the castings produced are employed in the transport and heavy equipment industries.[32] Engine blocks, crankshafts, wheels and turbochargers, pumps, valves and pipes, tools and machines have all benefited in some way from the use of sand in the manufacturing process. Impressive though these feats of engineering are, it is startling to learn of all the markets that are dependent on silica sand. Precisely because of all the properties listed above, it is very difficult to find a substitute that can do everything that silica sand does.

In short, regardless of whether it is used in its natural state or as a manufactured version, silica makes our lives much more convenient. However, it is important to recognise that while the number of uses may be growing each day, the places where this sand comes from aren't expanding. Silica sand is a valuable, scarce and non-renewable resource. It is obtained either by crushing sandstone, quartz rock and other sources that are equally non-renewable, or by surface mining, or by dredging, where there are particularly rich deposits. Dredging is the removal of sediments from the bottom of water bodies. In simple terms, dredgers are giant machines that vacuum up the sediment and everything in it, store it on board or transfer the material to barges for it to be deposited at specified locations. Some dredgers (e.g. cutter-suction dredgers) are equipped with cutting devices to break up hard substrates, such as rock. We will learn more about them in Chapter 11, 'The Currency of Development'. As demand explodes, governments might be forced to offer up more mining concessions. But, as the following chapters show, the trade-off is getting steeper as the social, environmental and economic costs pile up.

•6•

Why Mark Twain Would
Have Been Surprised

Buy land – they're not making it anymore.

When Mark Twain supposedly made that statement, creating land was not part of the psyche of the general English-speaking population, although land reclamation is not a new phenomenon.[1] Today, world maps quickly become obsolete given the unprecedented scale and pace of creation of new land.

In 1968, the Netherlands created the record for the largest artificial island reclaimed from the sea, the Flevopolder. Ever since, land reclamation projects have been steadily increasing. Several cities have been built on land reclaimed from wetlands, marshes, lakes, rivers, estuaries or the ocean, such as Rotterdam and large parts of the Netherlands, Tokyo in Japan, Boston and Washington DC in the USA, Rio de Janeiro in Brazil, Wellington in New Zealand, Fontvieille in Monaco and many others. But it is Dubai's palm-shaped islands that have unleashed the creativity and courage of modern developers, or not, depending on where you stand. Figure 6.1 illustrates the global scale of land gained between 1984 and 2015.

It seems highly profitable to create ultra-modern, futuristic cities with swanky offices, residences and leisure facilities.

Developers think it is easier to create the ideal city than to deal with messy politics and inadequate infrastructure. Waterfront areas are particularly popular and developers are falling over themselves to come up with the latest 'innovative' property to rival Dubai. Lack of land is no longer a constraint. Gone are the days of pioneers who sailed the seas for years to discover unknown worlds. Today's adventurers create their own land in any shape they fancy. Lobsters (Azerbaijan), cedar trees (Lebanon), Federation Island in the shape of Russia (Russia), giant tulips (the Netherlands) are all proposals for fancy islands.[2] Many of these projects stalled in the initial stages, many more have vanished into thin air. The fact remains that all these projects were seriously considered by developers and governments at some point.[3]

Peculiarly shaped land masses are not the only worrying trend. While Israel was mulling over the construction of an island off the coast of Gaza, China built artificial islands among contested atolls and reefs.[4] These actions have environmental and geopolitical implications that we'll examine later but most projects don't cause a geopolitical stir. As a result, they have become mundane and easy to miss, although each one uses gargantuan quantities of sand, rock and other non-renewable resources. Several countries have created airports on massive offshore islands because of the difficulty of obtaining land inland due to noise regulations and cumbersome land acquisition processes. It is apparently easier and cheaper to just build your own land. Take the example of Kansai airport in Osaka, Japan, which opened in 1994 and started the trend of building offshore airports.[5] It was built 5 km offshore on an artificial island that is 2.5 miles long and 1.6 miles wide (4 km long and 2.5 km wide).[6]

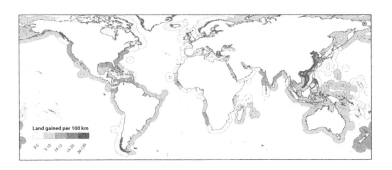

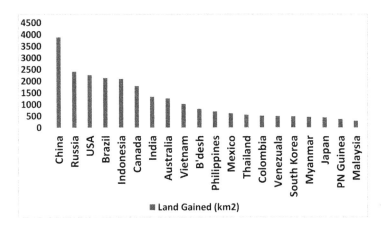

6.1 Global map of land gained between 1984 and 2015

Source: Sengupta, D., Chen, R., Meadows, M.E., Choi, Y.R., Banerjee, A., Zilong, X., 2019. Mapping Trajectories of Coastal Land Reclamation in Nine Deltaic Megacities using Google Earth Engine. Remote Sensing 11, 2621. https://doi.org/10.3390/rs11222621

The American Society of Civil Engineers gave Kansai airport a 'Civil Engineering Monument of the Millennium' award in 2001. It ranks as one of the most expensive civil engineering projects in world history (costing $20 billion in 2008[7]). The project took 20 years to plan and seven years to construct. The dredging of Osaka bay provided the landfill material and more was imported by barge from China and Korea. In addition, three whole mountains were excavated to provide 21,000,000 m^3 of landfill.[8] Thanks to engineering ingenuity, the project withstood a major earthquake and a typhoon. However, the seabed under the island was soft clay and while the engineers took this into account and anticipated a slight sinking or settlement, they underestimated how quickly it would happen. Upon completion the island began sinking much more rapidly than planned. The construction engineers relied on a technique called 'the sand drain method' to reform the soil of the seabed.

Reclaimed land is similar to a wet sponge. The water needs to be drained out of both it and the layers below before it is stable enough to build structures on. In this case, the soft clay of the seabed had been formed in the Holocene, over the last 10,000 years, but beneath it were several stable Pleistocene layers that had borne the weight of glaciers in previous ice ages.

The construction engineers poured a five-feet deep layer of sand on to the soft clay seabed and added vertical pipes of sand before adding the fill material. When the land began settling, the sand acted like a wick or a vertical drain up which water could travel to drain away or to evaporate from the surface. As a result, it sped up the settlement of the new land.[9]

Before the construction of Kansai airport, only 900,000 sand drains had been used in the country. But in a heroic effort to save the island, engineers used a million sand drains (20 m long and 40 cm in diameter at 2.5 m intervals) to stabilise the first part of the island and 1.2 million to stabilise the second part.[10]

The island is large and distinctive enough to be visible from space.[11] It has since influenced the construction of the New Kitakyushu Airport, Kobe Airport, and Chubu Centrair

International Airport (Nagoya) in Japan, Hong Kong's Chek Lap Kok International Airport, the Incheon International airport in Seoul, South Korea and several others.[12] In 2019, China was reported to be building a couple of offshore airports, including what was being billed as the 'The World's largest offshore airport'.[13] In Turkey, the Ordu-Giresun airport opened to air traffic in 2015 and the country is in the process of building another offshore airport, the Rize-Artvin airport, in the northeastern part of the country. Israel has commissioned a feasibility study for a $10 billion offshore airport in the Mediterranean.[14] The list keeps growing.

But offshore airports are not the only reason to create new land. Sometimes it facilitates revenue-generating activities that are unacceptable on the mainland. Take Macau, a special administrative region of China and the only location where gambling is legal. The Portuguese legalised gambling in the late 1840s and the Chinese have now done what only they can do, taken an idea and executed it on a grandiose scale. The gambling industry in Macau is massive, seven times bigger than in Las Vegas.[15] But the bed rock of this industry is land reclaimed from the ocean. Land reclamation began under colonial rule but Macau has increased its land mass by over one-third since 1999.[16] Although no commercial gaming is permitted on future new land, expansion plans are set to continue over the next 20–30 years.[17] Other provinces in China are not far behind in terms of land reclamation. Massive swathes of land are extending coastlines further out into the sea. Wade Sheppard, author of *Ghost Cities of China*, points out how reclamation to create new cities, ports, resorts and industrial zones has become 'an all out developmental free-for-all' in China.[18] Jiangsu province reclaimed land from the Yellow Sea equivalent to the size of London and Munich combined. Taizhou expanded into the sea by more than twice the size of Paris. Land for the city of Nanhui, designed to house 800,000 people, was reclaimed in five to six years. These parcels of land are called 'gift from the sea' by the local media.[19] It seems the sea has brought many gifts indeed (see Figure 6.2).

On the opposite side of the world there's a fascinating change in discourse. From the early twentieth century, the USA has been putting up a 'strong fight' against the sea with a huge emphasis on maintaining, protecting and enhancing its coasts. It has placed over 1.1 billion cubic metres (1.5 billion cubic yards[20]) of sand in over 400 projects along its coastline at a cost known to exceed $6.1 billion. The beach nourishment business is one of the biggest in the world. In China, beach nourishment is relatively small in terms of beach length, volume and investment in comparison with that in the USA or Europe, but this is changing rapidly.[21]

Beach nourishment, also called beach replenishment, is increasingly being used not just to replenish storm-battered sandy coasts but also to build sandy beaches where there were none. A beach, it seems, has become synonymous with sand. Mudflats and rocky shores are not as profitable as sandy beaches, which are tourist magnets. But, as we shall examine in later chapters, you don't get something for nothing. As giant dredging machines engage in 'underwater vacuum cleaning' to transfer the much-coveted sand from seabed to yet another 'paradise beach', the true costs are beginning to appear.[22]

The Caofeidian new economic zone built by Tangshan on reclaimed land twice the size of Los Angeles

Tianjin port, the largest in north China, constructed on 107 km² of land reclaimed from Bohai Bay

Jiangsu Province reclaimed 21 parcels of land from the Yellow Sea, totalling 1,817 km², that's the size of London and Munich combined

The city of Nanhui intended to house 800,000 people on 133 km² of land reclaimed within just 5–6 years

Taizhou expanded into the sea by more than twice the size of Paris

Sanya created an 'Oriental Dubai' on an an artificial archipelago with luxury hotels and an international cruise ship port

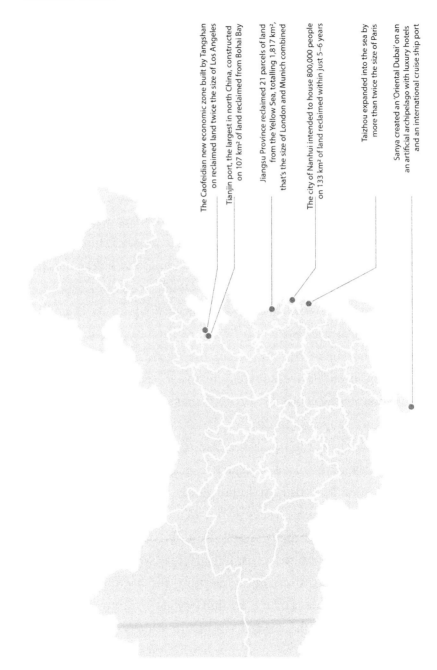

6.2 'Gifts from the sea', some of the land reclamation projects along China's coastline

Source: Shepard, W., 2015 "The gift from the sea" : through land reclamation,
China keeps growing and growing. City Metric © SandStories.org

•7•

In Pursuit of the Holy Grail

In 2014, researchers at the University of California, Riverside, created a sand-based lithium-ion battery that lasted three times longer than the current industry standard. One of the researchers chanced upon the idea when he was relaxing on the beach after surfing. He picked up some sand, took a closer look and saw that it was made up primarily of quartz, or silicon dioxide. He obtained sand from a creek that was known to be particularly rich in quartz and worked on it in the laboratory in collaboration with others. What they discovered created quite a stir and was published in the prestigious *Nature Scientific Reports*.[1] The researchers had finally found 'the holy grail – a low-cost, non-toxic, environmentally friendly way to produce high-performance lithium-ion battery anodes.'[2]

In the last few chapters, we examined how sand is used in previously unimaginable ways to sustain our current lifestyles. Sand is pivotal not only to the creation of places that house and entertain us, but also to the creation of nearly all the material objects we use in our daily lives in this modern world. In this chapter, we examine a new but growing trend that is employing sand and its components during either energy generation (via fossil fuels and renewable sources) or energy storage.

Although it is not yet widely recognised, rare earth elements (REEs) are also extracted from sand in placer deposits – targeted more for industrial than construction use.

Placer deposits are naturally concentrated mineral deposits that are formed by the action of gravity and water or wind. These deposits fetch significantly higher prices than ordinary construction sand, but more about that later. REEs are of critical importance to all advanced industrial economies and they have often allowed for big breakthroughs in technology. They are used in a wide variety of applications ranging from defence systems (such as missile guidance systems), jet engines and satellites, to rechargeable batteries and magnets used in hybrid vehicles and wind turbines.[3] Even everyday objects, such as smartphones and iPods, depend on these elements. Without them, none of these things would function the way they do. REEs have properties that no other elements have, which means they cannot often be substituted.

REEs are the 17 elements towards the bottom of the periodic table: cerium (Ce), dysprosium (Dy), erbium (Er), europium (Eu), gadolinium (Gd), holmium (Ho), lanthanum (La), lutetium (Lu), neodymium (Nd), praseodymium (Pr), promethium (Pm), samarium (Sm), scandium (Sc), terbium (Tb), thulium (Tm), ytterbium (Yb), and yttrium (Y). They are often found in minerals with thorium (Th) and, less commonly, uranium (U).

Nickel metal hydride batteries, use lanthanum (La), one of the REEs that is much in demand. Battery technology took a big leap forward thanks to La. Nickel-lanthanum hydride batteries are twice as efficient as standard lead-acid car batteries so they pack more power into a smaller space and are used extensively in batteries for hybrid cars, such as the Toyota Prius, and in the small mopeds used in China.[4]

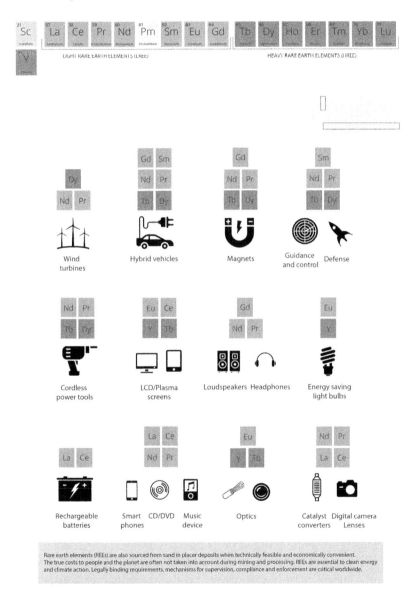

7.1 Rare earth elements and their uses

Sources: China Water Risk, 2016; National Centre for Biotechnology Information. PubChem Database © SandStories.org

In 2009, Reuters reported that each Prius motor uses 1 kg (2.2 lb) of neodymium, while every Prius battery uses 10–15 kg (22–33 lb) of lanthanum and that this number was set to double with efforts to increase fuel economy.[5] Today, whether one owns a Prius or not, REEs are very much an integral part of our daily lives. For instance, mobile phone batteries use terbium (Tb), dysprosium (Dy), erbium (Er), thulium (Tm), ytterbium (Yb) and lutetium (Lu), which are all found in monazite, which you'll learn more about in later chapters.[6] In the meantime, let's look at other uses for sand.

Sometimes, sand is mined not for itself but because it stands in the way of an energy source. This is the case when sand is indiscriminately dredged from or dumped in sensitive areas to make way for deep ports to ship resources such as coal, as in the case of Australia's Carmichael coal mine.[7] At the Athabasca tar sands project in Alberta, Canada, which is the world's largest industrial project, the sands lock away bitumen, which is a sticky and highly viscous liquid or semi-solid form of petroleum.[8] When the oil sands are relatively near the surface, they are mined by the surface method of open-pit mining.

The overburden, that is the non-target material, is moved out of the way so that the oil sands can be extracted and further treated. The overburden in this case includes old-growth Boreal forests, muskeg and more. Where the oil sands are deeper, in situ production techniques are used. In crude terms, you could say that no sand is extracted in this method. Instead, much like you'd heat butter to make it flow, the sand is cooked in place by injecting steam into the earth to reduce the bitumen's viscosity and to make it flow easily. The bitumen is then pumped out like conventional crude oil.[9]

Another shocking use of sand is in the hydraulic fracturing industry, more commonly known as fracking. Fracking generates energy by forcing reserves of shale gas out of the ground using a cocktail of high pressured gas, water and specific chemicals. Sand is mainly used in the process as a proppant, a role fit for Hercules. Its function is to prop the fissures open and let the gas escape. Often the pressures involved are so high that if you didn't have strong support between the layers to keep the gaps open, everything would collapse on itself. But not every kind of sand is suitable. Fracking requires sand with very specific physical properties, such as grains with a high crush resistance and a spherical shape.

This sand is often obtained by blasting apart once glaciated sandstone hills and bluffs. Each fracking well consumes about 5,000–7,000 US tons (4,536–6,350 metric tonnes) of sand, in other words about 50–70 rail cars of sand, but those numbers are growing enormously.[10] In recent years, fracking companies have been trying to 'frontload' profits for the first year of production by increasing the amount of sand pumped in. Just how much of an increase? Well, one super-sized fracking well can consume 10,000 to more than 25,000 tons of sand. To put that in perspective, 10,000 tons of sand is a mile-long train of a non-renewable resource to frac just one well (see Figure 7.2).[11]

What's the impact of removing such vast quantities of a non-renewable resource on ecosystems and the people dependent on them? What's the impact of leaving massive holes in the ground or blasted sides of hills that are never reclaimed? The surprising answer is that we don't know, despite the upbeat projections of the industry. But what we do know is that the process of removing this sand is shrouded in controversy, as you will learn in Chapter 12, 'Private Gain at Public Expense'.

Fracking companies use highly toxic chemicals during the process, which are often guarded as trade secrets. So, the sand, along with the earth and water, around fracking wells remains highly toxic and cannot be remedied until companies are willing to disclose what chemicals they use.

It is worth noting that unlike construction sand, fracking sand and other types of silica sand are routinely shipped across continents. Algeria, for instance, despite being so close to the Sahara desert, is scheduled to import 300,000 tonnes of proppant from a company in India during the 2020-21 financial year.[12] The country is said to hold the third largest shale gas reserves in the world and it intends to tap into this in order to supply the European gas market.[13]

Sand is also very important to the renewable energy industry. Although there are a variety of technologies to produce solar energy, the vast majority of solar panels today are made from silicon. Silicon is an excellent semiconductor but it must be very pure to be used in the photovoltaics (PV) industry. Elemental silicon is currently largely derived from quartz, the most common form of silica (silicon dioxide), through extremely expensive, chemically laden and energy intensive processes.[14] Chemical industries and metal foundries also depend extensively on silicon as a raw material. For instance, it is routinely used to make alloys of aluminium, iron and steel. But to qualify as solar-grade silicon or polysilicon (polycrystalline silicon), it needs to have purity levels of 6N (99.9999 per cent pure) to 8N (99.999999 per cent). Electronics require silicon that is even purer (9N (99.9999999 per cent) to 11N (99.999999999 per cent). The high manufacturing costs of photovoltaic cells has been an important limiting factor in their widespread use. It is estimated that the silicon used accounts for about 45 per cent of the cost of a traditional solar panel.[15]

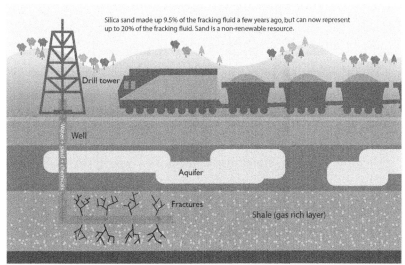

Silica sand made up 9.5% of the fracking fluid a few years ago, but can now represent up to 20% of the fracking fluid. Sand is a non-renewable resource.

Drill tower

Water + sand + chemicals

Well

Aquifer

Fractures

Shale (gas rich layer)

The fracking process lasts roughly 35-40 days. It can increase to 60-65 days depending on lateral length and other factors.

The increase in sand use per well:

A typical fracking well consumes an average of 50-70 rail cars of sand during the process

A super-sized fracking well can consume 100–250+ rail cars of sand

The frac sand market in the United States:

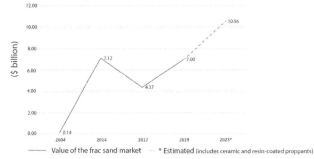

—— Value of the frac sand market   — — * Estimated (includes ceramic and resin-coated proppants)

7.2 The use of sand in hydraulic fracturing (fracking)

Sources: US Geological Survey; Reuters, 2014; San Antonio Business Journal, 2015; P&S Intelligence, 2018; IMARC, 2020; www.fractracker.org © SandStories.org

Solar cells use silicon derived from quartz not because it is the best material for the purpose but mainly because of historical reasons. The industry evolved from using waste material from the electronics/semiconductor sector. But in the late 1990s, the demand from the solar industry outpaced that from the semiconductor sector. Since the purity required was much lower, scientists looked for a way to make it cheaper. In the 1980s, scientists from the Siemens research laboratories in Germany described a way to prepare high-purity silica for solar-grade silicon production from a low-cost starting material, that is, 'abundantly available quartz sand'.[16]

Although much literature mentions quartz sand, some experts say that natural sand is too small a size fraction for this particular use. Instead, they say commercially viable quartz is sourced from quartz found as rock or river gravel. It is also sourced from quartzite, which is a highly siliceous and well-cemented sandstone. The sector is not transparent as the supply chain is highly fragmented and poorly regulated and we must remember that both rock and sand, although varying in size, share the same material composition and, most importantly, are both non-renewable resources in timescales relevant to policy makers. But could this reliance on silicon from specific sources pose a problem and are there any solutions? This is examined in Chapter 19, 'Racing Toward the Sunrice'.

Titanium dioxide (see Chapter 4) is also used to create solar cells in dye solar cell technology, which works well in all light conditions and allows the capture and conversion of energy without losing it through heat.[17]

As we shall see in later chapters, the extraction and convertion of titanium-bearing minerals have an extremely heavy environmental and social impact.

Can the world continue to extract sand in mind-numbing quantities with little regard to the consequences? Can we afford a lopsided focus on energy and carbon emissions at the expense of everything else?

SECTION 2

THE BIG PICTURE: HOW EVERYTHING IS INTERCONNECTED

•8•

The Dark Side of Development

The day started off pretty normally. She walked out of the front gate, helmet in hand, all set to start her motorbike. That is when she noticed that the fuel pipe had been cut. 'Petrol thieves!' she fumed and opened the fuel tank to check how much was left. To her surprise, the tank was full, just as she'd left it. She went back home to check CCTV footage of the night before. Sure enough, there it was. Two men on a motorbike stopped by hers shortly before midnight. One stayed on the bike ready to speed away. The other got off and did something to her bike. Then they left but came back again to finish the job. The angle of the video footage was not good enough to show her the precise details but it was enough to send a chill down her spine. Friends and family had warned her to drop the case, to stay quiet, to look the other way. But that was a price she wasn't willing to pay.

Sandhya Ravishankar is no damsel in distress waiting to be saved. She's a journalist on a mission to discover how 30 years of collusion has resulted in a massive loss to India's exchequer. She was awarded a Ramnath Goenka Award for Environmental Reporting in 2017. These awards are among the most respected in the country and they are given to journalists from the print/digital and broadcast media who maintain the highest standards of their profession, despite political and economic pressures, and who produce work that generates and sustains public trust in the media and impacts people's lives. Sandhya won the award for her extensive work on illegal sand mining in Tamil Nadu. She rides a motorbike meant for men and often goes where angels fear to tread. What started out as a routine job in this southern state led to the discovery of one of the biggest scams ever seen in independent India. It's weird to think that the commodity in question is sand.

It has not been an easy journey for Sandhya, and it is far from over. Looking over her shoulder, making a mental note of mundane details, such as a person's clothes and appearance, taking down the registration number of a vehicle behind her in case she is being followed, avoiding quiet lanes and staying on crowded ones – these are just some of the things she has to do every single day to ensure her own safety. Repeated complaints to the police have had little success, although they have been prompt to reassure her and offer her police protection at home whenever there has been an incident. And there have been a few. Enough to get her labelled as an 'attention-seeker' she says. But it's tiring to be on your guard all the time.

She is up against some extremely wealthy, politically well-connected and, frankly, dangerous foes. They have warned her that her activities are being monitored. Just to prove a point, the CCTV footage of her meeting with a source at a coffee shop was released on the Internet via a private blog. Further investigation revealed that the video footage had been collected from the coffee shop by police officers on the pretext of nabbing some petty criminals operating outside the shop. How it then found its way to an unconnected private blogger is anyone's guess. But it has serious implications. As a journalist who depends on information from reliable sources, it directly affects her ability to perform her job. In addition, it is a serious violation of her personal right to privacy. But, sadly, she is just one among several journalists facing similar problems, and some have faced worse.

Across the world, scores of people have been brutally beaten up, maimed, stabbed, shot, hacked to death with machetes, run over by tractors, mowed down by trucks, burned to death, buried alive – all for sand![1] Not all were journalists. They included farmers protesting against the destruction of their land, community leaders, forest guards, police officers, environmentalists and government officials on inspection missions. If you were looking for an example of how fact can be stranger than fiction, this is it. Sand is one of the commodities that is most sought after in places where 'development' is high on the agenda. The situation is particularly serious in India, but it is by no means restricted to India.

There's big money to be made by mining sand. In some places organised crime is involved, and in most others sand miners are opportunistic thieves working in groups. In India, you find both. When they enjoy political patronage, they are called the 'sand mafia'.

A study in the *International Journal of Comparative and Applied Criminal Justice* says:

> India's Sand Mafia, which illegally mines sand for construction, generates approximately $17 million per month in revenues. Despite the devastating environmental, physical, and economical harms caused, there is a dearth of criminological research on this organized crime group.[2]

The sand mafia can be ruthless. Much like organised crime in Italy or elsewhere, they are not a single organisation or entity. They carve up regions and are very territorial. They don't seek to exercise power directly. Instead, they infiltrate, corrupting the very systems meant to serve and protect people and the environment.

Getting involved in sand mining has been an easy thing to do so far. Nobody talks about sand in their daily lives. Yet, it is a critical resource. If there's no sand, there is no concrete. If there's no sand, there's no glass. These two things alone have become the mainstay of cities, no matter where in the world you are. You've read enough by now to know that sand is also mined for minerals that are critical to modern lifestyles. So people who object to the mining or who scrutinise the activity too closely are subject to intimidation, threat and violence if they fail to back off after the initial threats.

Sumaira Abdulali, the founder of Awaaz Foundation, a leading light in the fight to draw attention to this problem in India, has experienced many a threat to her life. In one incident in 2010, she narrowly escaped death when sand miners tried to topple her car off a bridge into the river below. She was lucky to survive that day thanks to some serious driving skills she learned from her husband, who happens to be a rally driver. Ten years after the incident her attackers still roam free, although, technically speaking, they face prosecution by the courts at some point. Fortunately for the world, Sumaira is extremely articulate, prolific and well-connected. She has been working relentlessly to document the problem and to drive change through a wide variety of means, including public interest litigation. She has influenced the work of many others, including my own.

In 2010–11, I did a Master's at King's College, London, on environment and development, and sand mining was the subject of my dissertation. But I could find few people in India who were willing to talk openly about it. Everyone I approached was too scared to talk about their experience because they were wary of the consequences. I was warned that it was wise to stay away because anyone who got too close was either kidnapped, or found their cameras being confiscated. The fear ran deep in all those who refused to be interviewed. The only people I could find who were willing to participate were Sumaira and the brave local activists she introduced me to, and I couldn't have been more grateful.

I travelled to Mumbai with my brother because I feared for my safety, and we did get a little taste of why the fear was so pervasive. We had hired a taxi for the days when we were scheduled to visit some of the villages affected by sand mining. Our local activist guide made us stop at a bridge to view the place where an embankment and a road had been built right into the river so that barges could be unloaded easily and the sand shipped to market much quicker – all illegally.

We had been on the bridge for all of five minutes when my brother noticed a youth on a motorcycle stop within earshot. He was clearly familiar with the local activist guide but what rattled me was that he was relaying a detailed description of my brother, of me, of the driver and of our car's licence plate to someone over the phone. He didn't look particularly menacing and I'm guessing we didn't seem a threat to him either. He let us go without incident. But I was afraid. Had I been alone, I would have turned back that very moment and given up altogether. It left a deep sense of unease.

It's hard to explain the feeling of being watched when you know there are big stakes involved, when a conversation can get people into trouble. Time has given me some perspective but I continue to wonder why this problem is so much more under the radar than it ought to be. What is this development that we chase after? And at what cost?

•9•

Cracking the Cradle

A beautiful young girl once lived with her cruel stepfather along the banks of the Yangtze. One day the stepfather decided to sell the girl in the market and he took her by boat on the river. En route though, he became intoxicated by her beauty and decided to take advantage of her before he sold her. The girl freed herself by jumping into the river and a powerful storm sank her cruel stepfather's boat. Shortly after the storm passed, a beautiful white dolphin was seen swimming gracefully in the river. Villagers believed it to be the reincarnation of that lost girl. She was called the Goddess of the Yangtze, a symbol of protection, peace and prosperity.[1]

Although sand has been mined for centuries, the current massive scale and frantic pace of this mining is unprecedented. Consequently, the impacts are hard to wrap our heads around. The key notion here is 'cumulative'. Even when projects are executed in a legal manner, that is, with the requisite permits and an environmental impact assessment statement for each project, what is rarely considered is the cumulative impact on the region of that and similar projects in addition to the impact from other human activities. There are important reasons to consider these cumulative impacts.

Take the case of the longest river in Asia, the third longest river in the world, the Yangtze. It had the rare distinction of being home to two species of dolphin – the Yangtze finless porpoise and the Yangtze River or Baiji dolphin. However, human activity in the region has changed this irrevocably. Building a dam for the world's largest hydroelectric plant to supply ever-growing energy demands changed the ecosystem, forced millions out of their homes and resulted in the loss of many species – but none more missed than the Baiji dolphin. Extensive sand mining, combined with other factors, culminated in the extinction of this iconic species, known as the Queen, or the Goddess, of the Yangtze.[2]

The Baiji dolphin had evolved to suit its environment with a highly developed sonar capability and greatly reduced vision because of the sediment in the river. The Yangtze River had long been the setting for the progress of civilisation. But the Baiji maintained its revered status and a steady population for millennia. Before industrialisation in the 1950s, there were an estimated 6,000 individuals in the Yangtze. However, with the advent of modern shipping, both sand and goods could be transported more quickly to their destination. Increasing traffic on the great river, combined with pollution and destructive fishing practices proved a death knell. The pollution left them vulnerable to disease and bereft of food.

The ever-changing sound environment drowned out their clicks and beeps and left them confused and exhausted. Popular author Douglas Adams, in *The Last Chance to See*, described their plight as being 'like a blind man trying to live in a discotheque. Or several competing discotheques.' They frequently collided with boats and many were hacked to death by ships' propellers. Many were caught as by-catch via gill nets, rolling hooks or electrical stunning. During the devastating Great Leap Forward, royal epithets notwithstanding, the Baiji dolphin was hunted for its meat and its skin was prized for gloves and purses.

China's economic boom meant an ever-greater requirement for building materials. So great was the scale of sand mining along the Yangtze that it began to affect navigation, destroy embankments and more. In 2000 the government banned sand mining in the Yangtze and tried hard to regulate fishing practices though education and workshops to protect the Baiji dolphin.

In 2006, 13 local officials were found guilty and punished for accepting huge bribes in Yongxiu county as they tried to monopolise the sand mining industry and to sell off the sand mining rights to Poyang Lake, the largest freshwater lake in the Yangtze river basin located in Jiangxi province. But it was too little, too late. That same year, after an extensive search in all known Baiji habitats, researchers failed to spot a single dolphin and the Baiji dolphin (*Lipotes vexillifer*), Goddess of the Yangtze, a symbol of protection, peace and prosperity, was declared functionally extinct.

The loss of the Baiji is of particular significance because it was the sole representative of the Lipotidae, an entire cetacean family that had diverted from other whales and dolphins. This was also the first extinction of a large mammal since the disappearance of the Caribbean monk seal in the 1950s. The Baiji had managed to change, adapt and thrive for millions of years. As Barbara Taylor at the National Oceanic and Atmospheric Administration's Fisheries Service put it, 'It's been here longer than the Andes Mountains have been on Earth'.[3] But we humans managed to erase 20 million years of unique evolutionary history in less than one-millionth of that time.[4]

In our quest for 'growth and development' at all costs, many more species are imperilled. Careless dredging results in sediment plumes that smother life underwater. Species that are mobile can move from the area. But those that are fixed, such as corals and plants, experience tremendous stress as their access to energy-giving sunlight is cut off. Scientists say that corals can shed some sediment but the process is very energy intensive and when they are already dealing with their access to sunlight being cut off, this added stress makes them prone to chronic diseases, such as white rot where their tissues waste away and expose the bare skeleton. Chances of a full recovery are slim as the tissues do not grow back.[5] Dredging has been linked with 'extensive coral mortality and critical habitat loss'.[6] Even the mobile species suffer. When they move away, they lose access to food sources and breeding sites.

Few species can tolerate high turbidity in the water column unless they already live in regions where this is natural. As a result, it changes the composition of species in the region. In turn, this affects larger species that depend on the smaller ones. Bottom-dwelling fish and other marine creatures lose critical habitat for spawning and feeding. Dredging impacts species during their most vulnerable stages. Sediment on floating eggs can disrupt nature's delicate dance and cause them to sink to the bottom, which affects the population's viability. Visual feeders such as fish, birds and marine mammals are affected by a lack of clarity in the water; while suspended sediments can clog the gills of fish and make them susceptible to infection and even death.[7]

In freshwater systems, such as lakes, rivers and wetlands, the removal of sand can leave behind only fine sediments, such as mud and clay. During the summer months, when water is most required, mud and clay tend to dry out and harden if there is no sand in the mix to allow the water to percolate to the lower layers. As a result, water levels can fall and bird and animal food sources can be impacted.[8] This affects not only those that live there but also seasonal users, such as migratory birds, who are deprived of the critical nutrition they need to continue their long journey.[9] Research comparing dredged and undredged sections of a river shows: reduced populations of fish; less variety of aquatic life in dredged areas;[10] flowing water species being displaced by still water species; and generalist and invasive species displacing native habitat specialists.[11]

For so long we have treated water bodies as mere dump yards and refuse sites. As we heedlessly dig and dredge, our past could come back to haunt us as the action of dredging resurrects long-buried chemical substances and reintroduces them into the water column.[12] Dredging also regurgitates normal dead and decomposing biomaterial, which uses up precious oxygen that is not readily replenished at those depths. Methods such as anchor dredging can leave deep pits that create hypoxic (low oxygen) conditions that affect how animals live and move on the seafloor.[13]

Evolution has empowered many species, such as terrapins and turtles, to find their way across hundreds of miles to lay their eggs at the very same sites where they hatched. Beach nourishment projects can bury nests so deeply that the little hatchlings have trouble getting out. This added strain must surely drain them of the energy they need to fight the elements and to evade predators. On other beaches, sand removal leaves these species homeless.[14]

Beach nourishment is a complicated business. As Samantha Muka, a historian in marine science explains, this habitat is not easily replaced.[15] Priorities depend on the stakeholder in question: tourists want picture-perfect beaches; engineers, politicians and tax payers want to minimise cost. Larger-grained sand is less likely to be blown or swept away but the added weight can crush eggs or make it impossible for hatchlings to uncover themselves. Finer-grained sand makes beaches that are great for humans to walk on but they become tightly packed and make it difficult for turtles to dig their nests.

In addition to grain size, there is another important factor. Scientists in Florida found that 'seemingly innocuous choices have unintended and possibly overlooked consequences'. They replaced one type of sand for another that looked similar but differed in only one characteristic, mineral make up. The study found there was not much difference in terms of the numbers that hatched and those that managed to get out of the nest. But turtle nests in aragonite sand were consistently cooler than those in silicate sand.[16]

Why did this matter? It turns out that the temperature of a nest during a particular stage of incubation determines the sex of many reptiles, including turtles. At 29.1^0C (84.38^0F) an even sex ratio forms in a clutch. Any deviation, even by one or two degrees above this temperature, during incubation has consequences. Above produces mostly females, while below produces mostly males. Messing with this delicate equilibrium drastically changes the availability of nesting females or males to fertilise the eggs. Rarely do beach nourishment project promoters take into account the need for such detail.

Muka thinks the gaps in the literature have been clear for a long while. She points to important studies that elaborate this conundrum. The most illuminating of these is one by Charles Petersen and Melanie Bishop in 2005. A review of 46 beach monitoring studies found that 'reform of agency practices is urgently needed as the risk of cumulative impacts grow'. Their review showed that over half of the studies arrived at conclusions that weren't entirely supported by the evidence available. Monitoring was typically carried out by project promoters and it wasn't subject to peer review. What was worse was that the results were rarely used to mitigate the damage inflicted on ecosystems.[17]

It is easy to picture a turtle or an otter and understand how they might be impacted. Yet there are countless other species, those known to science and those as yet undiscovered, that play an important role in maintaining the balance of the ecosystem but that do not get the attention they deserve. There is no shying away from the fact that humans are causing profound changes to the only life-sustaining planet that we are currently aware of. Some scientists say we are the root cause of the sixth mass extinction event in recorded history.[18]

Globally, freshwater megafauna populations declined by 88 per cent from 1970 to 2012.[19] These are species that can attain a size of 30 kilograms or more – such as sturgeons, river dolphins, crocodilians, giant turtles and hippos. They often live a long time but reproduce slowly. They can also travel long distances between spawning and feeding areas, which makes them vulnerable to human impacts on freshwater ecosystems. Since these species live long after their reproductive years, we may not even realise how bad things are for them. Human impact is felt even among saltwater species. Corals are among the most awe-inspiring living beings on Earth, but a startling study published in 2014 says, 'Over the last 30 years, hard coral cover has decreased by an average of 50% on Indo-Pacific reefs and 80% on Caribbean reefs.'[20] Coral diseases are a significant driver of global coral reef decline. Sediment and turbidity associated with offshore dredging have been found to increase coral disease on nearby reefs.

On the whole, the situation is quite dire for biodiversity. The Living Planet Index, an indicator of the state of global biodiversity and the health of our planet, shows an overall decline of 68 per cent in the populations of wildlife (fish, amphibians, reptiles, birds and mammals) between 1970 and 2020 – in other words, a decline by more than two-thirds in fewer than 50 years.[21] A landmark report released in May 2019, backed by the United Nations, says that humans are driving one million species to extinction.[22] One million! What kind of world are we making for future generations? As we recklessly plunder, dig and dredge mind-numbing volumes of sand from rivers, lakes, wetlands, ocean beds and inland sources to foster convenient lifestyles and to build shiny networked cities, we ignore the impacts of sand mining at our peril.

We move so much material across the world that we have overtaken nature as the force shaping our world. A press release from the British Geological Survey on 2 November 2018 is worth quoting:

Humans are the most significant global geomorphological driving force of the 21st century

We excavate the planet for minerals and modify the landscape to develop our expanding cities and infrastructure. A study by Dr Anthony Cooper and his co-authors estimates that 316 billion metric tons (a volume of about 150km^3) of sediment is currently created annually by humans through these activities. This is 24 times greater than the sediment shifted each year by all the world's major rivers.

A 100 years' worth of data on mineral, metal and cement production (and the waste materials these generate), plus construction, dredging and land reclamation estimates have been studied. These all show a dramatic increase in the amount of sediment created during the mid-20th century onwards as the world's population has grown.[23]

We are also making profound changes to the ecosystem by building dams on rivers. Dams prevent not only the natural migration of fish but also the flow of sediment downstream. As sand accumulates behind dams it lowers their energy output and simultaneously stops coasts and low-lying deltas from being replenished. Marc Goichot, who leads WWF's Freshwater Initiative across the Asia–Pacific region, uses the analogy of a conveyor belt to communicate how dams disrupt sediment flow, with dire consequences.

Concrete itself is problematic here. Hydropower dams use massive quantities. Let's remember that up to 75 per cent of concrete is made up of sand and gravel, not accounting for the sand it took to make the cement.[24] Where is all that sand coming from? The sediment in rivers plays a crucial role in the ecosystem. It builds up coastal wetlands and floodplains, replenishes nutrients in the soil, allows water to percolate into the groundwater table, provides critical habitat for species to spawn and is the source of sustenance in more ways and for more species than we have the funds to study. Floodplains have been the bedrock of agriculture and of civilisation. Without sand, all these ecosystem services are jeopardised, which could also affect our lives.

The next time you buy rice, do look up the country of origin. It is likely to have come from one of the countries in South Asia. The region produces about 90 per cent of the world's rice.[25] But many of the rice bowls of Asia are in deep trouble. Without the nourishment they need, these deltas are slowly shrivelling up. As cities grow and extract excessive groundwater, it leads to a phenomenon known as subsidence, where the land collapses. Without a constant supply of sand to act as a buffer against rising tides, coastlines are beginning to erode at abnormally fast rates. As long-standing mangrove forests are cleared to make way for sand mining to build cities and for shrimp cultivation and agriculture to feed these growing cities, these deltas are in a precarious position. As the seas advance, they encounter little resistance without sand to stem the tide. Several incidents of saltwater intrusion into freshwater systems have been recorded, which has a knock-on effect on the kinds of species that can survive in the river and on fisheries and agriculture. It's a stark reality for the people who live there.

The Mekong delta is a well-documented case study. The delta is shaped by the mighty Mekong river that originates on the Tibetan Plateau and runs for more than 4,184 km/2,600 miles through China, Myanmar, Thailand, Laos, Cambodia, and Vietnam before emptying into the South China Sea. But the

Mekong delta is a textbook example of how uncoordinated dam building in the upper reaches of the main stem of the river and on its tributaries are blocking the sediment flow so crucial to the region's economy and way of life.[26] The countries in the upper reaches of the river feel little obligation to those downstream and foreign investment is all too alluring. But the impacts are most noticeable downstream.

The Mekong delta is the third largest in the world, is home to over 17 million people and it ranks second only to the Amazon in overall biodiversity. The input of sediments used to be so strong that the shoreline advanced, meaning more land was being created than eroded. But human activities have altered this significantly and satellite imagery proves it. Several dams have been built upstream and many more are planned. Although no other factors have changed, such as wave and wind conditions, a study shows large-scale erosion and land loss between 2003 and 2012 that now affects over 50 per cent of the 600 km/372 mile coastline.[27]

Millions in the region depend on fish in the river for their sustenance and, in turn, the fish require free-flowing waters and abundant sediment in the river. Rivers are not static entities. Much like the tides that ebb and flow, rivers swell and contract with the seasons. Floods bring large amounts of nutrient into the deltas and communities learned to live with them. But the scale of flooding has changed dramatically, forcing people to migrate. As dam building unabashedly continues, many more people will be affected. South Asia is not alone in this situation though, there are similar cases in many other parts of the world.

There's a fierce fight going on to save the last wild rivers in Europe and the Balkans. A deluge of nearly 3,000 proposed hydropower developments threaten to destroy the culture and ecology of this forgotten region – 49 per cent of all these proposed projects happen to be situated in protected areas, including Ramsar sites, UNESCO World Heritage Nature Sites and Natura 2000 sites.[28] Is the word 'protection' simply empty rhetoric? *Blue Heart*, a beautiful documentary sponsored by Patagonia, is well worth a watch. It makes visible several interconnected threads. It records the battle to save Vjosa, the largest undammed river in Europe, and the effort to save the endangered Balkan lynx in Macedonia. It also tells the story of the incredibly brave 'women of Kruščica, Bosnia and Herzegovina, who were spearheading a month-long, 24/7 protest to protect their community's only source of drinking water'.

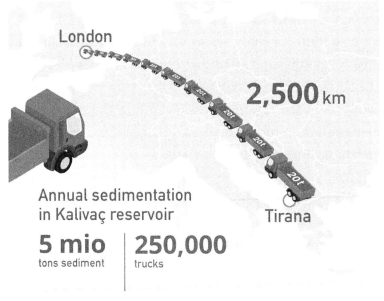

London

2,500 km

Annual sedimentation
in Kalivaç reservoir

Tirana

5 mio | 250,000
tons sediment | trucks

The Kalivaç dam would trap 5 million tons of river sediments (gravel, sand) annually. This amount equals a queue of trucks from Tirana to London (250,000 trucks).

9.1 Sediment trapped by the Kalivaç dam

Source: 'Measuring of sediment transport and morphodynamics at the Vjosa river/ Albania © Save the Blue Heart of Europe, balkanrivers.net

A recent study found that, every year, the Vjosa transports 5 million tons of sediment to the Adriatic Sea, that's equivalent to 250,000 big truckloads (see Figure 9.1). With these volumes of sediment trapped behind the dam, the study confirms there would be 'hardly any energy, no sand for the beach'.

A study published in the renowned *Science Advances* journal tells pretty much the same story from another part of the world. Scientists tried a natural experiment that reveals the impact of hydroelectric dams on the estuaries of tropical rivers. They compared two dammed and undammed rivers on Mexico's Pacific coast. They found that dams demonstrably affected the stability and productivity of the estuaries. The coastline associated with the two rivers dammed for hydroelectricity shrank rapidly on what should have been a growing coastline. The scientists don't mince their words as they calculate the economic losses to fisheries, biodiversity, coastal security and livelihoods arising from the coastal erosion caused by dams:

> We estimate that the cost of the environmental damages a dam can cause in the lower part of basin almost doubles the purported benefits of emission reductions from hydroelectric generation.[29]

> The world's rivers are arteries of sand transport across the continents.[30]

The health of our ecosystems depends on these arteries. The late twentieth century witnessed a dam-building frenzy that represents 'a recent, unprecedented, massive scale change'.[31]

Currently, there are 850,000 dams across the world that have been built for various purposes; 60,000 of these are large dams and they disrupt more than half of all river systems.[32]

Dams might have once been the symbol of green energy. But considering their collective and additive impacts, it is now past time that we disabuse ourselves of this notion.

I'd like to end this chapter with something shared by the late geologist Michael Welland. 'If the Earth is a year old, we [humans] appeared at seventeen minutes to midnight on December 31.'[33]

Can we afford to ignore the cumulative impact of all our actions? Can we afford to crack the cradle?

•10•

Builders Versus Fishermen

Bhaskar Rao Patil looks weary as he talks about his declining catches. He is the president of the fishermen's colony in Bankot, a small fishing village near Mumbai, on the western coast of India. The lines on his face tell the story of his life. He has seen better days. His hands are calloused, gnarled and strong. His clothes are clean but threadbare. Seated in modest surroundings he talks wistfully about bygone days while other fishermen nod in agreement.

> Gone are the days when we could fish easily. We could catch 50 pamplets [the local term for pomfrets, a high-value catch] in one hour. Today it's hard to find five even if we fish for the whole day. In the past, five people depended on one boat but today one boat can support only one to two people. Our life is under pressure.

Bhaskar's deep-set eyes turn to the far horizon. He points to the dredgers and the big barges on the river. They are his nemesis. The barges are filled up with sand dredged from the rivers and then taken to trucks waiting along the banks. He explains how the local fishermen live in constant fear for their livelihood because of them.

From a distance, the dredgers and barges look picturesque, but they're destroying the fishermen's way of life, and that of many others in the region. Up close, the barges look big enough to hold up to 20 fishermen's boats. And when they are full to the brim with wet sand, no prizes for guessing who wins if they crash into the smaller boats. The fishermen say accidents happen fairly often and that their nets are frequently damaged but that local officials are unwilling to register complaints against the barges as they are owned by 'Big hands' (i.e. elites). It feels like a losing battle. These local fishermen are up against a powerful, wealthy, well-connected and sometimes ruthless politician–builder nexus. The dredgers use pumps to suck up as much sand as they can, all of which is headed to the construction industry in Mumbai, the financial hub of the country. The commodity they take away to build a thriving city is the very lifeblood of these fishermen's livelihood.

Fishing is a seasonal occupation here as one cannot fish in the monsoon season, which lasts from June to August. What the fishermen earn in three to five months of the fishing season is what their families have to live on for the rest of the year. But seasons don't matter to dredgers and barges. They operate non-stop, all year round, shipping away precious sand to more profitable places. Most of the fishermen in these communities are illiterate. The few that can read and write have only completed primary education and most have no other income-generating skill, so they depend on moneylenders and fish traders to survive the lean period, which keeps them in perpetual indebtedness.

As the talk continues, Bhaskar Rao Patil's wife, Kanti Bai, enters the room with a tray of steaming hot tea and some snacks. The women play an equal role in village society. The men do the fishing, the women sell the catch in the markets.

With tears in her eyes she chips in with her part of the story, 'We'd like to send our children to good schools but we hardly make any money to spare these days.'

Rampant illegal sand mining has resulted in falling fish stocks because dredging destroys the spawning habitat of the fish and muddies the water. Only the most resilient fish survive and they are not as profitable a catch. When a boat is damaged by a barge, the villagers can't get a bank loan to repair or replace it without a registered police complaint or collateral property. So they are driven deeper into poverty. These people have been fishermen for generations and they know their river like the back of their hand. But indiscriminate sand mining is making their traditional knowledge obsolete as deeper channels make rivers more violent, which erodes riverbanks. The boats are forced to head out into the sea but they are ill-equipped for the dangers. Out in deeper waters, the tides have almost doubled in height, thanks to land reclamation around Mumbai. The fishermen are completely out of their depth in these waters and their only skills have become inadequate.

Around Mumbai, with no leader to show them another way, 80,000 fishermen have turned to fishing for sand.[1] They know their actions mean that their children will never be able to fish in these waters, at least not for the kind of fish they used to catch. They know that their identity and way of life is at stake. But it seems to be the only way to feed their families. They pin their hopes on getting their children educated and sending them to the cities so they will not have to live in hardship. The demand for sand has been increasing so, for now, they get by.

Mumbai is a city that never sleeps. With just over 22 million inhabitants, it is the most populated city in India and the eighth most populated city in the world. A massive growth that occurred over a relatively short time. In 1991 the city had just 9.9 million residents. Nearly half of the influx has been due to the search for better employment prospects. The number of super-rich has also increased exponentially. Out of 25 global cities, Mumbai has witnessed the highest growth in the number of ultra-high net worth individuals over the last decade. The world's most expensive home (at the time of its completion) can be found here, Antilia – 27 storeys tall, with three helipads, underground parking for 160 cars and a staff of 600. It is named after a mythical Atlantic island and is the fulfilment of a long-cherished dream for the owner.

Mumbai is the 'City of Dreams'. Millions of people flock to it hoping for a better life. It hosts a wide range of industries, from textile mills to cutting-edge technology. It houses two major stock exchanges and the headquarters of many multinational and large Indian companies. The city is also a hub for cultural export in the form of the thriving Bollywood industry and its ports are a critical part of its success. Mumbai alone produces five per cent of India's GDP.

There is no dearth of jobs or talent in Mumbai. But it is short of one thing, space. This is the most precious commodity in the city. Prominent journalist Bachi Karkaria says the built environment has increased fourfold since 1925 – and at its fastest rate over the past 30 years – all at the cost of green cover and wetlands: 'There's less than 0.03 acres of open space per 1,000 people. The global norm is four; London has a profligate 12.'[2] Most of the working class live in chawls, multilevel tenements with a family per small single room and a shared bathroom on each floor.[3] Middle-class families live in one- or two-bedroom apartments – a luxury in comparison, but still a tight squeeze.

There is a dire shortage of affordable housing. In the rest of the country, people manage to buy their own homes by their mid-30s. But in Mumbai people work well into their late 40s or 50s before they can pay off their mortgages. Demand is so huge that the government cannot keep pace so they turn to the private sector for help. This means developers are hungry for as much sand as they can get, which is in short supply. They blame the politicians and the environmental lobby.

Satish (his name has been changed), the director of a successful construction firm says: 'Roti, kapda aur makaan [loosely translated as food, clothes and shelter] is the dream of every citizen. How can you deprive them of this dream? It is easy to ban anything but it's important to provide alternatives. In 20 years of my career, I have never heard of such a thing. Shortage of sand?!', he snorts incredulously. 'It's not that there is no sand. This is all just a ploy to make you pay more'.

To Satish and his colleagues, the hullabaloo around the supply of sand makes no sense. To them, sand is abundant and they feel the whole situation has just been engineered to create an artificial shortage. Once the price goes up by more than 100 per cent, it never goes back to the original. Instead, it settles at a much higher price and that then becomes the new norm. 'In the end, it is the consumer who pays the price. I run a business, not a charity. I simply have to pass on the costs to the customers.'

On the condition of anonymity, he talks at length about how developers are forced to buy sand from certain suppliers, about how each region is controlled by powerful vested interests.

'You can buy sand from elsewhere but you have to still have to pay these guys if you want your consignment to actually reach you. So in the end, you might as well buy from them.' In sticky situations, some developers compromise on the quality of materials he says, while others like him compromise on the price. 'Sand used to be about 4–5% of the project cost. Now it is about 10–12% of the cost. We don't worry about cement anymore. We worry about sand. Cement, you can pay and tomorrow you will get it. Sand – you will not. The sand supplier used to be the last person who would get paid. We used to stock sand outside and when it rained, it would often wash away. Not anymore.'

Satish's predicament is common. Reports indicate that sand is in such short supply developers have to import it from Indonesia and the Philippines.[4]

While developers come to terms with the new reality, the government is working hard to promote affordable housing. The Mumbai Development Plan 2034 suggests that it intends to make additional land available for development by releasing No-Development Zones that include coastal wetlands and salt pans – used by scores of migratory birds in the summer. Fierce protests are taking place to save eco-sensitive zones, such as the Aarey Forest that was once part of the Sanjay Gandhi National Park. But many Mumbaikars have no time for this debate. With exhausting commutes and tough working hours, all they want is 'Roti, kapda aur makaan [food, clothes and shelter]' and some fun along the way. A Mumbaikar friend explains: 'Yaar [my friend], people buy apartments like they buy a pizza. You don't care about what goes into it as long as it looks great.'

Bhaskar Rao Patil and his co-workers are not alone. Even in the UK, where dredgers operate legally and are fitted with a black box to monitor movement at all times, there are very real fears about what is happening to fish stocks because of dredging. Interviews with UK fishermen show that they too avoid the dredging areas because of potential damage to their equipment. As a result, they find themselves being pushed into overcrowded fishing grounds, further jeopardising overexploited fish stocks.[5] A study by an independent marine environmental consultant and a member of the Marine Conservation Society, UK, Ray Drabble, shows: 'The majority of fish species have shown marked reductions in abundance since commencement of dredging [… when …] other environmental factors considered offer no explanation for the changes in abundance.'[6]

Drabble points out that some of the earliest studies from the UK government's £25 million Marine Aggregate Levy Sustainability Fund (MALSF) programme acknowledged that little work had been carried out regarding 'entrainment rates of fish in marine dredging', that is, fish uptake during the dredging process.[7] He feels it has remained an area of research that has been 'persistently neglected'. As early as 1992, scientists did sample studies to estimate the damage being done to marine life and concluded that they could only 'speculate on the amount of damage' until further studies were conducted.[8] But what is even more disconcerting is that, more than two decades later, Drabble says the industry still doesn't measure fish by-catch from dredging activity 'at source'. Affordable housing continues to be a mantra, even in the UK, and rightly so, although it remains a pipe dream for many. But, now that we have reached a critical point in human history, is there scope to do things differently?

There's a great need for a different approach because this is truly a global problem, and a growing one at that. A 2009 case study from Korea found that the value of lost catch over a one-year period was an estimated $38,851 due to a single mining site. Estimated cumulative damages due to recurring mining for 5 and 10 years were $1.5 million and $2.2 million, respectively, for 20 sand mining sites within a single district. Extrapolate that to a whole country and you can see why urgent measures are required to address the imbalance.[9]

The fishing industry is not the only one impacted by this lopsided focus on construction. Agriculture and eco-tourism are other sectors that are particularly vulnerable. Across Africa, Asia, South America and Europe traditional livelihoods are being jeopardised by dredging and other forms of sand mining.

Across the world, productive farmland and crops are being lost to various forms of sand mining or their impacts.[10] The impact on food and water security in one particular region bears closer scrutiny. An inquiry by a parliamentary committee in Ghana found that about 85 per cent of sand miners were operating illegally in 2017. Many operated at night and were armed with deadly weapons. Intensive sand mining was impacting food security, coastal erosion and causing a decline in fish catch in rivers. Sand mining, or sand winning as it is called in Ghana, was found to be 'a threat to economic productivity'.[11]

Across the world, the decline in fish catch in coastal areas could impact more than three billion people who depend on fish for their sustenance and their livelihood.[12] Can we truly eradicate poverty if people face forced migration and loss of livelihoods that have sustained them over generations?

Can we continue to ignore the trade-offs that are being made to facilitate the growth of our high-tech futuristic cities and lifestyles?

Can we achieve the global Sustainable Development Goals (SDGs) if we fail to take into account how sand underpins lives and livelihoods? Figures 10.1a–b illustrate how sand mining intersects with each SDG.

Global Sustainable Development Goals		Examples of how sand mining intersects with each goal
SDG1	**NO POVERTY** End poverty in all its forms everywhere	Heavy sand dredging for over a decade in the waterways of Cambodia's Koh Kong province has left a fishing community struggling to fill its nets. Source: https://southeastasiaglobe.com/sand-dredging-koh-kong/
SDG2	**ZERO HUNGER** End hunger, achieve food security and improved nutrition and promote sustainable agriculture	Productive farm lands in Ghana and other parts of Africa are being destroyed by sand winning (sand mining). A Parliamentarian has called this activity, 'a threat to economic productivity.' Source: http://ir.parliament.gh/handle/123456789/171
SDG3	**GOOD HEALTH AND WELL-BEING** Ensure healthy lives and promote well-being for all at all ages	Communities living around frac sand mining facilities in the U.S. are exposed to airborne pollutants, notably fine particulates and crystalline silica (quartz) that are known to cause respiratory diseases and cancer. Source: https://www.uwsp.edu/cnr-ap/clue/Documents/Mining/FracSand2014WebinarFinal.pdf
SDG4	**QUALITY EDUCATION** Ensure inclusive and equitable quality education and promote lifelong learning opportunities for all	Children in Uganda mine sand from the bed of the Nile River to earn enough for school books and other ancillary costs of education. The temptation to stay away from school is strong though as the rewards are immediate. The construction sector offers higher wages than traditional farming and the demand for sand is fierce. Source: https://www.youtube.com/watch?v=M5C5nI-Vz74
SDG5	**GENDER EQUALITY** Achieve gender equality and empower all women and girls	Mineral sand mining in Madagascar has had a severe impact on women's traditional livelihoods. They now spend many more hours at work only to make a fraction of what they once earned. Source: https://doi.org/10.1080/03066150.2012.671769
SDG6	**CLEAN WATER AND SANITATION** Ensure availability and sustainable management of water and sanitation for all	Uncontrolled sand mining in the Vietnamese Mekong Delta, a region that supplies 50% of the nation's food, has exacerbated saline intrusion, which is the movement of ocean saltwater into riverine freshwater. Source: https://doi.org/10.1038/s41598-019-55018-9
SDG7	**AFFORDABLE AND CLEAN ENERGY** Ensure access to affordable, reliable, sustainable and modern energy for all	The enormous demand for frac sand for unconventional oil and natural gas drilling projects in the U.S. has raised a lot of questions around environmental justice and the climate emergency. Source: https://halttheharm.net/2017/07/webinar-frac-sand-mining-frackings-hidden-connection-americas-breadbasket/
SDG8	**DECENT WORK AND ECONOMIC GROWTH** Promote sustained, inclusive and sustainable economic growth, full and productive employment and decent work for all	A land reclamation project in the bay of Makassar, Indonesia is having severe consequences for the fish stock, the beach and the lives of thousands of small-scale fishing communities who have filed a formal complaint against the Dutch Export Credit Agency Atradius DSB Source: https://www.bothends.org/en/Whats-new/News/Fisher-folk-in-Indonesia-file-a-complaint-against-the-Dutch-Export-Credit-Agency-Atradius-DSB

10.1a Sustainable Development Goals 1–8 impacted by sand mining

©SandStories.or

Global Sustainable Development Goals		Examples of how sand mining intersects with each goal
SDG9	**INDUSTRY, INNOVATION AND INFRASTRUCTURE** Build resilient infrastructure, promote inclusive and sustainable industrialization and foster innovation	Under the cover of COVID-19, Bali's provincial council has unravelled a hard-won campaign to save the mangrove-rich Benoa Bay. The zoning plan, approved in Aug 2020, allows for significant sand mining, land reclamation activities and the development of the inter-national airport. Source: https://news.mongabay.com/2020/10/in-bali-the-pandemic-unravels-a-hard-won-campaign-to-save-benoa-bay/
SDG10	**REDUCED INEQUALITIES** Reduce inequality within and among countries	Irresponsible heavy mineral sand mining operations in Mozambique put an entire coastal village of more than 1,000 people at serious risk of being washed into the Indian Ocean, Amnesty International released a report - 'Our lives mean nothing' in 2018. Source: https://www.amnesty.org/download/Documents/AFR4178512018ENGLISH.PDF
SDG11	**SUSTAINABLE CITIES AND COMMUNITIES** Make cities and human settlements inclusive, safe, resilient and sustainable	Between 1985 and 2016, rice crop areas within the São Paulo state in south-eastern Brazil decreased approximately 43% and the area covered by sand-mining lakes increased by 630%. Source: https://doi.org/10.1117/12.2278766
SDG12	**RESPONSIBLE CONSUMPTION AND PRODUCTION** Ensure sustainable consumption and production patterns	Lough Neagh, UK is a Ramsar site (wetland site of inter-national importance), SPA (Special Protection Area - safe-guards the habitat of wild birds, migratory, threatened birds) ASSI (Area of Special Scientific Interest). Unlawful dredging began over 30 years ago but was granted planning approval in Oct 2020. Source: Lough Neagh: Sand dredging approval 'assault on environment.' 2020.BBC News.
SDG13	**CLIMATE ACTION** Take urgent action to combat climate change and its impacts	Concrete contains 60% - 75% sand and gravel by volume. If concrete were a country, it would be the world's third-largest greenhouse gas emitter. Source: https://medium.com/@UNDP/why-development-results-should-no-longer-be-concrete-5214d2618b85
SDG14	**LIFE BELOW WATER** Conserve and sustainably use the oceans, seas and marine resources for sustainable development	Coral diseases are a significant driver of global coral reef decline. Sediment and turbidity associated with offshore dredging have been found to increase coral disease prevalence on nearby reefs. Source: https://doi.org/10.1371/journal.pone.0102498
SDG15	**LIFE ON LAND** Protect, restore and promote sustainable use of terrestrial ecosystems, sustainably manage forests, combat desertification, and halt and reverse land degradation and halt biodiversity loss	Asia's hunger for sand is taking a toll on several endangered species including migratory birds. Source: https://www.sciencemag.org/news/2018/03/asias-hunger-sand-takes-toll-endangered-species
SDG16	**PEACE, JUSTICE AND STRONG INSTITUTIONS** Promote peaceful and inclusive societies for sustainable development, provide access to justice for all and build effective, accountable and inclusive institutions at all levels	'The 'sand mafia' is currently considered to be one of the most prominent, violent and impenetrable organized crime groups in India' according to Aunshul Rege, an associate professor in the criminal justice department at Temple University in Philadelphia. Source: https://forbiddenstories.org/sand-mafias-silence-journalists-in-india/

10.1b Sustainable Development Goals 9–16 impacted by sand mining

©SandStories.org

•11•

The Currency of Development

Sand is the unsung hero of our world

Michael Welland, Sand Wars

A short flight away from ever-busy Europe lie the islands of the blissful, the islands of eternal spring, the islands of the Gods, the Canary Islands. Even closer to Europe, lie the Balearic islands, with classic Mediterranean postcard places like Mallorca. Millions of weary Europeans flock to these destinations to let their hair down and party, to find solace or as a refuge from the bitter winter cold. In 2017, two organisations, a golf course in Mallorca and developers of a luxury beach resort in the Canary Islands, were surprised to find themselves at the centre of a storm.[1] As far as they could tell, they had done no wrong. They'd been carrying out normal business practice. And yet, they were facing a media frenzy as people gathered to protest against them and their suppliers.[2]

At the heart of the controversy was the sand they had just imported from Western Sahara for construction and maintenance. The protesters held up banners that read 'protect the natural resources of Western Sahara for the Saharawi people' and 'Stop the Plunder'.[3] As far as the companies were concerned it had been a run-of-the-mill operation. Surely the consignment was legal or the civil guard would not have allowed it into the port, right? They had work to do, a reputation to live up to and guests to satisfy, and this media attention was for all the wrong reasons. The golf course was a thriving business. It was a short ride away from the city and it offered wonderful panoramic views and a varying landscape that catered to clients wanting to test their technique. But they were quick to admit that they didn't know the origin of the sand they had bought to replenish the bunkers. They normally sourced sand from inland quarries but this sand worked well for draining water off the golf course as it had very little organic content.[4]

The developers of the luxury resort had no qualms about using this sand. They had just spent over six million euros and had been building their resort for over 25 years. They had worked hard to get all the necessary approvals and had just received permission from the local council on condition that they complete the project within one year. They were proud of how they had transformed an unappealing black beach of volcanic rocks into a lush beach with blond sand, where people could walk without falling and hurting themselves.[5]

They had created a tourist magnet people would want to return to. Their promotional video depicted the international star footballer and local hero David Silva espousing their cause.[6] They were improving the region's economy by boosting tourism and offering much-needed employment. They had tried to get sand from other sources but had been denied and found no other option but to import it. They couldn't understand what the fuss was all about. After all, it was common practice to import sand and even Playa de Las Teresitas, one of the most popular beaches in Tenerife, had been built using imported sand more than 40 years ago. As far as they were concerned, such sand was routinely used in construction projects across the Canary Islands.[7]

The above issue has been highlighted several times over the years by Western Sahara Resource Watch (WSRW), an international network of organisations and activists researching and campaigning against companies working for Moroccan interests in occupied Western Sahara – and working to preserve the natural resources for its people. The Canary Islands have been importing sand from the occupied territory of Western Sahara for decades, ever since the local council realised that it was cheaper to import that sand than to use the local but rare and expensive black volcanic sand.[8] The first recorded import was in 1955, when Western Sahara was a Spanish colony.[9] Today however, this land is occupied territory and 165,000 of its people live in refugee camps in the middle of the sweltering desert in neighbouring Algeria.[10] They long for the right to self-determination and are bitter about having to depend on humanitarian aid when they should have been one of the richest countries in North Africa.[11] Meanwhile, exports of phosphates, fish and sand from their region continue unabated.

With an economy that is largely dependent on tourist money, developers in the Canary Islands will stop at nothing to create picture-perfect spaces for people to unwind in. WSRW says, 'The exploitation of sand is the most important non-energetic mining sub-sector in terms of production and generated value. It even tops phosphates.'[12]

Florent Marcellesi, Member of the European Parliament for the Equo party from Spain says, 'We are not talking about benefits, as is usually done, but about consent, it is a democratic issue and at the same time we are not talking about local populations but about the Saharawi people, which is different because with local populations they could be the settlers, we talk about the people with the right to decide on the future of Western Sahara.'[13] In the context of trade deals, it is worth mentioning that the EU Court of Justice, the highest court of the European Union, upheld the rights of the Saharawi people in 2016 and again in 2018.[14]

When asked whether they have consent from the Saharwi people, the companies respond with, 'Why should we? It's a problem in their country, not ours.' Some suppliers say they import from Morocco but deal with Saharwi families. However, in response WSRW says the region of extraction is heavily controlled and exporting companies have deep ties to the Morocco government.[15] They contend that the government of the Canary Islands is granting impunity to offenders by not imposing traceability checks on raw material imports from a disputed territory. Although imports went down during the financial crisis, they increased considerably after 2004.[16]

The model is so successful that even Madeira (a Portuguese territory) has jumped on the 'artificial beach from imported sand' bandwagon.[17] There is good money to be made. Developers get loans and special concessions for helping the economy and, for practical purposes, they're in it for the long-term. Unlike natural beaches that are created and maintained because of natural tides and currents, these beaches need to be replenished ever so often. Once the demand has been created, no one wants to lose part of their economy, or their reputation for welcoming tourists.

The supply of sand is critical. Even more so for countries planning to expand their territory. Singapore has received much attention over the last few years for growing at the expense of its neighbours.[18] Although the country is seen as a leader in sustainability initiatives, some question its green credentials.[19] Singapore requires sand not just for creating artificial land but also for growing vertically.[20] The demand is fierce since it offers all its citizens housing and top-notch infrastructure facilities. The country also has plans to use underground space. It has mapped out its entire subterrain and has begun building deep cavernous concrete tunnels in select locations. The tunnels are not intended for housing but to free up precious space in the sunlight. So they are designated as storage facilities for fuel and ammunition, sewerage and waste services, underground transport and the like. All these plans would come to nought without sand. So the country maintains reserves in closely guarded inland locations. They are so strategically important that they've been taken 'off the map'.[21]

Singapore has also benefited from hosting some of the biggest pure-play foundries that manufacture semiconductor chips. Its ability to process silicon for high-end uses has served it well.[22] The country has established itself as a world-class technology hub and as an attractive destination for companies looking to increase their footprint in Asia. According to Singapore's Economic Development Board, 80 out of the top 100 tech firms in the world have operations there and electronics play an important part.[23]

With so much at stake, it is little wonder that the government washes its hands of any responsibility for sand imports. In response to allegations from NGOs such as Global Witness, it has clearly stated that this is a purely commercial interaction and the responsibility for good governance lies with the country that exports the sand.[24]

Not everything is made in Singapore though. The country is heavily reliant on food imports, such as eggs, wild-caught fish and shrimp, from neighbouring countries such as Malaysia. But if events in 2018 are anything to go by, Malaysia is intent on asserting itself. It announced multiple bans on specific food exports at critical times during the year.[25] In a more controversial move, the country announced that it was extending its territorial waters. Singapore has objected and claimed that the move infringes on their territorial sovereignty. Old tensions have flared up and the region remains sensitive.

Meanwhile, within Malaysia, the government is tightening its control over a major land reclamation and development project, Forest City. Chinese developers own a controlling stake in the project and a minority share is owned by the Sultan of Johor Bahru.[26] The city appears to have been built for affluent Chinese, to the detriment of the local population who cannot afford to live there. Property costs MYR500,000–MYR3,010,00, when the average local salary is MYR51,968 ($113,272–$681,898, when the average local salary is $11,773).[27] As sales slow within China, developers are looking to Singapore. With sky-rocketing housing prices in Singapore, they can offer jet-setting individuals better living spaces at a fraction of the price. Forest City is strategically located adjacent to Singapore, approximately 5km from the Second Link and 40 minutes to Singapore CBD.[28] But the government in Malaysia has warned that it will not provide resident visas just because people own property in the country.[29] In 2019, it came to light that Malaysia had banned sand export to Singapore the previous year but 'the ban was never made public because of the potential diplomatic fallout'.[30] Malaysia had been one of the biggest sources of sea sand for Singapore. It's wait and watch to see how these developments play out in the future.

For now, South-East Asia remains a hotbed of activity with much action on the geopolitical front, particularly in the South China Sea. China, Vietnam, Malaysia, the Philippines and Taiwan have all reclaimed land, in other words, built artificial land. However, China has created '17 times more land in 20 months' than all the others have over the past 40 years.[31] It is hard to estimate the exact amount of sand that has been dredged from the bottom of the sea and dumped on contested coral reefs and atolls in a bid to build islands in the South China Sea.

So why are countries going to great lengths to build artificial land in this region? Because the South China Sea plays a strategic role in the modern world. Whoever controls access to these waters, exerts an outsized influence on everything that goes on there. Take the example of global trade, in which transportation by sea is dominant, 60 per cent of global maritime trade passes through Asia and the South China Sea accounts for a large portion of that. In 2016, roughly 21 per cent of global trade, an estimated $3.4 trillion, passed through the region.[32]

This region is also coveted for its natural resources. The South China Sea holds 'proven oil reserves of at least seven billion barrels and an estimated 900 trillion cubic feet of natural gas'.[33] It is also one of the world's most important fisheries, which generates billions of dollars each year and employs more than 3.7 million people.[34] Although it covers only 2.5 per cent of the Earth's surface, it accounts for 12 per cent of the global fish catch.[35] It is incredibly biodiverse and there are 3,365 known species of fish, thanks to the reef ecosystem.[36]

But this once-thriving ecosystem is heading towards collapse due to dredging, land reclamation and overfishing.[37] China has 'provided military training and sophisticated GPS and communications technology to its fishermen so they can call in the coast guard if they have a run-in with a foreign law enforcement vessel or alert the coast guard of the presence of fishermen from other countries.'[38] This bit of information acquires greater significance when you consider that China operates the largest fleet of fishing vessels on Earth and has been the world's leading exporter of fishery products since 2002.[39]

Understandably, Vietnam, Malaysia, Brunei, Philippines and Taiwan are all affected by China's aggressive approach. China's claims of historical rights in accordance with its 'nine-dash line' has been invalidated by an international tribunal set up by the Permanent Court of Arbitration in the Hague. In 2016, the tribunal ruled unanimously in favour of the Philippines in the arbitration instituted by the Republic of the Philippines against the People's Republic of China. However, China did not participate in the arbitration and has refused to accept or recognise the ruling.[40] Under the UN Convention of the Law of Sea (UNCLOS), 'Rocks which cannot sustain human habitation or economic life of their own shall have no exclusive economic zone or continental shelf'. Although islands can generate territorial waters and exclusive economic zones, UNCLOS also specifies that they must be 'a naturally formed area of land'.[41] So, in theory, artificial islands don't count. But there appears to be little these neighbouring countries can do as China flexes its might and uses dredging as a political instrument. The changing physical geography of the region brings with it new geopolitical challenges that these nation-states are ill-equipped to handle.[42]

Not only have the new islands been built to accommodate frolicking tourists who are proud of their nation's development, but they have also been designed with military infrastructure and airstrips capable of handling a 'fourth-generation fighter jet'.[43] There's no mistaking an intention to defend what China considers to be its territory.[44] The situation remains volatile as China continues its progress. Its shocking ability to convert a reef to a full-fledged island 'in less than a year' comes from upgrading its dredging fleet.[45] It owns dredgers that 'simply did not exist 15 years ago, yet now China can deploy dozens of them simultaneously in the South China Sea.'[46]

In November 2017 China launched *Tian Kun Hao*, an autonomous dredging vessel that has been hailed as a 'magic island maker'. The vessel can be controlled by GPS and operated without a crew. It can dredge the seabed at '6,000 cubic metres an hour, the equivalent of three standard swimming pools, from 35m below the water's surface'.[47] China appears well-poised to turn its ambition of a new maritime silk route into a reality. Despite the posturing, it is worth noting that this need for speed pales in comparison with what European dredging vessels currently have to offer and the fleets that are being built.

China has only recently joined the big boys club. But, the global open dredging market continues to be dominated by European companies, especially those from Benelux (Belgium, Netherlands and Luxembourg).[48] In 2012, the four giants – Van Oord, Boskalis, Jan de Nul and DEME – controlled approximately 60 per cent of the global dredging market. Experts point out, 'They still possess a competitive edge over China in terms of equipment, technology, and name recognition.'[49]

Take the example of cutter suction dredgers (to compare like-with-like, the evaluation is based on total installed power capacity). The *Tian Kun Hao*, built in 2017, has a total installed power capacity of 25,843 kW, whereas Belgian company DEME built the largest cutter section dredger way back in 2005, with a total installed power of 28,200kW (and called *D'Artagnan*, the swashbuckling hero of *The Three Musketeers*). In 2003, Jan De Nul built *JFJ* with an installed power capacity of 27,240kW.[50] These two dredgers are dwarfed by what's being built at the moment. Just as China was celebrating the largest cutter suction dredger in Asia, DEME, in collaboration with other partners, unveiled plans for *Spartacus*, the 'World's Largest Cutter Suction Dredger' with an installed power capacity of 44,180kW. It can dredge at a depth of 45 metres. Not only is it self-propelled but it also runs on liquefied natural gas (LNG).[51] Jan de Nul is also building a vessel that is 'approximately 150 per cent larger than its largest current cutter.'[52]

This chapter mentions four names but there are scores of other companies in this space.[53] In fact, the European Dredging Association (EuDA) says, 'Dredging activities are not well known by the wider public, but as a matter of fact, the European dredging companies, members of EuDA, are world market leaders with about 80% share of the worldwide open dredging market and a turnover of 7.7bn Euro in 2016. Although 70% of operations take place outside Europe, 90% of the returns flow back to Europe.' EuDA says that European dredging companies own a combined fleet of approximately

750 seaworthy EU-flagged ships.[54] This is an understatement, if ever there was one. In 2020, just one of the largest dredging companies, Boskalis, owns more than 800 vessels and auxiliary equipment, despite undergoing a 'fleet rationalisation' (taking vessels out of service by scrapping, selling and laying them up).[55] Many of these dredging vessels are state of the art.

Among the smaller companies operating in this space, many out of EU waters for expediency, several have vessels that are active but are not EU-flagged, nor seaworthy for that matter (but that's another book). Suffice it to say that dredging is seen as a key economic engine for the EU, although responsibility for the activity's impacts often appears to lie in no man's land. Serious allegations against many of these companies appear to be par for the course: bribery of public officials; undisclosed donations to political parties at election times; turning a blind eye to human rights violations; a blatant disregard for local environmental laws; and more.[56]

In conclusion, to weave it all together, sand is the currency of development. There needs to be greater regulation, monitoring and evaluation as this currency is produced and traded in a wide variety of contexts that have implications for geopolitical, social, environmental and economic outcomes, as well as for inter-generational equity. Prior to the global pandemic, the world was on track to build a New York City a month for the next forty years.[57] What we need now, more than ever, is 'big picture thinking' or 'systems-thinking'. For better or for worse, everything is interconnected and the following chapters tease out this concept in more detail.

•12•

Private Gain at Public Expense

As Chapters 2 and 6 showed, Dubai's example has spawned many a development. The latest reclamation project where work is continuing at a feverish pace lies in the heart of Africa, on Victoria Island adjacent to Lagos, Nigeria. The developers are creating a twenty-first-century city on land reclaimed from the Atlantic Ocean, using 140 million tonnes of sand and protected from rising sea levels by the 'Great Wall of Lagos' – an enormous sea defence built specifically to protect this feather in Africa's cap.[1]

Funding for this ambitious project comes not from government but from big name banks and private sector investors. The project has even been praised by former US President Bill Clinton.[2] As an aside, there have been reports that a member of the developer's family donated over $1 million to the Clinton Foundation.[3] In the 1990s that same family member was said to have been closely associated with the corrupt dictator Sani Abacha, who defrauded the country of billions, killed demonstrators and executed the environmentalist Ken Saro-Wiwa who protested against Shell.[4]

Eko Atlantic City is being touted as Africa's answer to Dubai, a multi-billion dollar residential and commercial development that will stretch over 10 km² (3.86 square miles).

The project aims to 'solve the chronic shortage of real-estate in the world's fastest growing megacity'. It will have its own light rail system, efficient road networks and a pedestrian lifestyle.[5] Energy efficient buildings will be the norm and the developers are preparing for 5G and autonomous cars.[6] They guarantee an uninterrupted power supply and potable water on tap. The developers also claim that this city will become the financial hub of West Africa. It is interesting to see how every marketing term in the pack has been used, from 'defence against coastal erosion' to the oft-heard 'creation of jobs'.

This project has also been called 'an act of climate apartheid'. It is seen as a place where the rich can escape the worst effects of the climate crisis while the majority are left to deal with the aftermath. But this criticism does not stem from envy. Experts say the project may cause its neighbours plenty of problems. Hard structures such as sea walls can offer protection but a storm surge then moves along the wall until it finds a weak spot or a target where the energy can dissipate. All around this fancy development are low-lying villages. The region used to be characterised by mangroves and fishing communities. But in a drive for modernity and massive urbanisation, the mangroves were all destroyed and the fishing communities displaced.

Organisations such as Community Conservation and Development Initiatives (CCDI), Environmental Law Research Institute (ELRI) and Heinrich Böll Stiftung (HBS) have raised serious concerns about the environmental and social impacts of the Eko Atlantic project.[7] This is especially significant given that the Nigerian coastline is low-lying and has the fastest erosion rates in the world.[8] The Environmental Impact Assessment (EIA) was submitted three years after dredging activities began, in contravention of national law. The project underwent public consultation in November 2011, although reclamation work had been going on since 2008. Not all of the affected communities were consulted when the project was being planned. No data or evidence of long-term monitoring of the tides and wave strength were made available before commencement of the project. The international companies involved would not dare to behave like this within their home territories. So what makes it okay to behave this way elsewhere?

Professor David Aradeon, a respected architect and urban planner and recipient of the Nigerian National Order of Merit, thinks the project is 'firmly grounded on the exploitation and expropriation and use of our common wealth for private profit' and is simply a continuation of the country's British colonial legacy.[9] As the wetland ecosystems are filled in with sand, the city loses their precious services as a natural sponge to soak up excess rain or the spill-over from ocean floods. The draft final EIA, available on the government's website, acknowledged that the project might shift the erosion eastwards – and no prizes for guessing that the proposed mitigation was to build more hard structures.

In a region where hunting, fishing and farming used to be the main livelihoods, communities have been forced to deal with added pollution from urban waste disposal, dredging and shipping due to vastly reduced forests and wetlands. In a city where 70 per cent of the population lives in informal settlements, the informal economy continues to play an important role so Professor Aradeon is quite critical of the public-private partnership model of development. He believes that it allows the government to free itself of its social responsibilities and to focus on the grandeur of glamourous projects instead. He warns that the financial burden on the next generation will be enormous. In light of the climate crisis and the strong possibility that Victoria Island and the Lekki Peninsula will flood, he believes the project promoters, their bankers and insurers should be held liable for any collateral damage it causes.

CCDI, ELRI and HBS have all warned that the project is likely to increase social differences and to entrench divisions between the rich and poor in Lagos. The nature and number of permanent jobs hasn't been made clear; nor is it clear where the support staff – the security guards, drivers and housekeepers – would live or find affordable food. Evacuation plans for worst-case flooding after an ocean surge haven't been made public and neighbouring communities are likely to have difficulties coping with increased pressure on their infrastructure. Truly sustainable mega-cities, they say, will be judged by their capacity to offer all citizens decent housing, education and employment, regardless of whether they are rich or poor. Meanwhile, bombastic marketing efforts to promote 'THE BEST PRIME REAL ESTATE IN WEST AFRICA' continue.

Elsewhere in Africa, there are troubling signs that mineral sand mining is not as benign as it is made out to be. Even though there are supposed to be well-established regulations around mineral sand mining, compared to mining sand for other purposes, it is still deeply problematic. It is commonly believed that for companies to obtain the social licence to operate they need to show that corporate responsibility is a core focus. One analyst I communicated with believes that, in general, companies with institutional shareholders that are listed in the

UK, US, Canada and Australia have such a pressure that they cannot afford any faux pas and they run good operations.

But there are definitely 'Multiple perceptions, contested realities'.[10] British-Australian Rio Tinto's ilmenite mine in Madagascar is a well-documented example. This is the fourth-largest island in the world and it is famous for its biodiversity. It is home to an incredible array of plants and animals found nowhere else on Earth. The old-growth forests are teeming with so much life that biologists cannot keep pace with naming newly discovered species.[11] But Madagascar is also one of the poorest countries. Ninety-two per cent of the population lives on less than two dollars a day and most of them live in extreme poverty. Studies have found that nearly 50 per cent of children under the age of five are chronically malnourished.[12] Spurred on by the World Bank's structural reforms, Madagascar has attracted several large mining projects to boost its development, but the country hasn't benefited as much as it had hoped to and it may have lost more in the bargain.[13]

Rio Tinto is headquartered in London and is listed on the London Stock Exchange. In 2019 it was the fourth-largest mining company in the world. The company has been in Madagascar since 1986. The mineral sand mine is run by a wholly owned Canadian subsidiary, QIT Madagascar Minerals (QMM), while Rio Tinto holds 80 per cent of the mine and the Malagasy government holds the remaining 20 per cent. The World Bank brokered the deal, the largest foreign investment in Madagascar's history.[14] QMM's mining operation is based in Tolanaro (also known as Fort-Dauphin from when it was a French colony) in the Anosy region on the south-east tip of Madagascar and it covers 6,000 hectares. Operations began in

2006 and are expected to last for 40 years from first production.[15] The Fort-Dauphin deposit contains nearly 70 million tonnes of ilmenite, around 10 per cent of the world market in 2013.[16] As Chapter 4, 'Fashion for Food', described, ilmenite is a raw material for titanium dioxide, the white pigment that is used extensively in paints, paper, plastics, toothpaste, sunscreens and more. Demand for it is fierce and is growing each year. But this project has had a troubled track record right from the outset.

Rio Tinto's mine features prominently in a scathing report 'The New Colonialism – Britain's scramble for Africa's energy and mineral resources' produced by activist group War on Want in 2014.[17] In the report, Gemma Holloway, sustainable development consultant to Rio Tinto says, 'There is much work to be done before the stories of communities affected by their [QMM] mining operations in southern Madagascar match the descriptions of the same areas in corporate communications documents.' But it is not just human rights groups or environmental activists who are concerned about mining operations in the region.

Rio Tinto first gained the social license to operate in this highly sensitive coastal forest zone mainly because it made a radical promise not only to reduce poverty in the region but also to ensure a 'Net Positive Impact' (NPI) on biodiversity.[18] Based on a need to demonstrate to governments and investors that it was the best firm to carry out projects with major social and environmental risks, the company went all out to argue the 'business case' for NPI wherever it could. The CEO even went out of his way to participate in environmental conferences around the globe to reiterate their commitment.[19] Conservationists saw this as a great opportunity and partnered with the company to help it 'make good' on its promise. But it seems to have been made without fully understanding what it would take to deliver. The 2008 recession affected ilmenite prices and Rio Tinto's priorities. By 2016, the company had reneged on its grand conservation promise of NPI and had adopted a vague goal instead.[20] QMM's Biodiversity Committee, an external panel of experts with an advisory role, felt compelled to make a public statement and resign. The following extract from the statement is quite telling:

> Each member of the Biodiversity Committee has over the last 13 years served in an individual capacity and has provided, free of charge, considerable time and effort towards assisting QMM and Rio Tinto in their effort to achieve the goal of NPI, and in particular to ensure that there is no net loss of critical habitat (littoral forest) or extinction of species during the lifetime of the project. The loss of Rio Tinto's corporate commitment to biodiversity, coupled with the fact that mention of the environment is totally absent from the five stated corporate priorities of Rio Tinto, as well as our lack of confidence that adequate long-term resourcing and capacity will be provided for the biodiversity program at QMM, have produced an untenable level of reputational risk for the Committee members to continue being associated with both RT and QMM in our present capacity.[21]

A top official of the International Union for Conservation of Nature (IUCN) has admitted that the project was a 'dismal failure' in terms of social and environmental outcomes.[22] Interestingly, the Biodiversity Committee's resignation has now been recast as a tenure that came to an end quite naturally and that had been planned all along. A collaboration between

QMM and its advisory committee seems to have been restored under a new name (the Biodiversity and Natural Resources Management Committee) and new experts have been brought on board.[23] Meanwhile, Madagascar has not only lost precious coastal forests that evolved over millennia but the people of the region haven't benefited as much as they had hoped.

Several academic researchers have documented what's been happening in Madagascar.[24] PhD researcher Caroline Seagle's body of work (including videos in the public domain[25]) is particularly illuminating and recommended for readers who are keen to delve deeper into these issues. She talks about the global trend of 'inverting the impacts', where multinational corporations conceal their biodiversity destruction by shifting the blame onto local people.[26] Seagle deftly unpacks the Rio Tinto/QMM narrative of 'the forests would have been destroyed anyway' and shows how Madagascar became the testing ground for neoliberal narratives, such as a biodiversity offset ideology that implies that the destruction of biodiversity in one place can be offset by preserving it in another region. QMM's offset programme claims that the loss of 6,000 hectares (23 sq. miles/60 km^2) of endemic littoral forest on the south-east coast through mining ilmenite, will be offset by forest conserved in three other sites (see Figure 12.1).[27] As you might expect, the biodiversity offset program in Madagascar has been deeply problematic.[28]

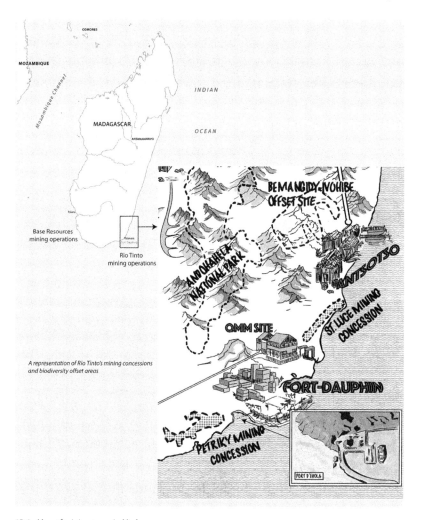

Figure labels within map:
- COMORES
- MOZAMBIQUE
- Mozambique Channel
- INDIAN
- MADAGASCAR
- ANTANANARIVO
- OCEAN
- Base Resources mining operations
- Rio Tinto mining operations
- A representation of Rio Tinto's mining concessions and biodiversity offset areas
- BEMANGIDY-IVOHIBE OFFSET SITE
- ANDOHAHELA NATIONAL PARK
- ANTSOTSO
- ST. LUCE MINING CONCESSION
- QMM SITE
- FORT-DAUPHIN
- PETRIKY MINING CONCESSION
- PORT D'EHOLA

12.1 Map of mining areas in Madagascar

Source: adapted from Huff, A., Orengo, Y., 2020, 'The QMM resource environment in south-eastern Madagascar'. Illustration by Tim Zocco, 2019 [Used under CC BY 4.0]

Aside from questions about the veracity of the offsetting achievements, the social aspect of the offsetting programme has been fraught with difficulties.[29] Reports show that villagers were not involved in a full, prior and informed consent process on the biodiversity offsets.[30] They complain of being misled about QMM's intentions and that promises of tree-planting work have not materialised. Most shockingly, the offset programme prevented the community from maintaining agricultural practices and pushed them on to infertile lands, with a resultant lack of food security or the means to maintain their traditional livelihoods.[31] Although almost one in two children are chronically malnourished, locals are forbidden to use prime agricultural land and are fined heavily if they are found using the forest and its peripheral regions – for instance, they can no longer cut trees from the forest to make their traditional dugout pirogues (canoes) for fishing.[32] Those who can't pay a fine are put in prison. The company has not compensated the villagers for loss of access to the forest.[33]

The pattern of failed promises and lack of compensation is a repeat of the initial land acquisition process during the mine's start-up phase. Hundreds of villagers were displaced to make way for the port, the mine, and the infrastructure, but were inadequately compensated for their losses. Community members felt that the company had taken advantage of them because they could not read. Customary land rights were not respected and illiterate families without formal land title were persistently disadvantaged in the compensation process, despite Rio Tinto's stated commitment to respect traditional land tenure.[34] The organisation not only acquired land without adequate compensation for the locals, but in its bid to 'green' the mine it also locked them out of the forests they depended on for food, firewood, medicines, construction material and more.[35]

Without a regular cash income to buy alternate supplies, food security for mine-affected communities is a real concern.

Rio Tinto/QMM's operations have also affected food security and livelihoods in other regions. Dredge mining of ilmenite requires enormous quantities of well-managed levels of fresh water, about 72,000 cubic metres per day, for the mining basin.[36] To manage this at their Mandena site, QMM constructed a weir (a wall built under the water across a river, over which the water flows from one level to another in a controlled way) in the estuary that links the interconnected rivers and lakes to the coast. The weir had a significant impact on the lake water, changing a naturally brackish estuary to fresh water and led to the 'collapse of a formerly highly productive fishery'.[37]Fishing provides both food for subsistence and an additional income and labour activities for local communities. As a result, villagers now struggle to survive despite the QMM-funded construction of artificial basins for fish production.[38] The World Bank says that, 'chronic malnutrition is the main impediment standing in the way of optimal growth and development'.[39]

A traditional fishermen's launching site was forcibly changed to accommodate QMM's port construction. The fishermen protested that they then lost boats through damage and lost fishing days when conditions were too dangerous to launch their pirogues from the unsafe new site. As these fishermen fell outside the formal compensation process they had to protest to the regional authorities to finally receive compensation.

The loss of lands, livelihoods and traditional practices, and in particular the failed promises and the lack of compensation, have been the cause of considerable contestation and conflict at a local level. Attempts by the company and/or its partners to pacify and manage both expectations and disappointments have highlighted contradictions in the company's policy of trusted relations and equitable dialogue.

A joint field investigation by the NGOs World Rainforest Movement (WRM) and Re:Common, who visited communities affected by one of the biodiversity offsets, about 50 kilometres north of the mining concession, shows how the company – along with Asity, a Malagasy affiliate of the international NGO Birdlife International – appears to have used religion and the ingrained local culture of reciprocity against the locals. After a particularly difficult meeting, when villagers requested a resolution of the outstanding issue of compensation for lost access to the forest, the local affiliate and the company decided to change when and where they held public consultations. They held the meetings in local churches instead and started them with a church service in an attempt to neutralise confrontation and demands.[40]

In 2011, over a thousand village claimants began a class-action lawsuit against the company in a UK court around the failed compensation for land acquired for the mining concession. They were assisted by a UK-based human rights law firm, Leigh Day. However, the case was quickly neutralised when cash payouts were made to over half the claimants, leaving too few to sustain the case.[41] Contestation over compensation continued. In January 2013 local Malagasy armed with spears and slingshots carried out a fierce week-long confrontation with mining executives.[42] Things turned particularly ugly when the protests culminated in a hostage crisis at the QMM site. The protesters blocked nearly 200 staff and the CEO inside the premises and demanded higher payment for the land purchased by the company and more permanent jobs for locals within the project. The company threatened to pull out of Madagascar completely.[43] The military was brought in, tear gas was used to disperse the crowds and protesters were brutally beaten, handcuffed and dragged along the tarmac.[44] In 2016 dissent erupted again over failed compensation for land deals brokered by QMM for additional areas to expand the mine around the Mandena site and, in 2018, locals blocked access roads to the mine site. QMM took legal action that resulted in the imprisonment of protestors.[45]

Numerous researchers have pointed out how unequal the relationship is between the people and a company that appears to enjoy 'quasi-state power'.[46] *The Guardian* reports how a Malagasy farmer who was due to address the company's annual general meeting in 2017 had his UK visa rejected on the grounds that he was not qualified to speak about environmental and human rights concerns. But what is most disturbing is that just after he made his visa application, he received a call from QMM asking him about the purpose of his visit to the capital and why he wanted a visa. As London Mining Network, a coalition of anti-mining campaign groups, points out, it is not clear why a foreign multinational company had access to such information, nor is it clear what gave them the authority to interrogate Malagasy citizens in this manner.[47]

It is hard for locals to question or hold the company to account over its social and environmental abuses. For example, in 2019 Rio Tinto admitted that QMM had breached the legally required environmental buffer zone at its Mandena site and had encroached on the bed of Lake Besaroy, adjacent to the mine.[48] This admission was only made after protracted investigation and campaigning by the Andrew Lees Trust

(ALT UK), a British charity that has been serving the people of Madagascar for 25 years.[49]

This breach is critical because the buffer zone is vital to protect people and the environment from potentially toxic mine tailings. Rio Tinto did eventually retreat from this sensitive zone but had already destroyed precious littoral forests. Moreover, the process of acknowledging the breach, and changing the mine's plan to avoid similar encroachments in future, had taken an inordinately long time and a huge amount of effort. ALT UK observed that 'A dialogue process of this kind would be impossibly onerous for the majority of the affected communities in Anosy, who are living on less than $2 a day and struggling to put one meal on the table.'[50] ALT UK also raised concerns that the QMM breach was potentially exposing local lakes and waterways to radionuclide contaminants from the mining basin, either through leaching or overtopping of the mine's dam.

An independent radioactivity study commissioned by ALT UK found elevated levels of uranium in the lake adjacent to the mine, in some places it was 50 times higher than the World Health Organisation's safe drinking water guidelines.[51] Local people fish and draw their water from the lakes and waterways around the mine so the presence of high levels of uranium and lead is a health concern. A lack of data or monitoring studies by QMM questions the extent to which the elevated uranium levels in the lake are being caused by the mine's extraction activity, which concentrates uranium in the mining basin during the mineral sand separation process. Rio Tinto/QMM has claimed that elevated uranium levels occur naturally but has been unable to evidence this assertion.[52] Indeed, the company's monitoring of the water environment and the ingestion pathways around the mine was reported as 'unacceptable' by ALT UK's radioactivity expert, Stella Swanson.[53]

What is worth noting is that the breach of the buffer zone violated national law, and exceeded permissions granted by the Malagasy Government in respect of the mine's social and environmental plan. Yet the multinational company faces no sanctions or penalties for its actions; while Rio Tinto's legal action against protesting locals in 2018 resulted in their imprisonment.[54]

Rio Tinto is not the only mining enterprise in Madagascar to encounter widespread protests or to divide communities.[55] Western concepts of development have been foisted upon local communities without adequate consultation on the country's new mining code and they live under an increasing threat of 'green grabs'.[56] There has been much unrest in 2019 over Australian company Base Resources Limited's mining plans in Toliara, south-west Madagascar. The company claims to offer one of the highest profit margins of any mineral sands project in the world but the true price is being borne by the indigenous communities who have lived there for generations.[57] Not only are their livelihoods at risk, so is their culture and sense of place and identity.

The company has insisted on moving ancestral tombs that are sacred to the ethnic groups in the region. Removal or relocation of tombs, particularly by foreigners, is seen as extremely problematic and very disrespectful, regardless of the compensation offered.[58] There have been several protests over the years.[59] In July 2019, nine people were detained without trial for several weeks following an act of civil disobedience against the company.[60]

The true price is also being paid by the environment and those endemic species that are disappearing fast as protected areas shrink because of successful lobbying to extend mining concessions for minerals that are then shipped off to South Africa.[61] Initial optimism has given way to disillusionment as the Toliara Sands project 'reneged on agreements made with representatives of local communities. Some locals have expressed the opinion that operators "tricked" villagers who live in the vicinity of the Ranobe mine site in order to receive the mining permit and lease surface rights…'.[62]

The complete litany of grievances against these heavy mineral sand mining companies is well beyond the scope of this chapter but there is reason to hope, as we will discover in Chapter 24, 'The Final Answer Lies in the Sandpit'. There is one last comment I wish to make before I move the focus. Mining heavy minerals from mineral sands (such as ilmenite, rutile and leucoxene) and converting them to bright white titanium dioxide is a highly toxic but less visually arresting process than other forms of mining and consequently there is a very real danger that we underestimate its impacts. The mining industry doesn't seem to think of it as true 'mining', while experts from outside the mineral sand mining industry appear to believe that it is 'extremely well regulated'.[63] Much is falling through the cracks between these two views while we allow mining companies the freedom to self-regulate and self-report on their adherence to what are essentially voluntary standards for mine tailings management, biodiversity conservation and sustainability.[64]

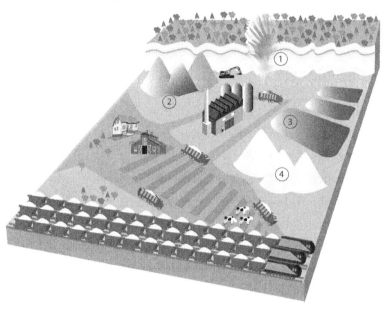

1. Blasting of sandstone bluffs that permanently alters the landscape and ecology of the region

2. Unprocessed sand

   • Modern fracking operations can use a mile-long train full of sand to frac just one well. Increased fracking requires intensive rail use and subsequent delays in train car deliveries to grain elevators can cost farmers hundreds of millions of dollars, as soybeans, wheat and corn cannot be moved without them

   • Very high water use and potential groundwater and surface water contamination (e.g. in 2013 in the USA, 18 operators consumed more water for frac sand preparation than 67 of the 70 public/municipal/community water systems in all 10 Wisconsin counties)

3. Retention ponds containing water and chemicals to process the sand

4. Frac sand ready to be dispatched

   • Heavy impact on farming, tourism and fishing industries, and potential loss of real-estate values up to 25% in the immediate neighbourhood

   • Residents report 'significant anxiety and stress from truck traffic, noise, light pollution, and uncertainty about environmental health impacts'

   • Exposure to silica dust makes neighbours vulnerable to respiratory diseases, such as asthma and silicosis

12.2 Health and environmental impacts of frac sand mining

Sources: Chapman et al., 2014; San Antonio Business Journal, 2018; Concerned Health Professionals of New York, Physicians for Social Responsibility, 2019, Fractracker.org © SandStories.org

Before you think such problems are only common to developing economies, allow me to present you with an example of private gain at public expense from a developed economy. The best example comes from the fracking industry, where silica sand is extracted for use as a proppant. In 2019, 73 per cent of industrial sand and gravel produced in the United States was used as frac sand, while the rest was utilised for glassmaking, foundries, ceramics, fillers, recreational facilities and other purposes.[65] The sand that is being removed from lands in Wisconsin and other places are from 500 million-year-old sandstones.[66]

In Chapter 7, 'In Pursuit of the Holy Grail', you've read about how the industry concentrates 'booms' in production by using extra sand, water and chemicals rather than spreading production out over a longer well lifespan. We still don't know enough about the impact of removing such vast quantities of a non-renewable resource on ecosystems and the people dependent on them. What we do know is that the process of removing this sand remains shrouded in controversy as the costs are externalised and rural communities are forced to pay the price. What is concerning is that there is significant variability of fracking data and its availability to the public, which is 'a barrier to regulatory and industry transparency. The lack of transparency also impacts public education and broader participation in industry governance'.[67]

FracTracker Alliance, has done a tremendous amount of work to advance our understanding of the risks and impacts of frac sand mining. You can access photos, videos, maps and many more resources on their website. In addition, the 'Compendium of Scientific, Medical, and Media Findings Demonstrating Risks and Harms of Fracking' by Concerned Health Professionals of New York and Physicians for Social

Responsibility makes a compelling read for anyone who cares to dig deeper.[68]

First, some context to understand the industry better before we delve into the David and Goliath kind of battle being fought in the Upper Midwest. The hydraulic fracturing, or fracking industry was reliant on sand from Oklahoma and Texas until about 2006, after which the industry moved north. The frac sand mining industry followed. Things really took off in 2008 when new horizontal-drilling methods transformed an industry formerly dependent on vertical boring. During the initial rapid onslaught, local officials from small rural towns, with limited or no experience in dealing with mining lease negotiations, found themselves up against savvy industry lawyers from multinational corporations. You can make a pretty good guess at how that turned out.

Until about 2018, western Wisconsin was the epicentre of frac sand mining in the USA, but the 'gold rush' has moved once again to the Permian Basin of west Texas, despite the fact that the sand there is not ideal for the fracking industry. Diminished oil prices have made this region attractive once again. It is closer to the oil wells and that eliminates the need for rail transport and makes it 50 per cent cheaper.

But, as mentioned, there's a great battle being fought in the Upper Midwest that could impact the future of frac sand mining in the United States and possibly further afield. Silica sand mining has transformed rural landscapes into industrialised zones and has introduced complex health risks that local authorities are ill-equipped to deal with. Silica dust is a known carcinogen and the processing and transport of frac sand exposes communities in the vicinity to ultra-fine crystalline silica particles such as PM 2.5 that are associated with a wide range of health problems, including asthma and silicosis (more commonly known as potter's lung disease). Silicosis is treated as an occupational health hazard and precautionary measures have been put in place within the industry, but precise exposures of downwind communities in the neighbourhood remain uncertain. There are also several other known unknowns and unknown unknowns around fracking emissions, waste, landscape change, water impacts and more. See Figure 12.2.

In November 2016, Winona County in Minnesota created history by passing the first countywide ban in the USA on the extraction of silica sand for use in drilling and fracking operations. But a frac sand mining company filed suit in the district court. The bone of contention was that the ban did not apply to other uses, such as construction. The company claimed that there is no real difference between mining for industrial minerals and mining for construction minerals. They also claimed that the ban violated the US Constitution's interstate commerce clause by outlawing sand mining for out-of-state use while allowing it for local use. Winona County argued that there is a substantive difference between frac sand and normal sand, and that the county was well within its rights to adopt an ordinance that protects citizens' health and the environment. Winona County won. The case was taken to the Minnesota Court of Appeal, which also ruled in favour of Winona County.

But the sand mining company took the case all the way to the state's highest court, the Minnesota Supreme Court. We will return to this case in the very last chapter.

Much hangs in the balance though. As of this writing, across the globe, the markets for frac sand, construction sand and other industrial mineral sands occupy very different worlds in terms of policy, regulation, or education for that matter. These worlds rarely coincide, even though the sand may even come from the same place, as the Winona case demonstrated. A market intelligence report suggests that the global proppant market is set to grow into a $10.6 billion industry by 2023.[69] What is clearly missing is the oversight to manage sand resources across all uses in a responsible manner.

Frac sand miners in the USA often use groundwater research publications, such as the groundwater atlas series of the United States Geological Survey as 'valuable prospecting documents' for determining the location and structure of sandstone rock.[70] But this couldn't be more short-sighted or ill-advised because the sandstone formations are often associated with precious water sources, such as groundwater aquifers that feed both human and non-human life. You simply cannot remove one without affecting the other.

Not everybody is opposed to frac sand mining. The industry has divided neighbours and families and pitted those who stand to make a quick buck against those who choose to continue living in the region. There have been multiple rallies, protests and petitions from local communities. But to give you a sense of the scale of discontent, in 2014 more than 75 civic and environmental organizations came together to submit a resolution to the Governor of Wisconsin, to members of the Wisconsin legislature and to state and federal environmental regulators, calling for a ban on frac sand mining and a halt to attacks on local democracy.[71] The resolution especially called for the rejection of SB 349, a bill designed to outlaw local ordinances from regulating frac sand mining, local air and water quality, or blasting. Unfortunately, a similar bill is in the works in 2020 in Michigan, where frac sand mining and sand mining in general is a huge topic, especially along the beautiful, priceless and irreplaceable Lake Michigan coasts.[72]

The frac sand industry is also working on circumventing local control in other places. Look up Wisconsin's Non-Metallic Mining Parcel Registration program on the FracTracker Alliance website.

Campaign organisers and communities have fought long and hard to ensure that their voice is heard. It has been especially difficult for them because, thanks to the 'Halliburton Loophole' in the Energy Policy Act of 2005 and other laws, the fracking industry and its attendant infrastructure in the USA is exempt from most provisions of:

- the Clean Water Act
- the Clean Air Act
- the Safe Drinking Water Act
- the National Environmental Policy Act
- the Resource Conservation and Recovery Act
- the Toxic Release Inventory Reporting
- and the Comprehensive Environmental Response, Compensation, and Liability Act (the Superfund law).[73]

It is worth noting that the USGS, which publishes annual reports on various minerals, receives annual production data from individual mines voluntarily and can't give that data out, otherwise they will no longer receive it. FracTracker Alliance have been told that this data is 'proprietary' and cannot be released, even under the Freedom of Information Act.[74]

What would the preeminent thinker Aldo Leopold, famed author of the *Sand County Almanac,* have had to say about what's happening in the region right now? As hills are razed to the ground in this feeding frenzy, the neighbours of frac sand mines cannot even open their windows and doors without fearing for their health, for their grandchildren, or for their livestock. They fear for the land that has been passed down over generations, for their livelihoods that will be jeopardised by this industry, for their right to peace and quiet in a fast-vanishing rural landscape, for the beauty that will be no more. What price would you put on such things?

•13•

White in a New Light

Can you recall the first time you brushed your teeth? Did you spit out everything or swallow some of the wash? In 2016, scientists from the Dutch National Institute for Public Health and the Environment (RIVM), Bilthoven, and RIKILT (Wageningen University & Research Centre) conducted an experiment to find out just how much impact this innocent act has. Not the brushing but the act of swallowing the toothpaste. It turns out that young children tend to swallow toothpaste a lot, and most white toothpastes contain titanium dioxide. Chapter 4, 'Fashion for Food', showed how this substance is in so many products. So, while we are all exposed to multiple doses every day, children are particularly exposed to the highest doses of the pigment from toothpaste, candies, sunscreens, paints on toys and more. Since it is used in nearly everything around us – paints, plastics, papers, make-up – the market for titanium dioxide is as global as it gets and it stands to be impacted heavily by regulation.

In April 2019, France announced the ban of E171, the label for titanium dioxide in food items, starting on 1 January 2020, and it also said it would formally invite the EU to follow suit once the decree was signed into law. But a peek at what led to this decision could inspire many a thriller novel.

In late September 2018, the 28 EU member states, via the Commission's chemicals regulatory committee (set up under Europe's main law to regulate chemicals, REACH – the Registration, Evaluation, Authorisation and Restriction of Chemicals) was meant to decide whether all forms of titanium dioxide (including the nano form) should be classified as a 'suspected carcinogen' when inhaled. If titanium dioxide was to be classified as such, every product using it would have to carry a warning label on the packaging. The decision was meant to be based purely on data concerning the health and safety of all – people ingesting this 'natural' food additive or workers handling it before, during and after a product's lifetime, such as paint. Data that had been available for some time.

In 2006, the World Health Organisation's International Agency for Research on Cancer (IARC) declared titanium dioxide a 'possible carcinogen for humans' after tests on animals, with even larger risks in its nano form. The US National Institute for Occupational Safety and Health (NIOSH) also found that at nano scale it posed a higher risk, and in 2011 recommended that occupational exposure (by inhalation) to nano scale titanium dioxide particles should be considered a potential occupational carcinogen. In 2017, the European Chemicals Agency (ECHA) advised the European Commission that all products containing the substance should carry a warning that it was a suspected carcinogen when inhaled.

Nano titanium dioxide consists of extremely small fractions of the compound. Although the chemical formula may be the same, nano materials behave very differently. For one, they have a much greater surface area and can be much more reactive. Think of how smaller vegetable pieces cook faster because more surface area is exposed to the heat. Despite industry claims to the contrary, the use of nano materials has been increasing. For instance, a greater number of sunscreen manufacturers are turning to nano titanium dioxide because normal titanium dioxide tends to leave a white residue on the skin while the nano version makes it more transparent. Aesthetics aside, this is a problem.

Nanoparticles are small enough to penetrate critical body barriers such as cell membranes (see Figure 13.2). The body takes a very long time to get rid of such particles. The Dutch scientists mentioned at the start of this chapter found evidence that titanium dioxide accumulates in the human liver and spleen, which raises the concern that health risks due to oral exposure 'cannot be excluded'.[1] Other studies across the world have also shown that nano metal oxides, such as nano titanium dioxide, are highly toxic to corals and other acquatic life. Titanium dioxide, especially in nano form, is definitely not as 'inert' as the industry believes.

13.1 The titanium dioxide industry's response to classification

Source: © Corporate Europe Observatory

But it is revealing how the industry responded to ECHA's proposal. Instead of engaging with data that was being provided by top-notch institutions right across the world to make its products safer for people and the environment, it has spent more than €800,000 to retain lobby firms across the EU (most notably Fleishman-Hillard, the same organisation that defends Monsanto and ExxonMobil in Brussels) and to launch a PR blitzkrieg. In 2019, the EU decided to opt out of putting the warning label on the suspected carcinogen, which divided member states.[2] There was also talk in 2019 of dropping the classification altogether because of the discord.[3]

Several civil society organisations and NGOs have raised serious concerns about the deluge of lobbying to dilute standards meant to protect public health and the environment. Among them are: the European Environmental Bureau (EEB), Europe's largest network of environmental citizens' organisations that works for sustainable development, environmental justice and participatory democracy; and Corporate Europe Observatory, an NGO whose policy is to reject funding from the EU, governments, political parties and corporations. They have pointed out how the industry ran an 'unprecedented' lobbying campaign, 'despite not being registered on the Transparency Register. [European Commission] Officials met with up to 24 lobbyists at a time and felt "ordered around".' Corporate Europe Observatory made another startling observation:

For the Commission's Scientific Committee on Consumer Safety (SCCS), which assessed the nano form of titanium dioxide, 70 per cent (14 members) of the committee's members were found to have a conflict of interest, with only 30 per cent free of conflicts.

TiO2 has many potential health and environmental impacts and
engineered nanoparticles (NPs) of TiO2 can be particularly damaging

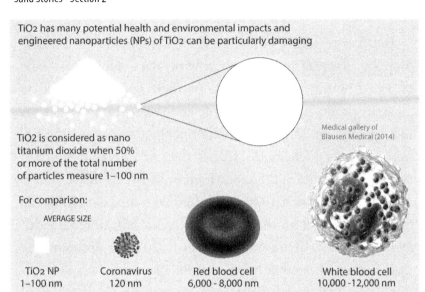

TiO2 is considered as nano
titanium dioxide when 50%
or more of the total number
of particles measure 1–100 nm

For comparison:

AVERAGE SIZE

Medical gallery of
Blausen Medical (2014)

TiO2 NP	Coronavirus	Red blood cell	White blood cell
1–100 nm	120 nm	6,000 - 8,000 nm	10,000 -12,000 nm

Ways in which TiO2 and TiO2 NPs can enter the environment

Run-off from paints

From sunscreens that
get into the water

Sewer overflows releasing
untreated sewage containing
TiO2 used in food, cosmetics,
pharmaceuticals, toothpaste
and other industries

Application of treated sewage
sludge in agriculture

Disposal at landfill

Please see Kaegi *et al.* 2008; Gondikas *et al.* 2014; Park *et al.* 2016; Loosli *et al.* 2019

13.2   Potential environmental and health impacts of titanium
dioxide (TiO$_2$) as highlighted by independent studies

Studies have found that TiO2 and TiO2 NPs are toxic to some acquatic organisms (e.g. coral), soil organisms, mammals and other vertebrates

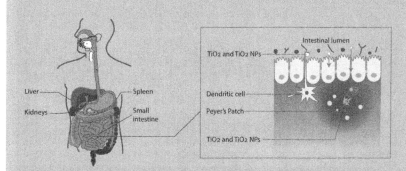

Healthy coral
Zooxanthellae
Coral polyp

Stressed coral

Individual TiO2 NPs

Phytoplankton

TiO2 can enter the food chain and can 'bioconcentrate, bioaccumulate and biomagnify'
(Jovanovic 2015)

Aggregated TiO2 NPs

Seawater

Scallop

(adapted from Wang et al. 2017)

Please see Skocaj et al. 2011; Miller et al. 2012; Mielke et al. 2013; Jovanovic and Guzman 2014; Jovanovic 2015; Sendra et al. 2016; Wang et al. 2017

Studies show that TiO2 accumulates in the liver, spleen, kidneys and small intestine in humans.

Liver
Kidneys
Spleen
Small intestine

Intestinal lumen
TiO2 and TiO2 NPs
Dendritic cell
Peyer's Patch
TiO2 and TiO2 NPs

TiO2 NPs may penetrate across or between cells of the gut membrane and accumulate in tissues such as Peyer's patches.

Lifelong exposure through oral intake of food and pharmaceutical products could present a health risk.

People with chronic conditions such as inflammatory bowel disease (IBD) are particularly at risk.

Children may receive the highest exposure due to their lower body mass and from consuming pastries and candies.

Please see Winkler et al. 2018; Weir et al. 2012; EFSA ANS Panel 2016

©SandStories.org

Sources: Kaegi et al., 2008; Gondikas et al., 2014; Park et al., 2016; Loosli et al., 2019; Skocaj et al., 2011; Miller et al., 2012; Mielke et al., 2013; Jovanovic and Guzman, 2014; Jovanovic, 2015; Sendra et al., 2016; Wang et al., 2017; Winkler et al., 2018; Weir et al., 2012; EFSA ANS Panel, 2016; www.marinebiology.co © SandStories.org

These organisations have especially criticised the industry's approach and the European Commission's response to the problem, which seems to rest on the socio-economic impact of the decision instead of putting people first.

The European Commission has not had it easy though. Member states with significant ties to the chemicals industry, such as Germany and Slovenia, have been quick to highlight impacts on trade – as was the UK. The USA also raised objections and the US trade representative explicitly called for a delay, telling the Commission that the regulation may be 'unnecessarily disruptive to billions of dollars of US–EU trade'. Other members of the World Trade Organisation, Canada, Australia, New Zealand and Japan jumped on the bandwagon to highlight its downstream economic impacts.

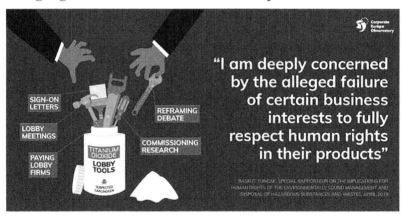

13.3 Observation by the UN's Special Rapporteur on the industry's response
Source: © Corporate Europe Observatory

Meanwhile, the concern was serious enough to draw comment from Baskut Tuncak, the UN's Special Rapporteur on the implications for human rights of the environmentally sound management and disposal of hazardous substances and wastes.[4] So, while the debate rages on, several fundamental questions remain unaddressed. The most important of these being, where does the feedstock for titanium dioxide come from? What are the impacts of the supply chain? A lot more research is required, but titanium dioxide appears to be the poster child for the marriage between big mining and big chemical – blessed by big oil.

Since 2000, much of the feedstock has come from mineral sands (ilmenite, rutile, leucoxene) mined in developing economies such as South Africa, Mozambique, Sierra Leone, Kenya, Senegal, Madagascar, India and Vietnam, where problems have been reported on multiple fronts (see Figure 13.4). There has even been fierce resistance to mineral sand mining in Stradbroke Island, Australia. China is the largest producer of titanium minerals in the world but it also imports these mineral sands from Australia, Kenya, Mozambique, India and, up until 2013, Vietnam.[5]

The process of transforming sand or rock ore into this shiny white powder is not only highly energy intensive but it is also very chemical intensive. There are two main manufacturing processes: the older sulfate route, and the newer chloride route.[6] Both processes leave behind highly acidic toxic waste that creates numerous environmental problems upon disposal. For every tonne of titanium dioxide, over eight tonnes of waste can be produced. While the chloride process is 15 times cleaner than the sulfate process, it is more expensive and requires relatively scarce, high-quality titanium ores, such as rutile.[7] The sulfate process generates the greatest amount of environmentally harmful waste per unit of titanium dioxide produced.

1 Senegal
Land grabbing and water grabbing has uprooted farming communities and disrupted lives and livelihoods

2 Gambia
Corruption at the highest levels; demonstrations violently repressed; activists criminalised

3 Sierra Leone
Extractives (including mineral sands) constitute > 80% of exports but generate only 15% of total revenues

4 South Africa
Activist opposed to mining shot eight times outside his house; threats and violence against opponents

5 Mozambique
Irresponsible mining led to flash floods that put >1,000 people at serious risk of being washed into the Indian Ocean

6 Kenya
Forced displacements of 5,000 indigenous Digo and Kamba people

7 Madagascar
a Secret deals; lack of public consultation; no environmental impact assessment
b Widespread protests against inadequate compensation; mass mobilization; violence; arrests
c Demonstrations commonplace about land rights, cultural and economic displacement

8 India
a 3,000 people go on a relay hunger strike for one year against mineral beach sand mining in the coastal area
b A major Public Sector Unit ordered to be shut down due to the absence of an effective effluent treatment plant
c 5,000 people converge to protest; concerns include loss of water security in a region with sparse rainfall

9 Vietnam
a Coastal villages left vulnerable to storms as barrier forests (casuarina, poplar) destroyed; groundwater depleted
b Three companies ordered to suspend operations, but continued for three years after licences expired
c Violent protests; serious health problems; drastic reduction of groundwater sources; impact on agriculture

13.4 Some reported impacts of mining mineral sands for titanium and titanium dioxide

Sources: EJAtlas; Vietnamnet; Corpwatch; The Hindu; Amnesty International; Reuters; The News Minute; Mongabay © SandStories.org

Up until the late 1980s, the sulfate process was used in nearly two-thirds of global production and nearly all European production. Sites were chosen for easy availability of water and the ability to dump the waste in it. The industry was notorious for dumping large quantities of sulphuric acid in the North Sea, or in connecting waterways, or on soil and decimating life in those regions. Also, the factories released dust and emissions of sulphur or chlorine gases into the air. Thankfully, we have come a long way from those days in most parts of Europe but there is no shying away from the fact that extracting titanium dioxide is an expensive, high carbon and chemically intensive process, regardless of which production process is chosen or which raw material is used.

In 2016, major producer Cristal, which had been acquired by another mammoth company, was fined £3 million after one worker was killed and another was left with irreversible lung damage by an explosion at the titanium dioxide production plant in Stallingborough, Lincolnshire in the UK.[8] According to the BBC, 'the explosion was so powerful a thick, toxic, cloud could be seen pouring out of the factory and across the Humber Estuary. Shipping movements were stopped for several hours and the public was put at risk.'[9] I hasten to add that industrial accidents are not the norm and they could happen anywhere. But the point is, this is not an intrinsically benign process.

In 2017, in a major crackdown on pollution, the Chinese authorities closed down tens of thousands of companies in various sectors. While companies would once have been able to use their social capital (guanxi in local parlance) to wriggle out of compliance, these audits were top-driven and influence at a local level was impotent. Factories were forced to cease production immediately and indefinitely until they complied – 72 non-compliant titanium dioxide production plants were closed down permanently.[10] It would have made headlines if something similar had happened in the western world.

Even progressive countries like Norway have struggled with the aftermath of titanium dioxide production. It was this very struggle that birthed the modern environmental movement in Norway when a young man named Frederic Hauge and his friends took direct action against the disposal of hazardous waste from titanium mines into the Jøssingfjord. Hauge went on to co-found the Bellona Foundation, an international environmental NGO that works in Norway, the EU, Russia and the USA. Between 1960 and 1984, 2.5 million tonnes of mining tailings were dumped each year into Jøssingfjord in southern Norway.[11] Thirty-five years after this action was stopped, the place is still pretty much an underwater desert, where the mining waste covers everything and only the most resilient species survive.[12]

So it is all the more surprising to learn that Norway has once again considered permitting toxic titanium waste to be dumped into another spectacular fjord. In 2015, the authorities approved a plan for open-pit mining for rutile and garnet that meant 250 million tonnes of mining waste would be dumped into the Førdefjord.[13] There have been fierce protests by local communities, fishermen and tourism operators whose livelihoods depend on the fjord. They have used civil disobedience to prevent construction work by the mining company.[14] This particular fjord has been designated as a National Salmon Fjord and is an important spawning grounds, not just for salmon but also for cod, halibut and herring. It is home to wonderful cold water corals, orcas, whales and sea eagles.[15] It's truly hard to make sense of it all.

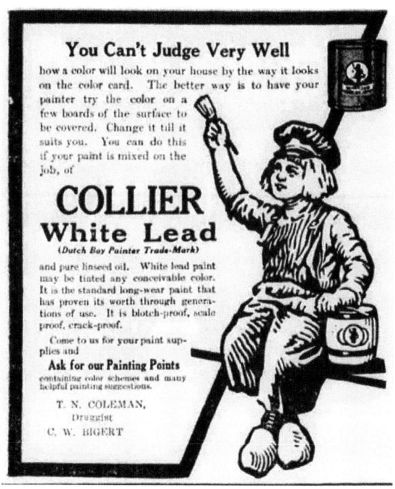

13.5 Dutch Boy paint advertisement from 1912

Source: The Daily Ardmoreite (Ardmore, Oklahoma), 20 September 1912. Chronicling America: Historic American Newspapers. Public Domain

That leads us to question how this product became so indispensable. Before titanium dioxide came into the picture, the paint industry used white lead. Today, we know beyond a shadow of doubt that lead is a poison. But it wasn't always so.

13.6 Has Your Child Had A Lead Test Yet? from circa 1970

Source: US National Library of Medicine. Public Domain

In the USA, although the first reports of lead poisoning were published over a century ago, many generations paid a terrible price because of the delayed adoption of meaningful regulation. When ingested, lead impedes children's mental and physical development. The US National Library of Medicine states that 'Until mid-century, lead industry-sponsored research dominated the scientific literature on the origins of lead poisoning and consistently understated or ignored the true threat posed by lead.'[16].

It was not until the 1960s that a series of well-publicised cases mobilised public concern, and it took until 1970 for lead poisoning to be officially recognised as a health problem for the first time. The Lead Paint Poisoning Prevention Act was passed the following year. It prohibited the use of lead-based paint in federal buildings and housing units and in the manufacturing of cooking utensils, toys and furniture. In the meantime, much damage had been done. In the late 1970s, an estimated 15 million children had unsafe lead levels in their bodies. By 1991 that number had been reduced to 1.7 million. In 2002, around 890,000 children had elevated blood lead levels.

This toxic legacy is thanks to industry whitewash. But as titanium dioxide became available in the post-war years, it seemed to be the perfect solution. Since then a lot has changed and yet very little has changed. The industry continues to extol the virtues of titanium dioxide while downplaying or ignoring its impacts, especially those of nano titanium dioxide. As trade bodies continue to meddle in medical matters, preventing meaningful legislation in pursuit of profit, it seems old habits die hard. Titanium dioxide may well be the perfect solution for hundreds, even thousands, of applications worth billions. But we must tread cautiously, especially when it comes to its use in food, feed, sunscreens, pharmaceutical products and other applications from which it can be released into the environment. The damage cannot be set right.

•14•

When the Edges Start Fraying

'How Do You Save a Million People From a Cyclone? Ask a Poor State in India' said a *New York Times* article in May 2019 when India was hit by a major hurricane that ripped through towns at 120 miles per hour.[1] In the end, it didn't turn out to be as big a 'natural disaster' as feared because the authorities acted swiftly and in a coordinated manner to ensure that people moved out of harm's way. There's definitely something to be said for how humans galvanise into action against urgent and immediate threats. But why do they fail to notice or react appropriately to long-term changes that are potentially even more disastrous? In 2018, the Intergovernmental Panel on Climate Change (IPCC) issued a stark warning that we had fewer than 12 years to avoid a catastrophic and potentially irreversible climate crisis.

Global sea-level rise and its impacts on coastal cities and countries may be 'the biggest threat that human civilization has ever faced'.[2] Sand offers a crucial ecosystem service in the form of a storm energy buffer, but our global sand flows are in jeopardy. Dams block the supply of sand to coasts worldwide (see Chapters 9 and 19) and man-made coastal defence structures block the flow of sand around the coasts. River sand mining removes sand that was meant to nourish coasts, while beach sand mining actively destroys coasts. For those who wish to learn more, Coastalcare.org is a great resource for the latest news, a sand mining database and a photo gallery.

A deeply problematic underlying trend is our desire to build along the coast. As coastal storms increase in frequency and ferocity due to the climate crisis, this mode of development is ill-advised as it eats away at our most important line of defence, our beaches. As explained beautifully in the award-winning documentary *Sand Wars*, beaches respond to the seasons. In the summer, they swell and as winter sets in and the seas become harsher, they absorb the sea's energy and move in toward land. This way they protect the hinterland. But as developers build more and more beachfront properties and build closer to the coast, they leave no room for beaches to respond. Pushed against hard structures, the beaches have nowhere to go and they become vulnerable to erosion. And then there are those industries that have ignored this crucial consideration, even though they rely on sand extracted from the coasts.

The eastern coast of India is rich in heavy mineral sands called placer deposits. Placer deposits are ideal because, unlike the processing of rock ores, companies do not incur a cost to separate the overburden, which is anything that restricts them from accessing the minerals – extraneous rocky material, trees, soil and so on. The minerals are already concentrated in situ due to their long exposure to the elements that have weathered away the more vulnerable material. All that is needed is a transport infrastructure and relatively cheap equipment to whisk them off to market.

With this kind of sand mining, the minerals are extracted and the spent surplus sand is returned to the location. Or at least it is supposed to be. But in many cases it isn't, especially in places like India. Most of the minerals extracted are exported for use in high-tech manufacturing facilities abroad. Until 1993, only government agencies and public sector companies could mine and process beach sand for export. The fear of losing out to neighbouring Sri Lanka enticed the country to welcome private players.[3] But this hasn't gone so well for the country. Regulations do exist. But the implementation, monitoring and enforcement mechanisms are inadequate. In an interesting turn of events in 2018, India banned private players from mining and exporting sand directly. However, reports suggest it has faced strong lobbying from the USA, Australia and Germany to overturn the ban.[4]

International market analysts speculate that the reason for the ban was the re-nationalisation of the economy. However, within the country, the scores of plot developments, and their twists and turns would give *Game of Thrones* a run for its money. Put simply, there is a lack of coordination between central and state governments, while district governments appear to lack the capacity to appreciate the significance of the minerals or the impact of their indiscriminate extraction. As a result, there is many a loophole open to exploitation.

In the south-eastern Indian state of Tamil Nadu one family has monopolised sand mining, and 71 out of 83 leases to mine and export heavy minerals out of India are owned by a band of brothers. They have been accused of illegal sand mining and especially of putting national security at risk by exporting monazite, a key REE-bearing composite mineral. They strongly deny these allegations and claim that they are being targeted by competitors.

The list of discrepancies is long and it is clear that corruption and collusion are rife.[5] Multiple cases are still being heard, particularly in Tamil Nadu. Some of the court proceedings show that:

- Mining continued despite a statewide ban
- Mining leases have been operational in ecologically sensitive coastal regulation zones (CRZs) without environmental clearance from central government
- Mining areas have often exceeded their permits by several orders of magnitude
- Coastal dunes have been destroyed using heavy machinery
- Transport licences have been issued for much larger amounts than those stated in mining permits[6]
- Mineral exports from one port alone show losses to the exchequer to the tune of INR 5,800 crore (nearly $790 million) from unpaid royalties and the cost of illegally mined minerals.[7]

One District Collector (DC) who conducted a raid on mining areas was unceremoniously transferred within eight hours – and a DC is a pretty high-ranking official within the Indian bureaucracy.[8] Nonetheless, government officers are vulnerable to the whims of politicians. The main driving factor in this case are exports of rare earth elements (REEs, sometimes called rare earth metals) and heavy minerals.

Despite their name, many are relatively plentiful, although they occur in a dispersed form more often than in a concentrated ore form. As a result, their extraction may not be economically feasible everywhere they occur. REEs are used in trace amounts but their unique properties make them indispensable to modern technology, as we shall see later.[9]

Heavy minerals refer to a wide variety of minerals with a high specific gravity, in other words, they are very dense. 'Heavy minerals are usually volumetrically insignificant. However, there are a large number of heavy mineral species, each of them having their own story to tell.'[10] Their economic significance makes mineral sands a hugely coveted commodity.

The minerals that are in huge demand are ilmenite, leucoxene, rutile, garnet, zircon, sillimanite, monazite and more. Each of these have a growing list of applications. For instance, with growing awareness about the possibility of silicosis with the use of silica sand, many are now turning to garnet sand for use in abrasive blast cleaning and water-jet cutting, used extensively in aircraft manufacturing and shipbuilding.[11] The petroleum industry is one of the leading garnet consumers for cleaning drill pipes and well casings and sometimes as a proppant in fracking.[12] Zircon is used to make ceramic tiles and alloys for golf clubs and tennis rackets.[13] It is also used in foundries and in the nuclear industry to make control rods and the cladding for nuclear fuel rods.[14] Zirconium, the element found in zircon, is used to make mobile phone circuit boards. The display colours of mobile phones are made possible due to elements such as praseodymium (Pr), europium (Eu) and gadolinium (Gd).[15] Gd-based compounds are also used widely in medical technologies as a contrast agent to image tumours with MRI (magnetic resonance imaging).

As global economies attempt to implement higher environmental standards, the demand for monazite sand, once just a by-product of mineral sand processing, is rising rapidly.

Monazite is one of the most important REE-bearing minerals, which are critical for all advanced industrial economies (see Chapter 7).

The rare earth elements neodymium and praseodymium (also known as NdPr), are crucial for the lightweight and powerful rare earth magnets used in electric vehicle and robotic motors, in missile guidance systems for the defence industry, and in wind turbines for the clean energy industry.[16] Both elements can be obtained through an ion exchange process from monazite sand.

On a global scale, China is the dominant supplier of REEs and, although there is strong demand from established markets outside the country, it has cut back on exports, leaving other countries to scramble for other sources. For instance, Japan, a leading importer, has negotiated supplies from India and Vietnam.[17] Monazite can sometimes occur with other minerals, including ilmenite and rutile. Rutile, ilmenite and leucoxene are critical raw materials for titanium dioxide and even the metal titanium. Chapters 4 and 13 illustrated the significance of titanium dioxide. The lion's share of titanium dioxide goes to the pigments and paints, paper and paperboard, and plastics industries, mostly in the Global North, although this equation is changing pretty rapidly.[18]

The ore recovery ratio is extremely low in India compared to that in countries such as Australia or South Africa. Therefore most of these minerals are shipped in a crude form to processing facilities abroad. Also, the technology to crack open composite minerals and extract specific elements is owned by relatively few players.[19] So developing countries like India really do not benefit as much as they could from their natural resources. However, India has now joined an elite list of only seven countries that are able to produce titanium sponge, the precursor of titanium metal, which is used extensively in the aerospace, submarine, defence and medical industries since it is extremely lightweight yet strong in comparison to other metals. This makes it ideal for aircraft and space applications, for which it takes 11 kg of titanium mill products to make 1 kg of finished product.[20] Titanium is hugely bio-compatible, meaning that the human body does not reject it as a foreign element. So it has huge applications in medical (orthopaedic and dental) implants and surgery. Titanium is also very compatible with carbon fibre and is increasingly finding a use in the automotive sector as the drive for fuel efficiency and low-carbon emissions takes the world by storm. But much greater attention needs to be paid to where it is being mined and, importantly, under what circumstances.

Monazite also contains thorium, a radioactive element that can potentially be converted to uranium-233, a fuel for nuclear power generation, through the process of neutron capture. Monazite is classified as 'atomic sand' in India and its export is forbidden. Thorium is yet to be used (in 2019) for nuclear energy development programmes across the world, although it has been a tantalising prospect for many years. The World Nuclear Association says that 'Extracting its latent energy value in a cost-effective manner remains a challenge, and will require considerable R&D investment. This is occurring pre-eminently in China, with modest US support.'[21]

Since India was excluded from the Nuclear Non-Proliferation Treaty due to its weapons programme and was under sanctions and trade bans, it was excluded from trade in nuclear plant and materials for 34 years. This hampered its development of civil nuclear energy until 2009. The country does not have substantial uranium reserves but it does have one of the biggest deposits of thorium in the form of monazite sands. Indian Rare Earths Ltd. (IREL), a central public sector enterprise (CPSE) under the administrative control of the Department of Atomic Energy (DAE), has a mandate to process monazite and stockpile thorium for future use.

In 2017, world monazite resources were estimated to be about 16 million tonnes, 12 million tonnes of which were in heavy mineral sand deposits on the south and east coasts of India.[22] Based on data from the Atomic Minerals Directorate for Exploration & Research (AMD), a unit of the DAE, this corresponds to about 1 million tonnes of thorium oxide. So it has developed a largely indigenous nuclear power programme in which thorium is the substance meant for application in the third stage.

In the neighbouring southern state of Kerala, mineral sand mining has been taking place for 60 years. Today it is controlled by two public sector companies and there are reportedly many private players vying for a piece of the action. There have been huge protests from the local population that have largely gone unheeded. But, in response to a mass protest, the state minister for industries said:

> Mineral sand is to Alappad what petroleum [sic] to the Gulf countries. The state can earn crores [tens of millions] of rupees from it and our economy will be strengthened. There are huge deposits of minerals in the coastal line from Neendakara to Kayamkulam. It's the state's fortune. Besides, the mining is being undertaken by the state and central public sector companies. So the opposition to the mining can be seen as an attempt to sabotage the state's industrial growth.[23]

Those opposing the mining say indiscriminate sand mining threatens a way of life, a sense of place and identity. They say that villages along coastal Kerala are disappearing as their land is devoured by mining activities and there are scores of 'Abandoned houses, temples, schools and many more buildings where people once lived. Red coloured ponds and dried up mangrove forests are another painful sight on this coastline.' Protesters say, 'more than 6,000 fishermen families have vacated over the years due to beach erosion, drinking water scarcity and lack of fish availability.'[24] The Chairman of the Save Alappad Protest Committee, K. Chandradas, says 'Our concern is, should progress and development come at the cost of uprooting lives of 25,000–30,000 people who reside in Alappad? We don't support this kind of development. We have the right to live and die on this land. We will resist anyone who questions this right.'[25]

In response to a right to information (RTI) request from The Lede, an online consortium of journalists founded by journalist Sandhya Ravishankar (see Chapter 8), the public sector organisation Chavara, a division of IREL, admitted to selling the heavy minerals to private buyers but refused to disclose their identity.[26] In an email response to The Lede's queries, they strongly refuted villagers' claims that beach sand mining was the cause of erosion in Alappad. The jury is still out on this one. But when you put all this information in context, you begin to see how sand is so much more than 'just sand' and that there is a vital need to manage it better. Our current economic models do not reflect the true cost of mining sand. We are amplifying the risks by not taking into account people's exposure to hazard or their vulnerability to extreme events, which will only become more pronounced with the climate crisis.

India is hugely vulnerable to tropical cyclones (hurricanes) and storm surges. The National Disaster Management Authority (NDMA) says that the Indian subcontinent is exposed to nearly ten per cent of the world's tropical cyclones, most of which originate in the Bay of Bengal and strike the eastern coast of India.[27] Sand dunes are key barriers against storm surges but they are rapidly being mined away in the face of fierce economic pressures. I'd still argue that it should not be framed as a problem of developing economies alone. In the UK, the controversy around the dredging of the Goodwin Sands (located in the English Channel between England and France) is a good example of how sand dunes are simply viewed as a source of cheap aggregate, despite the fact that they lie in a Marine Conservation Zone (MCZ), and that the Sands hold the remains of many brave pilots who crashed there in World War II, giving up their lives and so making the Goodwin Sands an area of immense cultural heritage for the country.[28]

Marinet, a community-based marine campaigning organisation incorporated as a non-profit limited liability company, has been campaigning against marine aggregate dredging for the last 20 years or so in the UK. Marinet maintains that the EIAs demanded by the government's licensing procedures are 'not fit for purpose, being deficient in their content, lacking in meaningful evidence and partisan to the commercial profit and short-term economic gain aspect only'. In 2010, Marinet, along with the North Sea Action Group (NSAG), made a submission to the UK Parliament's House of Commons Treasury Select Committee to consider 'the Management of the Crown Estate' with specific focus on the Crown's Marine Estate Offshore Aggregate Dredging Licensing provision. Marinet and NSAG raised concerns that are especially serious in light of the current context, where multiple industries are competing for the same resource and the cumulative impact of offshore dredging grows with each approved project. Below is the extract from Marinet's submission to the Parliament.

'(d) Licence Provision

For licence granting the DETR, later DEFRA, now the MFA [all UK government licence issuing departments or agencies], only take into account the information contained in EIAs (Environmental Impact Assessments) made for the dredgers licence applications by those selected, appointed and paid by the dredgers themselves. No other evidence is acknowledged and no second opinion is allowed. These EIAs intentionally do not research those issues that would provide meaningful evidence, nor do they follow up with post dredging research. It can take one or more years before the erosion results from a distant offshore dredging operation.

(e) Evidence of Impact

The MFA (and their predecessors) refuse to recognise any non-partisan independent research, and require no empirical research to qualify the computerized assumptions maintained to attempt to prove that offshore dredging is benign. Yet numerous independent scientific research projects show that erosion results from cumulative offshore aggregate dredging. The levels of resultant erosion of each area correlate quite powerfully with the levels dredged offshore, as does the lowering of the seabed when related to the cumulative active dredging areas.'[29]

Marinet contends that because aggregate dredging fleets require a significant capital outlay at the outset, operators are not open to other, far more sustainable options. In researching for this book as a concerned world citizen, I tried to understand the dredging industry by listening to their podcasts and watching their webinars and I discovered that the industry does indeed appear to care about sustainability. However, they seem quite narrowly focused on carbon footprint and fuel efficiency to make operations as economical as possible. They also focus on 'resource efficiency', by which the industry often means making machines bigger to achieve economies of scale, a trend that one also sees in the shipping industry. Such a focus is no doubt important, but if the industry fails to engage with the fact that they are essentially mining a non-renewable resource, how will it end?

A webinar by the International Association of Dredging Companies (IADC) offers a great insight into the evolution of the dredging industry. However, the environmental impact of removing vast amounts of material from the seabed isn't addressed at all in this webinar, nor does it elaborate on how technology has evolved to mitigate the impact. Working on these massive scales can be very high impact, and not just locally but over a much wider area. Over the last 50 years the size of dredging equipment has grown tremendously to enable the construction of large maritime infrastructural works within a short time. The carrying capacity of 'mega' dredgers doubled within just ten years.[30] While the maximum power on cutter suction dredgers in the seventies was about 3,000 kW, a European dredging company launched 'the most powerful Cutter Suction Dredger that has ever been built', with a total installed capacity of 44,180 kW, in the summer of 2019 (see Chapter 11).[31] These achievements bear testimony to our remarkable engineering proficiency, and we must acknowledge that. Nonetheless, the industry must also take responsibility for the spatio-temporal mismatch between their operations and its impact, whether inadvertent or not.

Much more research is needed on the cumulative impact of these industries on the ecosystem. The dredging, shipping and finance industries seem to be convinced of an ever-increasing need for bigger ports and larger deep-water land reclamations to accommodate bigger and bigger ships. But what we must not forget is that most marine life is found in coastal habitats, rather than in the open ocean. The dredging industry boasts about being able to exert dominion over any kind of substrate – soft sediment or hard rock. Right across the world, from Germany and the UK to India and beyond, rivers and estuaries are being modified to fit ships that are growing ever larger, regardless of the ecological consequences.

As convenient as it sounds in economic terms, isn't it putting the cart before the horse? When I think about how many millions of years it took to create the contours of our oceans and land and how life evolved over millennia to adapt to these conditions, it feels very reckless and imbalanced. Each dredger operates 24 hours per day, seven days per week, only stopping for maintenance or in poor weather.[32]

Figure 14.1 illustrates how our coastal areas, which are responsible for 95 per cent of the world's marine production, are being overrun by human activity.

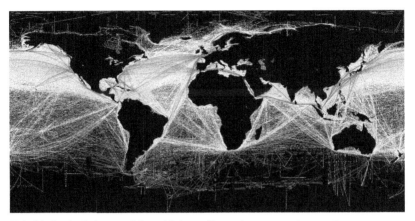

14.1 Shipping density (commercial) – a global map of human impacts on marine ecosystems

Source: B.S. Halpern (T. Hengl, D. Groll) Wikimedia Commons CC BY-SA 3.0 'Shipping density (commercial)', 2012

What is the impact on life? To answer that we only need to look at the landmark assessment and report by the Intergovernmental Science-Policy Platform on Biodiversity and Ecosystem Services (IPBES) in May 2019.[33] The scientists have issued a clarion call. For the first time at this scale and based on a thorough analysis of the available evidence, they have identified 'five direct drivers of change in nature with the largest relative global impacts so far. These culprits are, in descending order: (1) changes in land and sea use; (2) direct exploitation of organisms; (3) climate change; (4) pollution and (5) invasive alien species.' One million animal and plant species are now threatened with extinction, many within decades, more than ever before in human history – that is, more than 40 per cent of amphibian species, almost 33 per cent of reef-forming corals and more than a third of all marine mammals.[34] The scientists could not be clearer: 'The health of ecosystems on which we and all other species depend is deteriorating more rapidly than ever. We are eroding the very foundations of our economies, livelihoods, food security, health and quality of life worldwide.'

From earlier chapters, you have seen how sand underpins industries that make our modern life possible and yet it has received surprisingly little attention. Whether the industries mentioned simply cater to demand or create it is a chicken and egg story. The key questions before us are: what kind of world are we going to leave behind? Where does the buck stop?

In the third section of this book, I'd like to invite you to follow the stories of some inspiring men and women who are working on potential solutions. Time will tell which turn out to be useful but, for now, it is time to move on to constructive and positive action. As Greta Thunberg and so many young leaders across the world have reminded us, we have no time to lose.

SECTION 3

EXPLORING SOLUTIONS

•15•

The Anthropocene Circle of Life

Humans have overtaken nature as the largest force shaping our planet and, for better or worse, we now live in the Anthropocene, an epoch in which we are the masters of our fate. What could help us to deal with such an enormous responsibility? To answer that question, we must look to an industry that is the biggest consumer of resources in the world, the construction sector. In later chapters we will learn more about various aspects of the sector that require change, but the most important, overarching change required is to transform its linear model of 'take, make, dispose' to a circular economy where resources are used in line with planetary boundaries. Readers who would like to learn more about the circular economy in general should refer to the Ellen MacArthur Foundation and to Professor Kate Raworth's book *Doughnut Economics: Seven Ways to Think Like a 21st-Century Economist*.

A circular economy can be applied to any industry, but the positive impacts from this particular sector far outweigh any other. Instead of being disconnected and wasteful, this approach ensures that our built environment is designed in a regenerative way that supports communities, the ecology and, of course, the economy. So how does the circular economy work in practice?

In the EU, construction and demolition waste (C&DW) is responsible for one-third of the waste stream. In the United States, it accounts for about 40 per cent of the solid waste. A 2016 report from the World Economic Forum states that less than a third of C&DW waste is recovered and reused across the world.[1] So there's huge potential for change. There's a thriving market for post-consumer waste such as steel and other metals. But, what about sand? Is there a similar demand? Considering the massive environmental and social impacts of sand mining, shouldn't we explore this option rather than hunting for virgin material all the time? The answer is complicated by a frenemy in the picture, recycling – a word that is as loosely defined as the word sustainability, and both can be used to mean anything you want them to mean.

In general, recycling has been a growing trend, driven by a clear business incentive. However, not all recycling is virtuous and therein lies the catch. It is far easier to downcycle materials than it is to upcycle them or to maintain an equivalent quality. Which means that when materials get reutilised in lower value applications, they cannot be recycled again thereafter. When C&DW is recycled as road fill, very little can be done to recover and reuse this material at the end of life. Whereas, when materials are reused in similar or even value-added applications, potentially, they could be reused. How many times? The answer, as always, is, it depends. It is easier to recover and reuse materials if they were designed for this in the first place and if the appropriate quality is maintained during recovery and storage. Basically, one has to think about its end of life before a product is brought to life. So the design stage is quite critical to the circular economy.

The difference between theory and practice: recycling glass

Glass is infinitely recyclable, at least in theory. But that is not what you find in practice. I turned to the glass industry to find out more. Well, 'industries' would be a more accurate description because of the sheer diversity of glass use. The renowned engineering consultancy firm Arup has done some great research on architectural glass and the circular economy. How the glass is removed, stored and transported are all factors that influence whether that glass can be recycled at the highest value. Any contamination with other materials means the entire load needs to be rejected – for instance, for good quality glass, the cullet (broken glass) needs to be free from the element nickel, otherwise the finished glass could end up breaking all of a sudden. The requirements are so stringent that even minor contact with stainless steel at any stage can result in significant contamination that may cause critical inclusions.[2] Safety glass – the kind used for windscreens or balustrades – is made up of laminated glass. Laminating glass impacts its ability to be recycled because a plastic interlayer is sandwiched between two panes of glass and they are moulded together at high temperature and pressure. At the end of life, this plastic layer becomes a contaminant that hampers the recycling of this glass. New technologies use steam and high pressure to remove the plastic layer, but this raises whole new questions about emissions and carbon footprint.

There are several more barriers to recycling. Remember the cheerful tourist guide at the beginning of Chapter 3? We're not so different from our great grandfathers. Tax incentives can have a profound impact on how we behave. Standard rates for landfill tax have been increasing across the world. But in many places it is still so cheap to send glass to landfill that there is little incentive to recycle it. In the UK, glass on its own attracts a lower tax rate when sent to the landfill.[3] This means that when glass from buildings built in the 1980s and the 1990s needs to be replaced, most of it finds its way to landfill. Some gets recycled, or more accurately downcycled, into aggregate for road fill or to make the reflective paint that is used on roads. A true circular economy for glass used in the construction industry is a long way off.

But there's good news from the container glass industry, which makes bottles, jars and other packaging for food, perfumery, cosmetics and pharmaceutical products. In the EU, container glass is the largest sector among the glass industries and accounts for some 62 per cent of total glass production in the region.[4] Many cities in the USA are abandoning their glass recycling schemes over profitability concerns and challenges in finding new markets for the material.[5] But there's a very different picture in Europe, which has some of the highest glass recycling rates in the world. Sweden, Belgium and a few other countries are doing an extraordinary job by recycling well over 90 per cent of container glass.[6] What's the key difference? Segregation at source.

Coloured glass is made by adding a cocktail of chemicals to the mix. When everything gets mixed during recycling, these chemicals become contaminants. So it is important to treat coloured glass separately. But many consumers just can't be bothered with this minutiae, which is the primary reason for low rates of glass recycling in municipal waste collections. However, the container glass industry in Europe has made significant investment in technology that automatically segregates coloured bottle waste.

The second largest sector of the European glass industries is for flat glass, about 29 per cent of total EU glass production. This includes building, automotive and solar-energy glass. The sheer diversity of applications makes its recycling particularly challenging. But there is a beacon of hope, Cradle to Cradle Certification™. This is 'a globally recognized measure of safer, more sustainable products made for the circular economy.'[7] It is based on design principles established by architect William McDonough and chemist Dr. Michael Braungart. The cradle to cradle (C2C) certification system evaluates a product's sustainability across its entire life cycle. To achieve certification, a product must meet strict standards in five categories in health and environmental protection: material health, material reutilisation, renewable energy, water stewardship and social fairness. Standards evolve through a stakeholder engagement process, with input from technical experts, market leaders and the public. The aim is to create change at the design and conception stage instead of wondering what to do with a product once it is no longer in use.

Glass is a particularly difficult product to make circular in the current manufacturing context for a wide variety of reasons, including those mentioned earlier. As shown in Chapter 3, 'The Gorilla in the Room', glass making is also an extremely energy intensive process. I was shocked to learn that once a float line begins production it cannot be stopped and cooled during its lifetime (10–15 years). This means that it runs for 24 hours a day, 365 days a year, year after year. This makes any downtime for repairs or maintenance extremely expensive. It is also a huge challenge for sand supplies because this is a non-renewable resource in human timescales. It is formed in nature over thousands and thousands of years.

There may be another factor to consider. In Chapter 3, we learnt how the use of molten tin was pivotal to the production of flat glass through the float process. As you see in Figure 1.1, tin is also mined from sand when it is available as placer deposits. In fact, most of the world's tin is produced from placer deposits in riverbeds and valleys or on the sea floor.[8]

The float process has been licensed in 30 countries with a combined output of nearly one million tonnes of glass a week.[9] The demand is so fierce that by some accounts we might have only 20 years of supply of high quality white silica sand used in glass making.[10] New reserves may be found with much difficulty and great cost to the people and the planet. In today's context, it is a crime not to recycle this material.

So I was delighted to learn about the first glassmaker in the world to be C2C certified for its large portfolio of glass products. AGC Glass Europe, based in Belgium, produces, processes and markets flat glass for the construction industry (external glazing and interior decoration), car manufacture and solar power applications. It offers the world's most comprehensive portfolio of C2C certified glass products at bronze, silver and gold levels. This is no mean feat. Over twenty suppliers had to provide detailed information on the composition of material used. They had to work with over forty plants in nine different countries. Their code of conduct had to be clearly stipulated in all procurement policies and supplier contracts to ensure all suppliers remain committed to their goal of social fairness. The world certainly needs more such behaviour and if you are in a position to influence purchase decisions, you know what needs to be done.

Is an image problem getting in the way of the circular economy?

There are other interesting developments in the global C&DW sector, with many players working towards a circular economy. In 2018, CDE Global, a company that produces wet processing equipment for recycling sand, organised the Circular Driven Economy Symposium to promote the benefits and opportunities of recycling C&DW material.[11] I presented the first talk to help set the scene and then stayed on for its two days to learn more. In the UK, for example, purpose-built crushers and separation plants can take this waste and produce recycled sand that meets regulations. But the industry has an image problem and nobody wants to be the first purchaser. Representatives say customers are more than willing to buy but do not want to be identified as buyers. For a variety of reasons, the word 'recycled' appears to be a stigma. 'We don't call it quarried sand, so if it meets the same specifications, why should it be identified as recycled sand?' asked a delegate.

We visited the Sheehan Group, an established processing plant in the UK that produces recycled aggregates. They seemed to be doing a brisk business, even if their clients did not want to be singled out. A smell of wet soil permeated the air along with a faint smell of something ever so slightly industrial and the wind kept blowing sand grains into my eyes. At the centre sat an enormous metal octopus with arms branching out in several directions. Here, the C&DW was ground up and fed to a gravity separation chamber filled with water where the material was washed free of impurities and then passed through a variety of processes. At the end, a sludge was left that was dried and pressed to form a 'filter cake' that was sent to landfill – not as waste but for engineering purposes. The filter cake could also be used to line water features or as a bulk fill material. The water was filtered and reused to minimise impact on the environment. At the end of each metal arm was a growing pile of sand or gravel. Considering how heterogeneous the raw material input was, I was surprised to find several neatly segregated heaps of sand and gravel of various size fractions at the end of the process. It was hard to tell the difference between natural sand and recycled sand. I was impressed to see how much waste the process could divert from landfill.

However, within the broader construction sector, industry perceptions about recycled sand ranges from 'not good enough' to 'you don't know where that comes from'. Some of these perceptions are easy to address with rigorous testing and relevant data sheets, as Sheehan has already done. But others are not so easily addressed without a wider policy change. For instance, a common feeling that the market is skewed towards 'the big boys' and that customers expect recycled sand to be cheaper than natural sand. After all, you don't expect to pay higher prices for second-hand goods. Natural sand is so cheap that it's not an even playing field.

Big players in the industry do recognise that the circular economy is a significant business opportunity. LafargeHolcim's subdivision aggneo® focuses on the production of high-quality recycled aggregates. Although it is still a small entity within the organisation, their Business Development Manager, Mark Tomlinson, spoke positively at the conference about its growth prospects, 'We have an opportunity to provide higher value and preserve natural resources. Recycling occurs close to the centre of cities whereas primary aggregates are supplied from outside which gives it significant haulage cost advantage.'[12] He stresses that for this to work, environmental regulations not only need to be in place but also need to be enforced. Public procurement must play a role to boost demand. But this is not a hypothetical discussion. There are real-world examples. LafargeHolcim, with partner Bouygues Construction, completed a successful urban circular economy pilot programme in the Marais area in the heart of old Paris. The project faced two main challenges. They were dealing with recognised heritage buildings and the renovation of all 21,000 m² had high building standards (HQE – High Environmental Quality).[13] The project took back, sorted and recycled 4,000 tonnes of demolition waste and produced recycled aggregates in a dedicated local platform, including 720 tonnes to make new concrete in a local concrete plant.[14] 'Projects like this signal the start of something bigger.'

One of the biggest C&DW recycling units in the world is in Norway, where public procurement is driving a low-carbon economy. The unit is run by a visionary family business, Velde Pukk, who believe they are doing the right thing, even though it is not all smooth sailing. Public users are sometimes sceptical, legislation has yet to catch up and nothing is cheaper than dumping. But they are not doing this out of the goodness of their heart, they believe the business has tremendous commercial potential and that it is definitely the way forward. After all, it offers several benefits, including: reduced landfill; reduced CO_2; improved transport logistics; and saved natural resources. On the whole, as of late 2020, CDE Global and its partners – such as Sheehan, Velde Pukk and many others – had diverted over 80 million tonnes of C&DW from landfill to be reused in construction projects. This is the kind of change we need at scale.

Closing the loop

The EU Commission is keen to promote the Circular Economy throughout the EU. Although most European countries seem to have exceeded the target of '70% recovery of C&D waste by 2020' by 2016, a closer inspection reveals that these high rates are 'mostly achieved by using recovered waste for practices such as backfilling and low-grade recovery applications (i.e. downcycling), reducing the potential to move towards truly circular waste management'.[15] To encourage a true circular economy, the Commission is working towards: acquiring reliable C&DW statistics; harmonising EU markets for C&DW recycled materials; and increasing cooperation among stakeholders in the value chain.

The city of Zurich, in Switzerland, is a prominent example of change at scale. In September 2019, the city won a prestigious award for the innovative and sustainable use of recycled concrete with CO_2-reduced cement and of recycled asphalt in urban construction projects.[16] Zurich is the largest city in the country, with 430,000 inhabitants and a public procurement budget of over €1.8 billion. 'It spends around €370 million (420 million CHF) per year on new public buildings, and around 15–25% (€55–90 million per year) of this cost is related to structural work, including the building's concrete structure and shell.'[17] In 2002, the city ran a pilot project to build the first public building with recycled concrete. The Im Birch school was constructed with 80% recycled concrete.[18] Following this success, the city made it mandatory in 2005 that all public buildings should be built with recycled concrete in line with specific standards. Since 2015, all public buildings have also been built using CO_2-reduced cement (CEM III/B), which uses blast furnace slag (BFS) instead of conventional clinker.[19] Although this kind of cement has been around a while, it wasn't popular with architects and engineers for a number of reasons, however intangible.

To address the concerns of architects and other stakeholders regarding the aesthetic quality of concrete made with recycled aggregate and CO_2-reduced cement, Zurich built 'a mock-up wall', which allowed for a direct comparison of the effects of various aggregate types (virgin v. recycled) and cement types (CEMII/B or CEM III/B) on the finished product. It worked like a charm. While architects and developers already knew about the environmental benefits, they could see first-hand that using recycled aggregates did not negatively impact the concrete in any way; and that the use of CO_2-reduced cement actually made the concrete slightly lighter in colour, 'an additional aesthetic advantage'.[20]

Numerous landmark buildings were built, and continue to be built, this way. Some prominent examples include The Kronenwiese housing complex (completed in 2017 with a 95% share of recycled concrete with CEM III/B) and The Kunsthaus (art museum, completion expected in 2022), with a 98% share of recycled concrete (produced in situ) with CEM III/B. Thanks to this pioneering approach of recycling concrete in buildings, the City of Zurich saved around 17,000 cubic metres of virgin materials (and landfill space) between 2005 and 2018.[21]

It is worth noting that, from an energy perspective, the use of recycled concrete only makes sense when it is available from within a 25-kilometre radius of the construction site – which is the case throughout the greater Zurich area.[22] However, Zurich's experience has also shown us that supply often follows demand. Ever since it became mandatory to use recycled concrete in public buildings, more and more suppliers have invested in production capabilities to meet demand. Zurich also uses recycled concrete for up to 30% of the foundation material (sub-base layer) of new roads and it encourages the use of the reclaimed asphalt for the road base layer (up to 60%, or up to 80% on pavements and places with low traffic volumes).[23] Zurich's example shows us that systemic change is possible where visionary leadership and informed constituents exist – which is what we need to create and maintain the circle of life in the Anthropocene.

•16•

Is Architecture the Bridge?

The stone age didn't end because there were
no stones. A more attractive alternative simply
emerged

Michel Baars, founder and CEO of New Horizon Urban Mining

For a circular economy to work in the construction sector, we
need to rethink several industries, which takes time – the
one thing we do not have since we have fewer than ten years to
limit climate catastrophe. It does seem like a tall order until you
learn about people like Michel Baars, who set up New Horizon
Urban Mining.[1] He exudes a strong sense of urgency and the
will to make a circular economy work. He says he has chosen to
work as an entrepreneur so that he can actively drive change by
assuming both the risk and the responsibility.

When he talks, he says things that make you wonder if it's
just bravado or if there's more to it: 'We're entrepreneurs with
guts'; 'We don't demolish, We harvest!'; 'We make circular
products lovable'; 'We try to prevent recycling'. When pressed
to explain what he means, he talks about how huge volumes of
material flow in and out of our urban areas every day:

We have given these streams labels: what goes in is a raw
material, what goes out is waste. Those worlds hardly touch

each other. And when they meet, it is very low in the value chain and is called recycling. Nobody will be happy about that. I think that new connections can lead to solutions that are much higher up the value chain. I am convinced that it has an economic model.[2]

New Horizon Urban Mining takes inspiration from the visionary architect Thomas Rau's statement 'Waste is material without identity'. This company aims to bring to market products 'with a story' because they say 'people like stories and stories are the best way to transfer knowledge'. In practice, this company is a network organisation with 15 partners who call themselves the Urban Mining Collective. They take care of risk management, contracts and raw materials and they even offer financing, branding, sales and management. By teaming up with established market players, they make life easier for contractors and prevent the creation of new warehouses, double shipments, administrative burdens and disruptions in the construction logistics process. It sounds like a one-stop shop to bring circularity into the built environment.

There are some big names in this collective such as ABN-AMRO bank, a name associated with a great example of circular economy in building design. The Circl pavilion next to its headquarters in Amsterdam's Zuidas district is a fantastic example of what is needed to make this concept work. It was a pioneering effort. Work on the design started in 2015 when hardly anyone knew what circular meant in practice. Every part of the building was carefully thought through and chosen because the materials could be fully reused. Everything superfluous was cut out, including the 'e' in the word circle because they felt it could be pronounced without it.

Given the large amount of CO_2 in the production of concrete and the qualification for easy recycling, they chose wood instead of concrete where possible. The insulation in the ceiling was made from 16,000 pairs of used jeans donated by eager employees, the window frames came from demolished office buildings and old furniture from the bank was lovingly restored and reused. Even the fire hoses, cable ducts and paving stones were pre-loved.

The website proudly states 'On the ground floor, a collection of hardwood taken from a former monastery and the bar of Dutch football club Top Oss was used to make the floor. The partition walls for the basement conference rooms came from a building in Hilversum that once belonged to Philips. They didn't quite fit, so some extra partitions were used in places to complete the rooms. In this case, "reuse" took precedence over aesthetics, although everyone thinks the finished walls look great. And it all makes a compelling story.'[3]

Five hundred solar panels were installed on the roof to produce more than enough power. Since devices such as laptops and smartphones run on direct current, the kind produced by solar panels, they decided to use it directly rather switching to alternating current. This meant minimum energy loss in conversion and eliminated the need for extra equipment such as inverters and adapters.

The team behind Circl challenged every single person who came in contact with this building and its construction process. They made sure to team up with people whose activities within and around the building reflected the same philosophy of care. Most importantly, they allowed themselves to be vulnerable, to share openly what worked and what did not work. When was the last time you heard about a multinational bank behaving this way? Since it opened in 2017 the building has evolved into a thriving meeting place and a hotspot for all things circular. What was meant to be just some extra conference rooms and hospitality facilities for the bank's staff has become an important venue in the drive to speed up the transition to a circular economy.

The circular economy won't fall in place naturally. It is an active choice. In the words of the team at Circl:

> building according to principles which are still totally unknown to many is an enormous challenge. Nothing is certain or a given. The likelihood of making mistakes is great … The development of Circl has also demonstrated that you need visionaries, headstrong individuals who aren't afraid to go against the grain. People who know that you can only bring about real transformation by accepting the challenge. Who have vision, want to inspire and persuade others and, in turn, are prepared to be inspired and persuaded. And who dare to take a leap in the dark and gain the support and confidence of others to do that.[4]

The construction industry is generally risk averse. With lives, livelihoods and liability issues on the line, this is understandable. But our window of opportunity to act is small and we need leaders who can show us the way quickly.

It is reassuring that Circl is not an isolated example. The BAMB project, an acronym for Buildings as Material Banks, received funding from the European Union's Horizon 2020 research and innovation programme. The project ran for four years, brought together 16 partners from seven European countries with the objective of enabling a systemic shift in the sector by creating circular solutions for the building industry.[5] BAMB tested concepts such as 'building material passports' and 'reversible building designs', and solutions such as new business models. Material passports tell users where the material comes from and the journey it has undertaken to its use in a building. Such documents give architects and engineers more confidence to specify recycled materials in their projects.

Take the example of structural steel. 'The building and construction sector is responsible for more than half of global steel consumption.'[6] Much of this is eventually recycled but, as many sustainability practitioners know, reuse is an infinitely better option than recycling, which also requires tremendous energy and, let's not forget, sand. The primary production of steel is an extremely energy-hungry process that has wide-ranging impacts. Researchers have found that mining-related forest loss in Brazil caused roughly ten per cent of all Amazon deforestation between 2005 and 2015. They were surprised to learn that the impacts of 'deforestation associated with mining extends remarkable distances from the point of mineral extraction.'[7]

Chapter 5, 'The Backbone of Nearly Everything', discussed how sand is fundamental to the critical industrial process of sand casting, which is used for 70 per cent of all metal castings worldwide. But this process is environmentally unsustainable because silica sand mining and its transportation to foundries damages ecosystems.[8] Few studies have been done on the specific impact of mining common foundry sand, such as silica, or specialist sands, such as zircon and chromite, which are used for higher temperature casting. This is a gaping hole in our knowledge that needs filling.

Wouldn't it be far better to find ways to reuse building material? Which brings us back to BAMB. The catch is that 'Re-used steel is estimated to be about 8–10% more expensive than new steel, taking into account all required reconditioning processes. ... Material passports can [... help reduce ...] costs in sourcing, testing, reconditioning and fabrication' of steel and other materials.[9]

Reversible building designs keep materials in the circular economy loop for much longer than current commercial practices allow. 'Change in market needs is a leading reason for [the] premature demolition' of many buildings.[10] At the heart of reversible building design, lies the idea that investors can benefit from investment risk reduction by decreasing 'the risk of low return-on-investment or even loss due to early demolition', by building structures that can be transformed in form and function.[11] The idea of circular architecture, far from being a theoretical construct, was tested on a real scale during this project.[12] The most exciting thing about BAMB is that 76, double-blind, peer-reviewed, open-access papers were published as part of their conference proceedings. So learning and development on circular architecture is accessible to anyone with an Internet connection.

Another movement that offers hope is Architects Declare. At the end of 2019, over 800 climate-conscious architecture practices in the UK were signatories, including some big names. The declaration begins with a recognition of the challenges ahead:

> The twin crises of climate breakdown and biodiversity loss are the most serious issue of our time. Buildings and construction play a major part, accounting for nearly 40%

of energy-related carbon dioxide (CO_2) emissions whilst also having a significant impact on our natural habitats.[13]

Time will tell if these practices deliver on what they promise.

This chapter would not be complete without addressing the most important topic, reusing existing buildings. Given that we have less than a decade to avoid climate catastrophe, the best solution is to work with what we already have, especially in developed economies. Refurbishing existing buildings must take precedence over building shiny new 'icons'. Once again tax policy plays a crucial role. In the UK, new builds typically pay between zero per cent and five per cent value added tax (VAT), while most refurbishment and renovation projects pay 20 per cent VAT.

The *Architects' Journal*, the UK's leading architecture magazine and the voice of architecture in Britain, launched the RetroFirst campaign in September 2019 as a call for action on three fronts: tax, policy and procurement.[14] They are collecting evidence to submit to the government. They're calling for the VAT on refurbishment, repair and maintenance to be cut to five per cent to 'promote the reuse of existing building stock and reclaimed construction material by introducing new clauses into planning guidance and the building regulations', and for public procurement practices that 'stimulate the circular economy and support a whole-life carbon approach in construction by insisting that all publicly funded projects look to retrofit solutions first'. As the *Architects' Journal* says, 'The greenest building is one that already exists'. Let's hope that policy makers across the world rise to the challenge.

•17•

Tapping the Untapped

a. Alternatives to construction sand and gravel

a.1. Desert sand

'Why can't you use desert sand?' is an oft-repeated question that has prompted researchers across the world to turn their gaze toward this, as yet, untapped and abundant resource. Although much of the popular and scientific discourse about deserts currently deals with combating desertification, the construction sector has been preoccupied with the question of making desert sands a viable industrial resource. So far, sand from the desert has largely been unusable in industrial concrete and land reclamation because the grains are too finely polished by the desert winds.[1]

Four young students – Carolyn Tam, Hamza Oza, Matteo Maccario and Saki Maruyama from Innovation Design Engineering, a joint Master's course at the Royal College of Art and Imperial College London – developed a composite material that can be made using desert sand or quarry fines. The product, named Finite, is still in the prototype and test stage. Finite is as strong as residential concrete but it takes half the energy to make as traditional concrete and at end of life it can be decommissioned and then reused to create the next structure or melted down to become part of the landscape once again. Although their target sector is the construction industry, Finite is not intended to create multistorey buildings. They want to target temporary structures and objects – think architectural pavilions, exhibitions, and more. Carolyn plans to develop Finite during independent study at MIT (Massachusetts Institute of Technology).

Finite has received a positive reaction at several exhibitions and festivals. However, they have also received an oversized dose of scepticism. Presumably, it does bend the mind to use a product that looks like concrete but can be decommissioned and transformed into a new project after the end of its life. In a society that is conditioned to flushing potable water down the toilet, few bat an eyelid at this enormous waste of resources. Thankfully, this is changing. Carolyn does not seem perturbed by the negative comments and says they envision a very different kind of building. She has her sights set on developing solutions that might be useful for those who live close to desert areas or those without access to concrete.

When I wondered if there were people 'without access to concrete' in this day and age, she spoke about how camps for refugees and internally displaced persons can deliberately be kept impermanent because any facilities that make a camp look or feel more permanent are often prohibited by host governments. Sometimes, political reasons prevent access to concrete. For instance, Israeli restrictions on basic construction materials, such as cement, aggregates and steel, has meant that thousands of people in Gaza have been destitute for years after losing their home.[2] Carolyn hopes a temporary solution could provide such people with some respite.

Alternatively, for one-off events such as the Qatar World Cup, particularly events near a desert, one could use the sand to build modular bricks for bus stops and small pavilions. After the event the material can be melted down on site and become part of the landscape once again. But all this is still at the idea stage. Tests, such as on compression, have given the team definitive answers about the material's properties but there are still many questions. For instance, just as reinforced steel or rebar improves concrete's tensile strength, would incorporating steel open up new possibilities? Can it withstand wind, rain and snow? We will know more once Carolyn has completed her tests and analyses of the chemical and physical properties of the product. For the moment, Carolyn's research on Finite is more academic than commercial.

Although a desert can be perceived as an empty space or a wasteland waiting to be put to good use, it is as much a habitat as a river or a beach. This perception is no different to the way earlier generations spoke of swamps, marshes and wetlands. We have since learnt about the ecological value of those habitats and their critical importance in maintaining water security and biodiversity. Deserts have evolved over millions of years and, far from being mere empty spaces, they are teeming with life, from insects and reptiles to plants and mammals, all highly adapted to deal with the harsh environment. There is much we can learn from them. Experts point out that using desert sand for mass producing construction material only transposes the sand crisis.

Choosing alternate building materials to sand might turn out to be a key solution after all.

a.2. Mycelium insulation and plant-based concrete

Another startup has been making waves in the construction sector, Biohm. Their product offering is not yet ready to take on concrete. But the direction in which they are moving is certainly exciting and promising. They wish to lead the construction industry toward a biomimetic future, where everything is inspired by natural systems and biological processes to create a healthier and more energy- and resource-efficient built environment. They believe that when you are guided by biomimetics, you perceive everything as a system, so you take into account every stakeholder involved in a building project and ensure that their health and well-being is looked after by using natural, biodegradable and breathable materials, by reducing toxins and volatile organic compounds in the air, by consuming carbon and waste during production, and by purifing the air during occupation.

The founder of the BIOHM, Ehab Sayed, studied civil engineering but the rigidity of the course made him feel like a human calculator. He turned to design engineering, where he found an outlet for his creativity and his calling. He excelled and won multiple awards. The company he has set up appears different from the very first. For instance, team pictures are in side profile, like a monarch on a coin, instead of a traditional front-facing shot. The company philosophy deserves to be quoted in full:

our philosophy allows nature to lead innovation in the
construction industry to create a healthier and more
sustainable built environment … we are driven by a
continuous stream of interdisciplinary ground-breaking
research through which we offer a range of services. we
collaborate with industrial and academic partners to
lead the construction industry toward a circular future
that is inspired by nature and driven by our human,
environmental and economic needs.nothing is ever-lasting
… everything is ever-changing … we do not design … we
refine what nature has given us[3]

The company operates at the convenient intersection of
bioengineering, biotechnology and the traditional building
industry. They are very aware that they cannot change the
system on their own and have developed deep relationships
with large companies that could scale up the transition rapidly.
'We wouldn't be here, were it not for support from the industry
and academia,' says Sayed. They offer a range of 100 per cent
natural materials, including mycelium (mushroom-based)
building insulation, which consumes waste as it grows, and orb
(organic refuse biocompound), which combines agricultural
and food waste with an organic binder to create a sheet material
for buildings and interior architecture. Waste products, such as
coffee chaff, corn husks, orange peels, cocoa husks and ground
blue pea flowers, are transformed into beautiful construction
products that are not only aesthetically pleasing but are also
rigorously tested to meet industry standards. Orb is robust
enough to replace dry lining products, such as MDF (medium-
density fibreboard) which is widely used in professional projects
and homes in flooring, cabinetry, furniture and more. MDF is
usually made using a binder that contains the toxic substance

formaldehyde (used to preserve biological specimens, so it's not the best product to use among the living). Orb relies on an organic, non-toxic binder derived from agricultural waste products. It has much to offer in terms of aesthetics and they have had a lot of interest in it.

The first product that the company is bringing to market is mycelium building insulation. Unlike traditional insulation, this product is not only breathable but also can be grown on a wide variety of substrates. It offers spectacular thermal insulation and is naturally fire retardant. Fire retardants are often packed with neurotoxins. So, it is fantastic to hear about one that puts human well-being at its heart and takes care of every stakeholder in the value chain. A BBC video shows Zoe Laughlin from the Institute of Making testing samples of this product with a flaming blow torch on one side and a chocolate ice cream on the other side.[4] That the ice cream does not melt, despite the extreme temperatures on the other side of the mycelium board, is testimony to the power and potential of the product. Their mycelium insulation outperforms almost every other natural and synthetic insulation product on the market.[5] Biohm is working with the social enterprise the Onion Collective to build the world's first community-led, bio-manufacturing facility that will divert 150 tonnes of waste from landfill and sequester 16 tonnes of carbon every month. The facility will be a catalyst for economic regeneration in the coastal town of Watchet, West Somerset, UK.[6]

Biohm is also developing a plant-based concrete and aims to expand their range of mycelium construction products. All Biohm's materials will eventually be combined to form an innovative interlocking construction system it calls Triagomy.

Inspired by the molecular structure of some of nature's strongest materials, it will be a revolutionary way to build. Triagomy offers 'near-limitless flexibility in design, enabling the creation of structures of all shapes and sizes using standardised components'.[7] It allows a building to be deconstructed at any stage, which means you can add a room or a window where there was a wall, you can easily move spaces without needing a whole 'construction project' to make a small change. It can also incorporate integrated foundations. The strength of the system does not come from individual blocks but from the structure of the interlocking grid. Such a radical approach would eliminate demolition and make the reconfiguration or relocation of buildings much easier. The significance of such innovation and aspiration cannot be overstated. Sayed's research shows that:

> To create our built environment (3 per cent of the earth's land), the global AEC (Architecture Engineering and Construction) industry has exhausted more than half of the earth's natural resources and contributed around 50 per cent of all greenhouse gas emissions. (Wilmott Dixon, 2010; Wines, 2016) … In the UK alone, a considerably large percentage of materials delivered to construction sites still go straight to landfill – estimated at 15 per cent in 2008 (Baker, 2008).[8]

These are shocking statistics. How can we be okay with this mode of development? The most widely accepted definition of sustainable development is 'development that meets the needs of the present without compromising the ability of future generations to meet their own needs' (Brundtland, 1987).[9] Inter- and intra-generational equity lies at the heart of any sustainability approach, so how we operate has got to change right now. Biohm have ventured into crowdfunding, which gives the ordinary citizen a chance to support the principle.[10]

Many practitioners are calling for increased use of offsite manufacturing techniques that make better use of resources, speed up build times, reduce costs and generally offer greater sustainability, quality and flexibility. There are many barriers to such an approach, including incompatible business models, supply chain issues, high up-front costs to set up manufacturing facilities and, not least, client perceptions. But the benefits are manifold and can offer ever-greater returns for multiple stakeholders. Research and testing, in conjunction with partners from industry and academia, continue on Biohm's regenerative design approach but evidence to date suggests that 'this approach could achieve significant reductions in environmental impact (120 per cent), build times (95 per cent) and costs (70 per cent) compared to conventional methods and approaches' (Sayed 2019, p. 434).[11] I am excited to see what the future holds for Ehab Sayed and his multi-award-winning team at Biohm, and for all other innovators who give as much if not more importance to the planet and to people as to profit.

a. 3. WasteBasedBricks®

WasteBasedBricks® are another beautiful example of upcycling waste and turning it into useful products. True to their name, these bricks are made from construction and demolition waste (C&DW) and they are truly aesthetically pleasing. The bricks are not only safe to use according to European standards but they also come in a wide variety of enticing palettes to suit design requirements –Aubergine, Blackpepper, Mushroom,

Nougat, Orange, Pistachio, Radish, Salami, Salt+Pepper, Truffle, Wasabi. They've been used all over the world for interiors and exteriors of high-end residential and commercial real estate.

The company, Stonecycling®, is on a mission to move towards 'beautiful building materials made from 100% upcycled waste with a positive carbon impact on the planet'. They 'envision a circular world where waste is synonymous with raw material: cities and its buildings are constructed of building materials that are made from 100% waste, are 100% recyclable at the end of their life cycle and absorb more carbon than it takes to create them.' What struck me when I spoke to Ward Massa, the team's business strategist, was how they worked within the existing framework of this traditional industry but were moving away from a 'one-size fits all' approach. Instead creating distinct, and even unique, building materials, from a clever combination of different waste streams. Unlike traditional bricks, these come in a wide variety of shapes, sizes and colours to suit project requirements. For a 2020 project in New York, on Manhattan's 11th Avenue, an incredible 260,000 kilograms of waste will be upcycled. Exciting times!

a.4. Straw bale buildings

Concrete might seem like the only suitable building material. But before concrete dominated our skylines, vernacular architecture was rich and vibrant as local materials and expertise imparted a distinct style and soul. Communities often came together to build. Concrete seems to have divorced us from this ethos of place making. Fortunately, some traditions continue in the natural building sector and modern methods are driving innovation in this sector.

As a building material for the twenty-first century, straw bales are extremely low impact. They are a great way to use a co-product from agriculture that is often discarded. Low nutritional-value straw from cereals such as wheat, rye or rice, does not compete with other uses, such as fodder; while barley and oat straw is often used as a feed supplement for livestock.[12] Straw locks in carbon dioxide as it grows and the co-products do not compete with food production, unlike other crops grown exclusively for biofuel.[13]

As long as they are built with care and protected from moisture, straw bale houses can offer extraordinary thermal and acoustic insulation.[14] That means you don't hear your neighbour's conversations, or other activities, and you save on energy bills. Straw bale buildings create unique and aesthetically pleasing spaces. At end of life, the straw can be safely composted, unlike artificial insulation products that are hard to dispose of, such as fibreglass and expanded polystyrene. With proper maintenance, these buildings can last a long time. The oldest known straw bale house is in Nebraska, in the USA, built in 1903; the oldest one in Europe was built in 1921 in Montargis, France.[15]

Straw bale buildings have also proven incredibly resilient to earthquakes, hurricane force winds and wildfires.[16] They have much to offer, especially in post-disaster reconstruction programmes when safe, affordable shelter materials may be growing all around.[17] Concrete and masonry construction require the use of high cost, non-renewable, energy-intensive materials and skilled labour, which are largely unaffordable for the poor. In the wake of an extensive natural disaster, the demand for these materials further increases their cost, while their production, transportation and use contribute to the climate crisis. In response to the 2005 earthquake that devastated northern Pakistan, non-profit organisation Pakistan Straw Bale and Appropriate Building (PAKSBAB) developed 'a unique straw bale building method providing exceptional structural capacity at about one-half the cost of conventional brick and concrete construction in Pakistan'. They used a simple load-bearing design in which the straw bale walls supported the roof load and could resist earthquakes and wind. It was also cheaper because they used renewable, locally available materials and local labour.[18]

Prefabricated panels have made this type of construction much more accessible. Even in the UK, where affordable housing is hard to come by, there are some promising examples. One outstanding one is the multiple award-winning LILAC (Low Impact Living Affordable Community) project in Bramley, Leeds. This was the UK's first ecological affordable co-housing project and it is proof that 'a modern lifestyle can be achieved without costing the earth financially or environmentally'. It was built using ModCell® technology, a modern low-carbon method of construction using panel timber walls insulated with straw bales. The buildings are equipped with solar panels and a mechanical ventilation heat recovery system, which enables the indoor air quality to remain high. As a result of the increased insulation provided by straw, the community has reduced its annual gas bills by nearly 90 per cent, compared to the average for Leeds.[19] Such results alone should make people sit up and take notice.

LILAC is a vibrant community that has inspired and supported the development of many similar projects in the UK. Which is just as well because research from the University of Bath shows that:

> up to seven million tonnes of straw remains after the production of wheat flour, and up to half this amount is effectively discarded due to its low value, to be used as animal bedding. This 'leftover' 3.8 million tonnes of straw could be used to build over 500,000 new homes, as an average three-bedroom house needs 7.2 tonnes of straw.[20]

The ModCell® technology is industry certified, which means that developers and house buyers can insure and secure mortgages against homes, schools and offices built using this sustainable construction method.[21] Given that the construction sector must reduce its energy consumption by 50 per cent and its carbon emissions by 80 per cent by 2050, radical changes are needed. Professor Pete Walker, Head of the Department of Architecture & Civil Engineering at Bath, believes, 'Building with straw could be a critical point in our trajectory toward a low-carbon future'.[22]

Such prefab construction methods can play a significant role in both developed and rapidly developing economies. Strawtec® is a German company based in Rwanda, East Africa, that has won multiple awards. It produces locally manufactured, sustainable, high-performance wall systems with a core made from compressed agricultural straw fibres. Strawtec® caters to both the affordable and the high-end, luxury housing markets. Unlike traditional straw bale buildings that have thick walls, prefabricated straw panels offer great space savings and are produced to exacting standards in a controlled environment.

Strawtech® strawboard panels have been tested extensively and meet international standards, such as the British Standard BS 4046 in the UK, DIN 4103 in Germany, CSTB in France and ASTM in the USA.[23] Structures can be built incredibly fast compared to traditional brick and mortar construction. Rwanda stands to benefit in many ways. Not only does the technology improve skills and create local jobs, it also empowers farmers and reduces the country's trade deficit. Rwanda imports many of the basic raw materials for mainstream construction, such as cement and gypsum; these materials represent up to ten per cent of the country's total imports.[24] Using locally sourced, renewable resources that can reduce the shortage of affordable housing makes it a compelling offer. Such win-win solutions can speed up climate action across the world and reduce the need to mine non-renewable sand and gravel.

a.5. Engineered wood or mass timber

There are many more examples that offer great promise. Modern technology allows traditional materials to be engineered with great precision. For instance, architecture is renewing its interest in timber. There's already a race to build the tallest timber tower, or 'plyscraper'.[25] One of the highest residential timber towers is being constructed in the Netherlands. At 73 metres and 21 floors, HAUT is set to receive the coveted BREEAM Outstanding label, the highest possible sustainability score.[26]

Cross laminated timber (CLT) and glue laminated timber (glulam) are engineered wood products that allow for the creation of mass timber structures. Both are extremely strong and surprisingly fire resistant. I was astonished to learn that timber can outperform steel in a fire because of how materials behave in a fire. Steel heats up pretty quickly in a raging fire, softens, and can collapse into a spaghetti-like mess. In contrast, hefty beams of timber develop an outside layer of char that protects the uncharred inner portion and maintains its strength for a longer period.[27]

Unlike non-renewable resources such as sand and gravel, we have stronger mechanisms for ensuring responsible sourcing by buying Forest Stewardship Council (FSC) certified timber. Timber also offers incredible carbon savings in comparison with concrete.

b. Recycled aggregates

b.1. Recovering aggregates and unhydrated cement from concrete

In Chapter 15, we learnt about companies that are recycling C&DW to produce high-quality recycled aggregates. But what about the cement used? Can that also be recycled? This is an important question because, as a key input to concrete, cement is a major contributor to climate change. To my delight, I found a product in the Netherlands that had won the construction category in the Circular Award Business 2019, for the second time in a row.[28]

Although most end of life concrete used to be downcycled as road fill, newer technologies are finding ways to preserve and recover valuable raw materials. Which brings us back to the contest winner, SmartCrusher, whose pitch reads:

> The concrete industry is one of the most polluting. In comparison: it produces twice as much CO_2 as the entire aviation industry, ten percent of the total CO_2 production in the world. One kilogram of concrete provides one kilogram of CO_2. This has a major impact on our climate. Our concrete machine returns all materials from old concrete, sand, gravel, cement – for reuse. With this we reduce CO_2 emissions by 75 percent. This machine pays for itself within a year and a half, fits in a shipping container and is therefore easier to move. [29]

The SmartCrusher is not an entirely new product but has evolved into a better version. In 2014 it won the ASN Bank World Prize in the 'Sustainable energy, nature and environment' category. At the UN Climate Conference in Bonn (COP23) in 2017, the innovation was hailed as one of the 'needed Game Changers'.[30]

SmartCrusher is backed by a company that operates in transport, road construction and recycling in the Amsterdam region – the Rutte Group and New Horizon Urban Mining (see Chapter 17). The SmartCrusher is used for all the concrete that is released when New Horizon dismantles buildings.

This technology has the potential to alter the future of the cement and concrete industry. The theory behind how it works is interesting. As concrete sets, not all the content reacts. In fact, around 30–40 per cent of cement in concrete can be extracted as unhydrated cement.[31] SmartCrusher is able to separate concrete into its composite elements in four fractions: unhydrated cement, hydrated cement (both are also referred to as fines), gravel and sand. One of the by-products of the SmartCrusher is heat. Consequently, the resultant aggregates are dry and ready for immediate use as resources for new concrete on site. Research shows that recycled gravel and sand from a SmartCrusher outperforms virgin aggregates because their prior use acts as an excellent pre-treatment.[32]

As shown in Figure 2.3, cement production is highly carbon intensive. It alone is responsible for eight per cent of global carbon emissions.[33] CO_2 is not only released from the limestone used for cement production but also from the burning of fossil fuels used to heat a cement kiln to around $1,450^0C$ ($2,642^0F$).[34] The unhydrated cement from a SmartCrusher can replace virgin cement to produce new concrete on site, reducing the concrete's CO_2 emissions. The hydrated cement fraction can also be used as a mineral admixture (additives used to control the properties of concrete for an intended end use) or as a substitute for limestone in cement kilns, eliminating the emission of CO_2 associated with the decarbonisation of limestone, and cutting the energy demand of the kiln in half.

Urban mining with a SmartCrusher offers a commercially attractive way to significantly reduce the carbon and environmental footprint of the construction sector and to help it transition to a circular economy. It can decentralise development and empower small- and medium-sized organisations to shift rapidly to a circular economy. Because governments are the largest consumers of concrete in infrastructure and utilities, this solution allows 'countries to meet their climate ambitions without compromising their ability to implement the infrastructure that is needed to build a low-carbon future'.[35]

c. Secondary aggregates

Secondary aggregates, also known as manufactured aggregates, differ from recycled aggregates. While recycled aggregates refer to the recovery of materials that have already been used in concrete, secondary aggregates refer to a non-traditional stream of resources that can take the place of conventional aggregate, such as, pulverised fuel ash (PFA), blast furnace slag (BFS) and incinerator bottom ash aggregate (IBAA). As long as the processes comply with stringent building industry standards, these can be viable resources.

Traditional rock quarries generate a huge amount of waste, sometimes up to 50 per cent of output, which can be developed as manufactured sand. However, I would urge caution in recommending crushed rocks as a major alternative before putting control mechanisms in place. It is better to establish systems for sand manufactured from C&DW or other waste streams before establishing systems for sand to be manufactured from crushed rock. Rocks are as non-renewable as sand and the context is critical. In developed countries, quarries are often highly controlled spaces when it comes to land zoning. Whereas in the developing world, where demand outstrips supply greatly, unregulated quarries can and do spring up anywhere and artificial sand is manufactured by deliberately crushing rocks. Without appropriate checks and balances, this solution could actually be worse for the environment, as it could lead to ecologically sensitive regions being razed to the ground – with deadly consequences for people and wildlife.[36] With that caveat in place, I'd like to present the next example.

c.1. Premium concrete sand from crusher dust and recycled glass

Despite being an advanced industrial economy, Japan has chosen to move away from sourcing natural sand for concrete by dredging. This move came out of necessity. Around 1975, Japan began to experience a scarcity of natural sand, especially in the western part of the country. In 1990, it proposed a ban on dredging and gave the industry ten years to find alternatives. At the turn of the millennium, Japan enforced the ban on dredging, except for what was required to keep shipping ways clear.[37]

In 2006, China decided to ban the export of natural sand dredged from rivers and the sea due to the 'loss of the country's natural resources, undercutting of river channels, the destruction of dikes and the impact on shipping'.[38] The Chinese authorities clamped down on Fujian and Guangdong, the two provinces that were crucial hubs for sand exports to Taiwan, Japan, Hong Kong and South Korea. The move may also have been politically motivated as it subsequently permitted limited exports to Taiwan, Hong Kong and Macau.[39]

This context made 'Western Japan almost totally dependent on manufactured sand for concrete', so Japanese industry and academia stepped up their R&D collaboration.[40] Kotobuki Engineering and Manufacturing Co. Ltd. (KEMCO), based in Hiroshima, started off by manufacturing sand using slag from the Japanese steel industry. Over time, they developed a way to manufacture premium concrete sand from crushed rock and recycled glass. The crushed rock was waste material from rock quarries that, until that point, had no market in Japan. I learnt about this Japanese technology through Kayasand, a company that is licensed to sell KEMCO's products. Kayasand is also a member of Marinet, an organisation described in Chapter 14.

Making the right kind of concrete is a complex science. 'Concrete producers require a very specific and consistent gradation in their sand that is not typically satisfied by the fines [waste crushed rock] produced in conventional rock crushing.'[41] The size of aggregate particles, their distribution, their mineral content and the presence of impurities, all influence the quantity of cement and water required and the workability of the concrete. If there are not enough small particles, swiss-cheese-like holes are left in the concrete, which impacts its strength. One could add more cement to solve this, but that is an expensive proposition in terms of both cost and environmental impact. On the other hand, an excess of angular material makes it difficult to pump the material and work the finished concrete as it binds too much.[42] In summary, effective concrete requires careful and consistent management of its constituents.

Kayasand promotes KEMCO's V7 technology because it meets the considerable demands of the industry: 'to produce a sand to completely replace natural sand in concrete, having both well-shaped particles throughout and the ability to make an evenly graded sand … the gradation can be adjusted and held at a level within any of the standards set by ASTM (American Society for Testing and Materials), JIS (Japanese Industrial Standards) or BS (British Standards). … [Operations are based on a dry system because] wet systems were considered unnecessary, environmentally difficult, wasteful of space (always at a premium in Japan) and expensive.'[43]

In general, concrete from crushed rock can require more water to ensure a workability equal to that of natural sand concrete, due to the higher angularity of the manufactured sand particles. However, independent research in 2013 by Cardiff University (funded via the Aggregates Levy Sustainability Fund for Wales in the UK) has shown that water reducing admixtures can be used to compensate for this if the manufactured sand does not contain clay particles. 'At the same water/cement ratio, the compressive and flexural strength of manufactured sand concrete exceeds that of natural sand concrete.'[44] KEMCO's proprietary technology allows surplus quarry waste to be reprocessed to completely replace natural sand in concrete.[45] It can produce well-shaped and evenly graded sand from a wide variety of raw material, such as basalt, granite, limestone and sandstone. And it offers many sustainability and environmental benefits for a low-carbon era.[46]

But technology alone will not drive change, especially when the environmental costs are externalised or are not immediately apparent. Socio-economic and political barriers can be powerful forces indeed. In Kayasand's experience, making headway in some traditional markets has proven difficult due to: conservative appetites for risk; a reluctance to rock long-standing relationships; substantial investment in dredging equipment and licences; and a lack of regulatory change.[47] Meanwhile, in Japan, as of 2015, more than 50 per cent of all manufactured sand was being produced using this technology.[48] Kayasand's business is continuing to grow in Australia, New Zealand and the Pacific Islands.

c.2. Carbon negative aggregates

An exciting solution from the UK is set to capture a growing share of the secondary aggregates market. OCO Technology, formerly known as Carbon8 Aggregates, was a spin-off from research at the University of Greenwich. In early 2020, carbon capture and utilisation (CCU) was more of an aspirational than a truly tangible commercial technology. But OCO Technology can permanently capture carbon and transform a cloud of smoke into something you can hold in your hand, a 'product' that can be used by industry. Their patented technology is called accelerated carbonation technology (ACT) and it is being used to transform thermal residues, such as air pollution control residues (APCr) from energy from waste (EfW) facilities into a high quality, lightweight, secondary aggregate.

ACT technology works by making carbon dioxide react with the residues under carefully controlled conditions. Binders and fillers are added to create calcium carbonate (manufactured limestone) which is similar to natural oolitic limestone.[49] The process captures more carbon dioxide than is emitted to create the finished manufactured limestone, resulting in the 'World's first carbon negative aggregate'.[50] Embodied carbon in buildings and infrastructure is a serious concern for those in the construction sector. This carbon capture product helps reduce the embodied carbon of the structures themselves. It also avoids the need to mine and dredge natural aggregates, saving our natural landscapes, ecosystem services and our biodiversity – crucial concerns in this era of climate crisis. It is heartening to know that 'for every tonne of carbon-negative aggregate used, 1.4 tonnes of natural aggregates are saved'.[51]

For EfW providers, who provide the thermal residue, it offers a chance to achieve 'zero waste to landfill' – as at the Lakeside facility at Colnbrook, near Slough, which became the UK's first zero waste to landfill EfW facility in 2017.[52] Manufactured limestone has many applications in construction. It can be used in: the production of concrete building blocks; precast and ready-mixed concrete; screeds; pipe bedding; and various road applications. As a manufactured product it can be tailored to specific requirements, unlike natural aggregate. OCO Technology currently recycles around 24% of the UK's EfW sector's APCr.[53]

The company operates three sites in the UK: Brandon (Suffolk), Avonmouth (Bristol) and Leeds. Together they process over 100,000 tonnes of waste each year, which would otherwise have been sent to landfill, and they produce over 200,000 tonnes of sustainable aggregate. They have their eyes set on international markets like Japan and Australia. The company has won many awards. In August 2019 it was mentioned in a UNEP report for the Pan-European region, which highlighted that these aggregates 'meet European "end of waste" regulations and materials performance standards, and make a demonstrable contribution to the developing European circular economy.'[54]

As you can see, there are numerous solutions to the looming sand crisis. They may not solve the climate crisis and, without question, it is far better to avoid waste and to avoid building or burning in the first place, before trying to reduce extraction, offset emissions or reduce landfill. Our imagination and creativity, our spirit of resilience and ability to collaborate with others are our critical assets. We need to nurture these as we adapt to what lies ahead. Hopefully, examples like these help to dispel the doom and gloom stories we hear every day.

•18•

Leaving a Beautiful Legacy

Quarry restoration

Can the future create a portal into the past? That is exactly what Park in the Past in the UK has set out to do.[1] They want to take visitors back to the first century, when the Romans arrived in North Wales, when conquest brought huge benefits to the Roman empire and when this region was famous for its mineral wealth. The Romans were renowned for their engineering prowess and were one of the most technologically advanced civilisations of the time. Once they'd conquered Wales, they extracted large amounts of gold, copper and lead and modest amounts of other minerals. But what was the life they conquered like? What kind of structures did people build? How did they survive in this forested, mountainous countryside? What was it like to hear hundreds of hooves, wood and metal clashing, the clamour of a Roman legion drowning out the gentle sounds of the countryside? How were the Romans greeted? We are about to find out.

The former sand and gravel Fagl Lane Quarry in Flintshire, north-east Wales, is being restored, primarily for local residents to appreciate their rich cultural and historical heritage. The site's 120 acres were once part of a stunning landscape dating back to the ice age, 2.6 million years ago. A prehistoric bison tooth and many man-made artefacts have been discovered in the vicinity. The varied topography includes a 37-acre lake, agricultural and grazing lands, woods and scrubland, a river and extensive wetland areas. A CIC (community interest company) runs it, a financial model for social enterprises that is a hybrid charity and commercial business. It operates like a company but is legally bound to ensure that its activities benefit the community that supports it and an asset lock is in place so that everything is reinvested in the project.

Park in the Past aims to ensure the long-term viability of the site in terms of nature conservation well beyond the short statutory aftercare period enforced under mineral extraction planning permission. They want to bring the local community closer to the natural and historical environment, benefiting their health and well-being. They are planning a fully functioning Roman fort and a Celtic iron-age settlement and want to create opportunities for involvement at multiple levels. They would like this space to be a National Centre of Excellence in experimental archaeology, ecological restoration and conservation. They believe there is huge potential because the site could appeal to a wide variety of audiences, including researchers, environmentalists, cycling enthusiasts, horse riders and even wild-swimming enthusiasts.

In June 2018, the company held its first crowdfunding campaign to raise £20,000 to build the main gate tower of the

Roman fort. They surpassed their target in under four weeks, thanks to the generous support of bestseller authors Ben Kane, Simon Scarrow and Anthony Riches and their fans. It was a winning combination. Since the authors specialise in historical fiction, particularly Roman military fiction, this project has a synergy. The authors tapped into a wide variety of methods, from auctions of Roman artefacts and limited collectors' editions of their books, to fundraising by following cycling trails over ancient routes. At the end of 2019, Park in the Past were still completing the final conditions of their planning permission before officially opening. But it is a great example of how, with good planning, societies can benefit from a quarry after mineral extraction is complete.

It was once common to use spent quarries for the disposal of waste.[2] Fortunately, at least in developed economies, this is mostly a thing of the past. Restoration is seen as a vital part of the licensing regime and licences often earmark the land for specific purposes, such as agriculture, nature conservation or recreation. The loss of habitat and its fragmentation is taking a toll on wildlife. As towns spread and industrial agriculture takes its toll, the biodiversity of the world is declining significantly and quarry sites can provide a much-needed refuge for wildlife. Progressive restoration is increasingly expected of mineral extraction companies, that is, restoring patches of land that have been worked while it is still an active quarry, rather than waiting for all operations to cease before beginning restoration work. This needs to become standard procedure across the world wherever mineral extraction happens, as long as the lack of capacity of regulatory bodies to monitor and enforce consents and permits is also addressed.

Quarries and biodiversity

There are some interesting developments related to sand extraction. One such is The Quarry Life Award, a competition run by HeidelbergCement, a multinational that owns and operates thousands of quarries across the world. As one of the world's largest building materials companies they claim to be 'No. 1 in aggregates production, No. 2 in cement, and No. 3 in ready-mixed concrete'.[3] They also say they are the first company in the construction materials sector to adopt group-wide guidelines for species protection. For a company this size, good PR is invaluable and what better way to get it than to involve stakeholders in a fun and rewarding exercise? The Quarry Life Award is an international research competition for the promotion of and education about biodiversity in quarries.[4] It is targeted at scientists, university students, NGOs and citizens (site neighbours).

The aim is to raise the awareness of the organic value of mining sites and to find new ways to enhance it further. The competition takes place every two years and runs simultaneously at national and international levels. To make the process fairer, the organisers have split it into two: a research stream and a community stream. The research stream focuses on scientific projects that increase knowledge of mining ecology and lead to improved biodiversity, landscape or water management; the community stream focuses on engagement and outreach projects that help the quarry to better connect with its local stakeholders. The awards are distributed at a lavish ceremony in Brussels and the excitement among the contestants is palpable. Anyone who thinks quarries are boring should watch the interviews with the winners. Their passion for biodiversity and their strong desire to make a difference speaks volumes for trying multidimensional approaches.

The Sand Motor experiment

Another development comes from the beach nourishment business in the Netherlands. The Sand Motor, or Sand Engine as it is sometimes called, is an experimental pilot on working with nature.[5] In a country so small that they have no hinterland to escape to, the Dutch keep their coastline constant, even in light of the climate crisis. Ever since 1953, when they had the worst flood incident in history, land reclamation has become central to the Dutch identity. They adopted not only hard engineering approaches, such as dykes and groynes, but also frequent beach nourishment to keep the sea at bay. However, as sea levels rise that task is getting harder by the day. The country knows the trajectory that lies ahead, what they don't know is how bad things are likely to get.

The Sand Motor project was also supported by the European Union's European Regional Development Fund. At $68 million in 2011 to create a two-kilometre-wide sand engine reservoir, the experiment was not cheap. But it was chosen because it offered a greater potential to deal with dynamic situations.

The key test is whether mega-nourishment is better than traditional beach nourishment. Is it better to deposit a humongous quantity of sand in a specific spot and let nature take care of forming coastal protection barriers, such as beaches and sand dunes? Or is it better to deposit smaller quantities more often and to artificially smooth the sand over the beach? In the case of the latter, the public sees the immediate benefits of their tax money. The jury is still out on the concept.

Traditional beach nourishment has to be repeated every four to five years. But with the Sand Motor, the dredging industry anticipates a much longer timespan of 20 years or more before it would need to be repeated, which they hope will give local flora and fauna more time to recover. The hypothesis is that species are tolerant of thinner blankets of sand via natural processes but cannot deal with being completely smothered by thick layers of sand through the standard process of beach nourishment. However, it is not clear from data in the public domain, which habitats had to be destroyed to create this new habitat. Neither is it clear which species were impacted the most by dredging such vast volumes of sand from the seabed. Other questions remain unanswered: was fish uptake measured in the process of dredging? Were any recovery studies/active seabed restoration activities undertaken for the borrow sites? Were any other industries impacted? If yes, how was this mitigated? Are potential borrow sites for future replenishment being monitored currently to establish a robust baseline? Would the monitoring and evaluation programme have been feasible without the EU subsidy? Is such support expected to continue in the future?

An official evaluation of the Sand Motor was completed five years after its construction (in 2016) and a final assessment is expected for 2021.[6]

The UK has also been inspired by this approach and is in the process of carrying out a smaller version near North Norfolk, tailored to the local context. Sandscaping, as it is known in the UK, takes into account the differences between the bathymetry of the UK and the Netherlands and a differing policy regime. Unlike the Dutch seabed, which slopes gradually, the Norfolk beach extends below mean sea level, plateaus for about 300 metres and then suddenly drops off into deep water.[7] Replicating the sand engine would be neither economical nor desirable because it would extend into protected seabed habitat and result in offshore losses of sand.

The drive for this project comes from the need to protect fossil fuel, critical infrastructure and the villages around it in the face of long-term coastal erosion and increasing damage from storms. The Bacton Gas Terminal in Norfolk, owned and operated by Shell and Perenco, receives up to one-third of the country's gas supply. Hard structures such as rock groynes could protect the terminal for the next 50 years, but at the expense of the neighbouring villages of Bacton and Walcott, where 200 homes are already under threat from sea-level rise. Experts say that these two villages are within 15 years of being engulfed by the sea.[8] Where could these people go? Who would pay for their relocation? Although the same could be said of many other coastal villages that are at risk from rising sea levels, protecting the country's energy security is a key priority for the UK.

Dredging industry experts believe that the sandscaping initiative is better suited to achieving the twin objectives of safeguarding the UK's energy security and protecting neighbouring villages, although it could cost up to £20 million.[9] As the sand gets washed along the coast, it would shore up the neighbouring villages and protect them from the sea for an extra 20 years or so. Funding for the project comes from a public-private partnership venture between the Bacton Gas

Terminal and the North Norfolk District Council (NNDC). Vast volumes of sand are already being brought in to shore up the gas terminal, so the extra price to replenish the beaches makes it more 'cost efficient'. The project aims to use 1.5 million cubic metres (1.96 million cubic yards) of sand to protect a 5 kilometre (3.1 mile) length of coastline.

The project has not been all smooth sailing though. It has received a large amount of unfavourable press thanks to netting on the cliffs preventing sand martins from nesting in their burrows. #CliffsofShame and #SaveTheBactonSandMartins have been rallying cries for many birders on social media such as Twitter. The depth of public sentiment took the dredging industry by surprise. Half the netting was removed thanks to the flurry of media coverage. The bottom half was left to ensure that the sandscaping project could keep to schedule and to prevent sand martins from being buried alive when large amounts of sand are deposited.

Conservation organisations have been fairly vocal about how the project should have avoided the nesting season, as the sand martins travel thousands of miles from their winter nesting grounds in Africa only to find themselves locked out of a nest and a future. There is a lesson here for future projects. Although this species is not at risk of extinction, designing projects with only human well-being in mind is ill-advised at a time when one in ten species are set to go extinct. Watching the little birds struggle for life as they are trapped in nets is inhumane and heartbreaking. Could the project have avoided this unnecessary situation by providing the birds with artificial nesting sites? Perhaps.

Nonetheless, the sandscaping project is well underway and the UK's energy security and Shell's gas terminal are safe for the moment. This project hopes to 'turn back the clock and restore beach volumes at Bacton and Walcott to what they were 20 years ago.'[10]

At this point however, we need to take a step back and look at the big picture. At a global level, the demand for sand for beach nourishment is likely to rise from 50 million cubic metres today (roughly 80 million tonnes) to 500 million cubic metres by 2050 (roughly 800 million tonnes).[11] Where will all that sand come from? At what cost to the environment and the communities dependent on that sand? The latest research is quite clear and compelling, in general beach nourishment is not a sustainable business. Parkinson and Ogurcak (2018) provide multiple lines of evidence to show how studies that promote beach nourishment or beach fill often fail to take into account: where the sand will come from (sufficient reserve volume); whether the sand is compatible with native beaches in terms of grain size, texture and mineral make-up; rising construction costs; and all the vulnerable geomorphic elements of the coastal zone and the full environmental impact.[12]

Numerous coastal scientists recognise that beach nourishment is and will continue to be big business. However, they urge governments to treat it as an interim strategy while an overarching strategy of managed withdrawal from the coastline is formulated and implemented.[13] If you already live by the coast, you may want to consider your options very carefully. Professor Gary Griggs, a world-renowned expert, says that planned retreat from the shoreline will become the only feasible long-term solution by mid-century and beyond. He lays out a clear and compelling account of the challenges facing our global coastal zones and the actions we can take to protect our coasts and oceans in *Coasts in Crisis*.

The best thing we can do to nourish our coasts

There is another movement that gives me hope, a crowdfunding campaign to open up as many rivers in Europe as possible. Thousands of old and obsolete dams currently block European rivers, disrupting the flow of sediments and the habitat of species such as sturgeon, salmon, trout, otter and stork. Thanks to this campaign, led by WWF Netherlands, several old dams, culverts and weirs have been removed in France, Spain and the UK, with exciting results as nature bounces back.[14]

The USA has a richer history of dam removal as 1,605 obsolete dams were removed between 1912 and 2018, 99 in 2018 alone.[15] In 2011, the largest dam removal in US history began on the Elwha river in Washington. Two hydroelectric dams, including the 210-feet-high (64 m) Glines Canyon Dam, were torn down to restore critical spawning habitat for endangered salmon species in the Elwha. A time lapse video by National Geographic is a treat to watch.[16] According to the USGS:

> Of the 33 million tons of sediment trapped behind the dams, about 8 million tons resettled along the river or at the mouth, and another 14 million dispersed into the ocean. It would take more than 70 dump trucks running 24 hours a day for five years to move that much dirt and debris downstream. Piled up, the sediment would form a

cone about one-third of a mile in diameter and taller than a 50-story building.[17]

The dam removal on the Elwha has had fantastic results. The seafloor near the mouth of the river has risen by about 10 metres (33 feet), creating a whole new delta and beach.[18] This has generated an incredible abundance of fish, crabs, clams, birds and other forms of wildlife. Considering the sheer volumes of sediment moved by rivers and how life thrives on free-flowing waters, this nature-based solution might be our best bet yet for leaving a beautiful legacy.

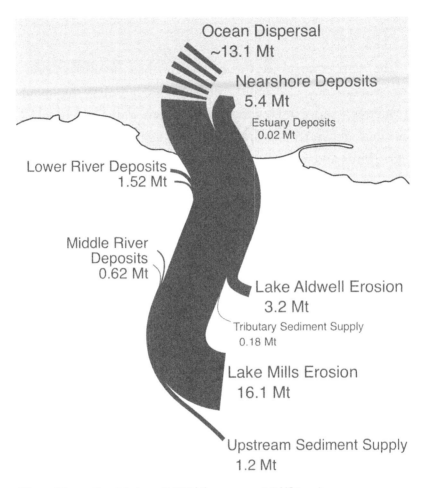

Ocean Dispersal
~13.1 Mt

Nearshore Deposits
5.4 Mt

Estuary Deposits
0.02 Mt

Lower River Deposits
1.52 Mt

Middle River
Deposits
0.62 Mt

Lake Aldwell Erosion
3.2 Mt

Tributary Sediment Supply
0.18 Mt

Lake Mills Erosion
16.1 Mt

Upstream Sediment Supply
1.2 Mt

Mt = millions of metric tons (1,000 kilograms or 1.1 US tons).

18.1 Diagram of Elwha River sediment changes, five years after dam removal began
Source: US Geological Survey (Public Domain)

•19•

Racing Toward the Sunrice

Soon after World War II, there was fierce competition between the United States and the Soviet Union to achieve military supremacy during the Cold War. Their arsenal already included nuclear weapons, hydrogen bombs and intercontinental ballistic missiles (ICBMs). Then both announced their intentions to launch artificial 'Earth satellites' for scientific research during the 18-month-long International Geophysical Year (IGY), which extended from July 1957 to December 1958.

Much to the dismay of the USA, the Russians got there first. They launched Sputnik 1 in October 1957 and a month later followed it up by successfully launching a dog named Laika into space aboard Sputnik 2. The pressure was on. US leadership had to show the American public that they could do it too. So, in less than ideal circumstances, the first US artificial satellite, Explorer 1, was successfully launched on 31 January 1958. Shortly after that, on 17 March, the USA launched Vanguard 1, the first satellite to be powered by solar power, which established solar cells as the preferred method of energy supply for satellites. Although it is now derelict, Vanguard 1 has been in orbit for over 60 years.

The man behind this feat was a German immigrant, Dr. Hans K. Ziegler. He was a much-respected scientist in the field of electronics and his conviction that solar was the way forward ultimately trumped objections from the US Navy, which still thought that solar cells were not a mature technology. Dr. Ziegler had told the US Signal Corps, 'In fact, in the long run, mankind has no choice but to turn to the sun if it wants to survive'.[1] We now know that it is time to let go of our addiction to fossil fuels and turn to renewable sources of energy. Solar energy has many advantages. There are no moving parts, it creates zero emissions and no noise. But its promise of clean energy is marred by some production practices that favour short-term profit over a long-term outlook.

Although there are a variety of technologies to produce solar energy, the majority of solar panels today are made from silicon. Elemental silicon is currently largely derived from quartz, the most common form of silica (silicon dioxide), through extremely expensive, chemically laden and energy intensive processes. Metallurgical-grade silicon is the precursor material for both electronic- and solar-grade silicons.[2] It is often produced in countries that have cheap electricity, reductants such as charcoal or wood chips and access to good quality quartz, either through natural deposits or via trade.

The primary process to produce metallurgical-grade silicon is the carbothermic reduction of silicon dioxide (quartz sand) in submerged-arc electric furnaces, where the sand is heated with a source of carbon such as coke, charcoal, or wood chips to about $2,000^{0}C$ (over $3,000^{0}F$). This process produces an awful lot of CO_2. Nonetheless, it is how most of silicon is produced today. But what if silicon could be obtained from renewable sources? What if you could grow sources of silicon rather than mine it? What if the process required much less energy and cost much less? What if it is already possible? How would that change our energy landscape?

Scientists have found 'a low cost, low energy route' to harvest silicon from rice husks, also known as hulls.[3] This is the protective outer covering that is discarded when the paddy is processed. Each year, the world produces about 800 million tonnes of paddy and the residue of straw and husk has little commercial value. It cannot be fed to livestock as it is high in silica. When incorporated into the soil, it is a major source of methane. So the husk is often burned to produce energy. But the ash still needs to be sent to landfill. The benefits of harvesting silicon from rice husks are manifold in terms of cost and of a significantly smaller environmental footprint through carbon reduction and waste management. There has been a lot of focus on the use of sand in construction and not nearly enough on its use in other industries. So this source of silicon is a significant solution.

One of the earliest papers on this subject comes from scientists in the Materials Science Centre in IIT Kharagpur, a renowned Indian scientific institute. Despite promising laboratory results as early as 1982, the project was not scaled up and commercialised due to 'internal politics' and the reticence of Indian funding agencies to fund a new concept.[4] It does seem like a wasted opportunity. India currently imports most of the polysilicon used to make solar panels, despite its ambitious plans for solar energy.[5]

Richard M Laine, Professor of Materials Science and Engineering at the University of Michigan and his colleague Julien Marchal patented a method in 2015 to directly distil high-purity silicon using biogenic silica sources including grasses (wheat, rice, barley, oats, etc.) that take up silicon dioxide in their stalks and seed hulls. The patent uses ash from rice hulls because rice hulls contains the highest silica content of all the grasses. However, other forms of biogenic silica such as corn stover may be utilised in the same process.[6]

Whenever you distil things directly from a reaction pot, you can make them quite pure. So the resulting silicon can be purified to specified values that meet the stringent requirements for photovoltaic and other applications. Professor Laine says the key is to dissolve some of the silica in the rice hull ash (RHA) to get the carbon to silica ratio correct for making silicon metal. This is an exciting green development as some of the energy required for the process comes from burning the rice hulls so it requires less energy. The process is 'kinetically much faster' because these biogenic sources already contain carbon that has been absorbed from the atmosphere, along with the silicon dioxide absorbed from the soil and deposited in the stalks and hulls to strengthen them and to ward off predators and diseases.[7]

Businesses in several countries, including Thailand, China, India, Japan and Germany, have shown an interest in Professor Laine's company, Mayaterials Inc., from those simply wanting to develop the chemistry further, from makers of commodity chemicals and from solar-grade silicon producers. Traditional silicon production is a capital-intensive business, so capital already sunk in the dominant technology could be an important reason this has not taken off sooner. However, in 2019, Mayaterials was in active talks with an undisclosed company looking to establish a pilot plant.[8]

Other sectors are vying for a piece of the rice husk pie, and in fairly advanced stages. In Chapter 5, 'The Backbone of

Nearly Everything', we learned how silica is part and parcel of our everyday lives. Specialty silica, such as precipitated silica, is widely employed in the manufacturing of green tires. According to market research agency Globe News Wire, the demand for green tires, particularly from Asia Pacific, North America, and Europe has been strong and is expected to have a positive impact on the market over the next seven years.[9]

In this technology silica is used as a reinforcing agent in tire tread compounds, currently in conjunction with, but increasingly instead of, carbon black, the traditional reinforcing agent for tires. Silica reduces rolling resistance and therefore improves a car's fuel economy. It also improves anti-skid performance – a tire's traction on wet surfaces. In short, silica allows tire engineers to reach the 'magic triangle' where trade-offs between grip, rolling resistance and treadwear, balance each other out.[10] Although adding silica does increase production costs.

The tire industry is making a concentrated effort to reduce its considerable carbon footprint and many manufacturers are exploring options for using only renewable resources. The Goodyear Tire & Rubber Company is one of the world's largest tire companies. It employs approximately 67,000 people and manufactures its products in 50 facilities in 22 countries around the world. The company is keen on sustainability measures and is exploring various options, including synthetic rubber and soybean oil instead of petroleum. Let us hope the soybean isn't coming from burning the Amazon or other old-growth forests. But silica from RHA is certainly good news.

Goodyear has tested silica derived from RHA at its Innovation Center in Akron, USA, and found its impact on tire performance to be equal to traditional sources. The company sees this as an economic advantage because most silica for tires is produced by incinerating sand at around 2,500°F (1,371°C), RHA can be converted into usable silica for tires at only 212°F (100°C). It is now working with companies in Asia to eventually process tens of thousands of tons of silica from RHA. Goodyear has reached a supply agreement with Yihai Food and Oil Industry in China for silica derived from RHA. In 2015, it was scheduled to begin using such silica in a consumer tire manufactured in its factory in Pulandian, China, and sold in China. Considering that over 1 billion tires are produced annually worldwide, sourcing silica from this renewable source could have a profound impact on the environment.[11]

Asia Pacific was the largest regional market for specialty silica with a revenue share of 40 per cent in 2018 owing to rapid production of tires and construction activity in the region.[12] The supply chain for RHA is still fragmented but as farmers learn of this beneficial use for their waste, I hope more entrepreneurs will leap in and academia and governments will help create the change we need. Precipitated silica is used extensively in rubber, food, healthcare, plastics, abrasives and coatings and we cannot continue to extract non-renewable resources at such rates without undesirable consequences on people and the environment.

We must also find a way to recycle these minerals. Nature does this seamlessly. For instance, scientists have found that hippos were responsible for 76 per cent of the total movement of silicon throughout the ecosystem in southwestern Kenya.[13] They acted as 'a kind of conveyor belt' transporting silica from land to water. This is vital to the ecosystem, because diatoms, single-celled algae in the water, need this element, and they in turn provide food for other plants and animals in the waterways.[14] I'm not suggesting we poop into waterways, that is not the lesson here, but humans seem to have perfected the art of taking what we want with little regard for other users of the resource.

Meet the microscopic giants of our world

There is an even more compelling reason to reconsider how we use sand in the current context of a climate crisis. In comparison with industry that uses tens of thousands of tonnes of sand per year in a one-way process to produce silicon, nature recycles several gigatonnes of sand through biomineralisation (a gigatonne is equivalent to a billion metric tonnes).[15] Before we go into what biomineralisation is, it is helpful to clarify some terms. You see, the element silicon is rarely found on its own in nature. Instead, it is found bound up with other elements in various forms. Silica refers to a compound of silicon and oxygen in a specific ratio. When this compound is dissolved in water, it becomes dissolved silica, also known as silicic acid. Biomineralisation is a process in which silica is incorporated as a structural material into organisms.[16] This happens at the micro-scale – such as single-celled diatoms, protozoa-like radiolarians and silicoflagellates – and in some higher orders – for instance, two of the three classes of sponges have skeletons composed of silica instead of the more common calcium carbonate.[17]

It turns out that these little diatoms play an inordinately big role in the ecosystem for several reasons and they are the dominant component of phytoplankton in both freshwater and oceans. An estimated 200,000 species of marine diatoms are currently known to science.[18] Some estimate the overall number of species across oceans, lakes and rivers to be up to 2 million.[19] Diatoms use dissolved silica to build their extraordinarily beautiful, intricate, symmetrical, transparent cell walls of glass, called frustules, which form their skeleton. You may be interested to know that their name is derived from the Greek diatomos, meaning 'cut in half', precisely because of their astounding symmetry.[20]

Diatoms are critically dependent on silicon found in water as silicic acid.[21] The main external source of which is via rivers that supply about 84 per cent of this dissolved silicon through the weathering of the continental crusts (i.e. the formation of sand and other sediments, which is often thought of as a physical process, but is also a fundamentally chemical process). Coastal wind also has an impact, especially around deserts. Aeolian transport is the second largest external source of silicon and is estimated to provide about 7.5 per cent of it in the oceans.[22] The third source of silicon is through weathering submarine basalts in the oceanic crusts.[23]

Interestingly, 'The production of silicic acid is intimately related to the sequestration of carbon dioxide'.[24] Diatoms are an important climate regulator.[25] They are responsible for '40% of the annual ocean carbon fixation' as part of the biological pump.[26] To put this in context, this has been equated to 'the total impact of terrestrial rainforests'.[27]

Diatoms are responsible for about one-fifth of the photosynthesis on Earth.[28] They are found in water across the world, wherever there is sufficient light and nutrients, including inland lakes.[29] For example, Lake Victoria is the world's largest tropical lake and it is critically dependent on the silicon supplied by rivers such as the Mara, which in turn depend on the hippos to supply silicon.[30] Diatoms alone account for approximately 40 per cent of marine primary production.[31] In other words, diatoms are 'keystone producers', a building block that we simply cannot afford to ignore.[32] They feed everything, from microscopic zooplankton to gigantic blue whales. Zooplankton include the immature stages of larger animals, for example larvae. In coastal areas, diatoms are important both ecologically and economically because they underpin productive fisheries.[33]

In open oceans, organic matter from diatoms is a significant source of food for deep-water organisms.[34] What doesn't get eaten, settles on the sea floor, and over geological timescales is sequestered into sediments, rocks and petroleum reserves. Thus, diatoms lock carbon in their bodies, in all the organisms they feed and thus lock in carbon in the oceans.[35] Over time, their skeletons collect at the bottom of oceans (and rivers) to form diatomaceous earth, or diatomite. We have many uses for diatomaceous earth, for instance, some types of kitty litter, in flea powder, insulation, toothpaste ingredients and, on a larger scale, to clean up after chemical spills. Diatomite is also crucial to the production of dynamite.[36]

As diatoms fall to the seabed, some of the silica in their cell walls dissolves to form silicic acid in the deep oceans, where the concentration of silicic acid is much higher than in surface waters. This is another critical source of silicic acid for diatoms. But humans are altering the environment in ways that are terrible for these microscopic giants of our world. The construction of dams on rivers has profound consequences on the distribution of nutrients and results in the subsequent change in species composition.[37] Dams hold back not just water

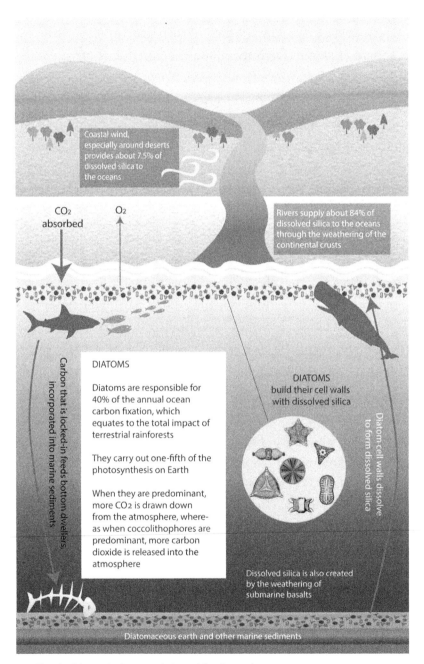

Coastal wind, especially around deserts provides about 7.5% of dissolved silica to the oceans

CO₂ absorbed

O₂

Rivers supply about 84% of dissolved silica to the oceans through the weathering of the continental crusts

Carbon that is locked-in feeds bottom dwellers, incorporated into marine sediments

DIATOMS

Diatoms are responsible for 40% of the annual ocean carbon fixation, which equates to the total impact of terrestrial rainforests

They carry out one-fifth of the photosynthesis on Earth

When they are predominant, more CO₂ is drawn down from the atmosphere, whereas when coccolithophores are predominant, more carbon dioxide is released into the atmosphere

DIATOMS build their cell walls with dissolved silica

Diatom cell walls dissolve to form dissolved silica

Dissolved silica is also created by the weathering of submarine basalts

Diatomaceous earth and other marine sediments

19.1 The role of diatoms in climate regulation and the silicon cycle

Silicon is rarely found in nature on its own. It is commonly found bound up with other elements. Dissolved silica ($Si(OH)_4$, also known as silicic acid) is a compound of silicon, oxygen and hydrogen

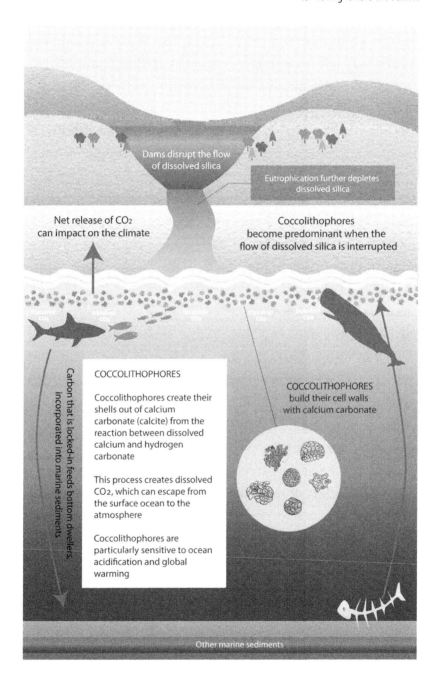

Dams disrupt the flow of dissolved silica

Eutrophication further depletes dissolved silica

Net release of CO2 can impact on the climate

Coccolithophores become predominant when the flow of dissolved silica is interrupted

Carbon that is locked-in feeds bottom dwellers, incorporated into marine sediments

COCCOLITHOPHORES

Coccolithophores create their shells out of calcium carbonate (calcite) from the reaction between dissolved calcium and hydrogen carbonate

This process creates dissolved CO2, which can escape from the surface ocean to the atmosphere

Coccolithophores are particularly sensitive to ocean acidification and global warming

COCCOLITHOPHORES build their cell walls with calcium carbonate

Other marine sediments

Sources: Tréguer, P. Pondaven, P., 2000; Harrison, K.G., 2000; DeMaster, D.J., 2001; Perry, C.C., 2003; Kudela, R.M., 2008; Armbrust, E.V., 2009; McWhan, D., 2012; Maavara et al., 2014; De La Rocha and Conley, 2017 © SandStories.org

but also sand and dissolved silica in the water. In addition, eutrophication in water bodies, caused by fertiliser run-off from farms, further depletes the dissolved silica that is so crucial for the diatoms.[38] When dissolved silica is available in the ocean, it favours the growth of diatoms, but when its availability is altered, other species of phytoplankton become dominant, such as coccolithophores.[39] This can result in harmful algal blooms that are toxic to wildlife, to fisheries and to humans.[40]

All phytoplankton form the basis of the food chain. However, we should be particularly concerned about altering conditions favourable to the growth of diatoms because it turns out that coccolithophores create their shells out of calcium carbonate (calcite), by the reaction between dissolved calcium and hydrogen carbonate. This process creates dissolved CO_2, which can escape from the surface ocean to the atmosphere (see Figure 19.1).[41] In an era when we're exploring all the means available to capture CO_2 from the atmosphere, we cannot afford to ignore this unintended source of carbon emissions and of harm to our ecosystems.

Diatoms are not only an important part of the global silicon and carbon cycles but they also play an important part in global nutrient cycles for phosphorus, nitrogen and even aluminium. It is estimated that every atom of silicon derived from the weathering of rocks is recycled about 39 times to build the cell walls of diatoms before it is buried in the seabed.[42] Can you imagine how different and wonderful our world would be if our industries followed such a model? There's so much we can learn from the magnificence of Mother Nature. Our understanding of how these cycles work is still rudimentary, but we cannot continue to operate our economies on a linear model.

For now, we certainly need to educate ourselves about industries that use sand with specific properties but that, inadvertently or deliberately, employ the narrative of silicon being the second most abundant element after oxygen to reassure the public. This huge gap in public perception needs to be closed. The goal should be to craft products and processes that are part of a circular, rather than a linear, economy. But until we realise that ambition for the industrial minerals we extract, using silica from renewable sources is a step in the right direction.

•20•

Can Big Data Save the Big Blue?

What treasures lie beneath the seas? How did the bottom of the oceans come to be as they are? As Sir David Attenborough says, for a planet that is mostly ocean, we know more about the moon than about the ocean ecosystem that regulates our planet's health.[1] Although humans have become adept at extracting an ever-greater volume of aggregate and minerals from the bottom of the sea, it is still largely uncharted territory. As you saw in Chapter 11, 'The Currency of Development', Belgian and Dutch companies are world leaders when it comes to dredging. Yet, knowledge of the morphology of the seabed and the consequences of altering it are at a nascent stage, at least in the public domain.

In Belgium, for example, decision makers have depended on a cautious yet subjective rule of allowing extraction to a depth of up to 5 metres from a reference level. Once this limit has been reached, the concession is closed and extraction moves elsewhere. But in a context where changing land-use patterns are driving ever-greater development towards the oceans, a growing number of competing users are laying claim to this sand. Precisely because mineral sands and aggregates are non-renewable resources, in timescales that are relevant to decision makers, every decision assumes a greater significance. How can authorities decide on the most appropriate course of action?

Dr. Vera Van Lancker, a senior researcher at the Royal Belgian Institute of Natural Sciences (RBINS), explains how the TILES project could be a step change. It's an acronym for Transnational and Integrated Long-Term Marine Exploitation Strategies. The transnational part is because it is a cooperation between Belgian and Dutch scientists to create a voxel model of the Belgian and southern Dutch part of the North Sea. Where pixels represent the elements of digital images or screens, voxels similarly represent a three-dimensional unit of space in terms of volume. This unit is frequently used in medical imaging and even video games. It is also in common use in land-based resource mapping and this is the first time it is being used in marine resource mapping.

The TILES project was designed to create a 4D resource decision support system, the fourth dimension being time. Since sand was formed over several millennia, sand extraction is not a sustainable activity because we can exhaust mines long before we come to realise the impacts. The ambition for TILES is to help decision makers ensure that any exploitation of sand is done with a view to long-term planning. Mathematical modelling allows the user to explore how each voxel will evolve naturally over time and what the impacts of extraction might be in that specific geography. It can demonstrate impacts not just locally but also at considerable distances. So it could be used to develop management strategies for all non-petroleum resources that are formed over geological time. Most importantly, it could be used to develop a legal system to ensure environmental limits are respected while trying to optimise the extraction of aggregate resources.

You can tell from the term 'exploitation strategies' in the the name that it is not designed to be anti-industry. But why would the extractive industry pay heed to something that could change the status quo? Industrial processes hinge on the uniformity of resource input. The economic feasibility of a mining project is greatly enhanced when there is a concentration of resources. TILES can offer a greater certainty for ROI (return on investment) by predicting both the quantity and the quality of sand in a given area. For instance, fine sands are of little use to the building industry besides being used to stabilise structures and in road construction. Medium/coarse sands are required for most concrete applications such as reinforced concrete. TILES can identify where the sand is fairly homogeneous and therefore better for exploitation.

What stood out though is that biological parameters were not included in the initial project design. How can we possibly talk about environmental limits without considering biology and the systems that are conducive to life itself? Fortunately, with the success of this project, there has been a new call for biology partners focused on habitat mapping and the relationship between extraction and recovery at mining sites. Once biological parameters are integrated into the decision support system, then predictions about marine life recovery will become more realistic. There will always be uncertainty, but we can hope that scientists will be better able to predict where adverse impacts will outlive the benefits of extraction and whether marine life will recover.

We cannot protect what we do not understand, so the TILES project is a great way forward. It can open up discussion among stakeholders. The amount of data it produces is huge and not only requires special hardware requirements but also advanced computational skills. Dr. Lancker from RBINS says there has been interest in this model from other countries, although many have to deal with significantly larger territories than Belgium or the Netherlands. Nevertheless, it is a promising approach and the team is keen on outreach. It has developed several interactive demonstrations, including virtual reality experiences. Users wade through sand bars on the sea floor, led by a guide who points out interesting features. This is an invaluable way to engage the general public, including school children, about our ocean home. The project and the marine researchers from the RBINS were featured in a Dutch documentary series called 'Er was eens...' [Once upon a time...] that showcased the RBINS and its scientists. This generated lots of interested viewers who wanted to learn more.

As with any international and interdisciplinary project, the challenge was finding and staying on common ground. Data is only as useful as its interpretation, which is not necessarily straightforward. The harmonised and transnational knowledge base aims to provide long-term adaptive management strategies within the context of Europe's marine spatial planning, the Marine Strategy Framework Directive (MSFD) and integrated coastal zone management.[2]

The UK is also exploring options to improve processes and has adopted a slightly more nuanced approach compared to how things were done in the past. The Regional Seabed Monitoring Programme (RSMP) aims to improve environmental protection by detecting unacceptable changes in sediment composition at an early stage. This approach also reduces monitoring costs for the aggregates industry and facilitates early intervention. In a paper published in *Nature* in 2017, Dr. Keith Cooper and J Barry from Centre for Environment, Fisheries and Aquaculture Science (CEFAS) suggested a big data approach to establishing a macrofaunal baseline assessment, monitoring and sustainable exploitation of the seabed. 'Big data' refers to a growing field of data analysis that deals with large, diverse, ever-growing sets of information from a variety of sources. Big data approaches require advanced computational techniques to analyse and systematically extract information from data sets that are too large or complex to be dealt with by traditional data-processing approaches, which are generally unable to mirror the complexity found in nature.

This paper states that, while we are getting better at predicting the impact on biodiversity on the seabed during dredging, the monitoring has not explained what is likely to happen to impacted sites after dredging stops. We are still unable to say whether original species can recolonise the area because 'recovery studies' are deemed too time consuming and expensive. Ironically, there are also 'options for active seabed restoration', but these are far from practical because they too are deemed to be expensive and the results are uncertain. It makes sense then to focus on preventing ecological collapse in the first place.

The big data approach has established a baseline of the kinds of organism that make up the UK's macrobenthic fauna (organisms larger than 1 mm) in and around sites of aggregate dredging.[3] It has helped to map the kind of sediment that is currently associated with specific families of organisms and it has developed a method for assessing the potential ecological significance of human-induced changes in the sediment composition. It remains to be tested if this approach of stopping dredging when critical thresholds are breached does work to protect the integrity of the seabed and the potential for recolonisation. But the key success factor has been that this study was made possible by 'using a dataset comprising of new and existing data belonging to government and industry sources'.

Although the study has many limitations, its approach has been adopted by the aggregate dredging industry in the UK as they have been able to reduce costs by 50% by adopting a regional approach.[4] Since the dredging industry appears to accept animal mass mortality as a given during the process of dredging in the service of building houses for people, of improving city infrastructure and of making a contribution to the exchequer through exporting aggregates, their focus has shifted to ensuring that the integrity of the sediment composition is not completely destroyed so that, hopefully, organisms can recover over time.

There are scientific advantages to the regional approach. Because data is collected in the same way, it is comparable and you get a snapshot view of the whole region and not just a single licensed site. Data from 33,198 samples from 777 grab surveys were integrated to build a comprehensive dataset of spatial and temporal patterns in how macrobenthic fauna (greater than 1 mm) were distributed around the UK in reference to dredging sites.[5] Although the exercise started with existing data, there were gaps and the dredging industry paid about £2.5 million over two years to collect more samples from the seabed and add them to the repository.[6] This large dataset allowed Dr. Cooper and his colleagues to determine not only the broad classification of the fauna and their distribution but also how rare and vulnerable they were across all sampled locations. Some classes of animal were widespread, while others were only found in relatively localised areas. This is very important for marine spatial planning because it means that in the future, when applications for dredging licences come up, the regulator will be able to examine the application in context to decide whether or not the activity should be permitted at the specific location. Before adopting such an approach, we didn't really have that perspective. Each application was examined on its individual merits but the significance of a species being lost was not analysed. The most promising part of this exercise is that the vast majority of this data has been made accessible to the public and to UK businesses under the terms of an Open Government Licence. You can access the Marine Aggregates Application Baseline data at https://openscience.cefas.co.uk/.

As the authors suggest, 'the harmonisation and integration of offshore monitoring programmes could deliver significant benefits for industry and government'. This approach can potentially be rolled out for other offshore activities, such as locating offshore wind farms, pipeline and more. Big data applications can help us improve our understanding of the natural world and could lead to better management and improved sustainability. There is a caveat though. Evidence-based monitoring can only work when there is a strong component of supervision and enforcement.

Particularly in a global context, studies show that many countries do not require offshore activities to undergo an EIA and, where they do, the EIA regulations for the marine environment are often less comprehensive than for terrestrial activities.[7] Even when we talk about seabed mineral extraction (for metals) and deep sea mining, it is important to know that although there is requirement for EIAs to be conducted in international waters, there is little information on the content of assessments and there is a lack of global, detailed, legally binding requirements or mechanisms for supervision, compliance and enforcement.[8]

Which makes comments by Dr. David Levy, the chair of Marinet (the organisation you learnt about in Chapter 14), all the more pertinent. He insists that 'the actual evidence needs to be published and placed in the public domain to inform debate and serve as an example for the future'. He believes that there is 'an urgent need to get all involved in the evaluation of projects so that blame is not the main issue but constructive learning is'.[9]

As Deborah Wright, author of *Conserving the Great Blue*, points out, aggregate dredging can have 'a devastating effect on shallow, coastal habitats. Both sand and gravel sea beds support rich and varied ecosystems and are important spawning and feeding areas for many types of fish. Aggregate sites are often located precisely in these sensitive areas, and intensive and repeated dredging can wipe out these habitats completely, before their value has been recognised.'[10]

The term for each license can last 15 years in the UK and may roll on even further. The *Good Practice Guidance* in the UK recommends both pre-dredge baseline surveys and post-dredge monitoring.[11] The objective is to measure the effects of dredging and assess the site's potential for recovery. Currently, the license holders (dredging companies who are project promoters) are largely responsible for providing this monitoring data. The onus is on the industry not only to report problems but also to come up with solutions. They are also responsible for commissioning the EIA studies that affect whether or not a project gets the go-ahead.

However, we may need a closer look at the prevailing governance structures. Many community organisations, such as Marinet and the Goodwin Sands Conservation Trust, find this practice deeply contentious. They maintain that project promoters are not exactly an impartial source and that, because of resource constraints, there is little unbiased supervision or enforcement by the statutory agencies involved (see Chapter 14). Many of these agencies now operate a project-based approach, which means they cannot work on anything unless someone (industry/government) agrees to pay for it first. Marinet says:

> The studies are currently composed by bodies who are sought for, located by, appointed by and paid for by the dredging companies themselves. Thus, they cannot be seen as being independent in their findings.[12]

Marinet has called for 'a scientific study of whether there is any measurable transfer of sand from the beaches where erosion is occurring to the offshore dredging sites.' All it requires is tracer material to be placed on the adjacent shoreline beaches, and its movement monitored and recorded over a period of seven years following offshore dredging.

Such studies have already been undertaken successfully on Lancashire's Fylde coast, and in the USA. They point out:

The UK dredging companies maintain that there is no movement of material from the beaches to the dredging sites, so this study would confirm if the dredging companies are correct in their presumption or otherwise. It is to be noted, with emphasis, that such a tracer study has never been done by the aggregate companies for the east coast, and has never been required of them by the government and its licensing agencies.

Marinet also insists that in the case of a dispute, a second opinion from a financially unlinked, non-partisan party should be permitted.[13] In the face of the climate crisis and 'an incipient sixth mass extinction', these demands acquire a greater significance.

The UK has been a forerunner in establishing a levy on aggregates sourced from land as well as from marine sources.[14]

The Marine Aggregates Levy Sustainability Fund (MALSF) was a £25m programme of marine research undertaken from 2004–2011, funded through a Government imposed levy on all primary aggregate production (including marine aggregates) to reflect the environmental cost of winning these materials. A proportion of the revenue generated was used to provide a source of funding for research aimed at minimising the effects of aggregate production ... The main aim of the MALSF programme was to promote environmentally friendly aggregate extraction in the marine environment in England or in English waters.[15]

The outputs of this research have been made available to the public for free at www.marinedataexchange.co.uk (MDE) under the terms of use of the Open Government License.

This platform facilitates evidence-based decision making through better information and sharing of survey data among stakeholders from a variety of offshore industries throughout the lifetime of a project. By making all the survey data available in one location, the MDE enables a strategic view across the seabed.

As of June 2019, 80% of the survey data comes from the renewable energy (wind) sector, 9% from the marine aggregates sector, 8% from the wave and tidal sector, while 3% comes from special research projects commissioned by the Crown Estate.[16] It is interesting to see that most of data on the MDE has been shared by a relatively new industry – maybe because the wind-farm industry has been compelled to share this data in the interest of the greater good. It would be a welcome move to see a similar regulatory approach with the marine aggregates industry that is well-established within the UK. 'Since 1955 in excess of 500 million tonnes of marine aggregate have been used in the manufacture of concrete products in the UK.' Each year, over 20 million tonnes of marine sand and gravel is extracted from over 65 licensed areas, located in seven regions around the coast of England and Wales.[17] Adopting a similar regulatory approach with the marine aggregates industry is even more relevant because the industry's sustainability statement clearly recognises that they are 'extracting a finite natural resource that will not be replenished'.[18]

We now have to ask ourselves:

- What do sustainability statements mean in practice, especially when the resource is non-renewable?
- How do our actions impact future generations?
- How do we measure cumulative impact on marine ecosystems from multiple industries (such as aggregate dredging, fishing, renewable energy

generation, dredging of ports and harbours, oil and gas operations, installation of cables and pipelines, and more?
- Who speaks for Nature?
- How can we respond adequately to the climate crisis, rising sea levels and the biodiversity crisis?

Artificial intelligence (AI), big data, machine learning and other technological approaches can certainly help with the pace at which we take action and provide a better context. They can even increase the scope of our actions, but these approaches can be most effective when fundamental assumptions and governance structures have first been tested and proven to be sound.

On a global scale, there's never been a greater need to break down silos and share learning and good practice across traditional industry and geographical boundaries – and the UK offers a great example of where to start.

•21•

Looking into the Magic Mirror

'We decided to take an ecosystem approach. What we need is an inclusive model that does not alienate an entire demographic.' explains Sangeetha Shenoy from Telematics4u (t4u), an Internet of Things (IoT)-enabled solution provider based in Bengaluru, India. The ecosystem she refers to has nothing to do with the flora or fauna but the ecosystem of different stakeholders in the supply and demand of sand in India. At the very bottom of the pyramid are the drivers and the people involved in digging up the sand from allocated sites. At the top, is the District Collector often referred to as the DC. A district in India is equivalent to a county in the US. It is a key administrative unit, in fact, India's GDP is tracked at district level. A DC runs their district much like a CEO runs a company. They are responsible not only for the revenue generated in the district but also for ensuring that natural resources are maintained for future generations. The other stakeholders in the ecosystem are the Public Works Department (PWD), the Directorate of Mining And Geology (DMG), lease owners, transport owners, law enforcement officers such as the police, the regional transport office and citizens.

T4u is trying an alternate approach, so their revenue model is not direct. Instead of charging the party that benefits the most, they offer their services to the government at no cost and monetise it through the stakeholders engaged in trade. But it is the government that gives them the mandate and sets the prices they can charge. 'Unlike other natural resources, the inherent problem with sand is that it is found everywhere but the advantage of sand is that it is not easy to store. You can't eat it. You can't convert it at source. But all the sand that is excavated has to be transported.'

**Being SMART about
local sand ecosystem touchpoints**

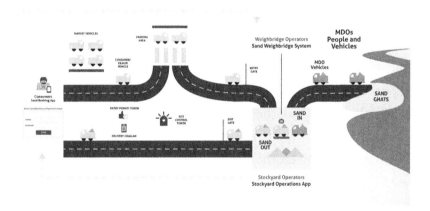

21.1 T4u's sand transport monitoring from source to destination
Source: © T4U

Pratap Hegde, the CEO and Managing Director explains further. Unlike other minerals, such as iron ore or bauxite, that are found in specific locations, sand is relatively abundant in several locations. With sky-rocketing demand, sand mining has become an appealing trade, but given its multiple points of mining it is hard to manage. Iron ore only becomes useful when it goes to the iron ore factory. But given the multiplicity of users of sand, there are numerous points of delivery, which again makes it hard to track. His solution is that what connects all these mining points and all points of consumption is that sand has to be transported and stored temporarily in sand yards, which is something that can be managed.

The company's core offering is based on GPS satellite imagery and allied mapping technologies that allows them to geofence a specific mining area. They have partnered with ISRO (Indian Space Research Organisation), the space agency of the Government of India. Once a district signs up, they issue a mandate for all trucks transporting sand to be fitted with a transponder that tracks it constantly. Knowing that they are being monitored deters drivers from selling the sand outside that district. If they do stray beyond the border, an alarm is automatically set off at the control tower in the DC's office.

'All the people at the bottom of the pyramid want to be included and they want to belong to mainstream society, but they have been given the short end of the stick,' Shenoy says. The IT revolution in India ushered the whole middle class into the organised sector but it mainly benefited those who spoke English. The rest continue to work in the informal sector.

> These people to want to belong and they are happy to comply if they're given an inclusive model of development. Unlike other countries where huge fleets of trucks belong to one company, in India most owners are individuals who run a service with one or two trucks. But these are the people who often have to deal with an aura of antitrust. They are stopped at every point and they have to bribe everyone along the route. With our permit they are recognised as authorised vehicles and they are able

to reach their destination unhindered. It makes life much easier for them.

Once they are brought into the formal sector, the implications are enormous. Banking and insurance companies can be brought in to provide services at scale. Tire companies can offer tire-on-hire services. All those who didn't have access to banking services can then be included in development. Inclusive development aside, this technology has the potential to bring much-needed transparency into the construction sector. Law enforcement officers have access to an App that helps them check the validity of the permit in real time. Consumers also have access to an App that allows them to place an order for sand directly with the supplier instead of going through many middle men.

There are vested interests at stake though and not everyone welcomes such technology-aided transparency. But the company says they find that more local governments are reaching out to them and they are working with 21 out of 30 districts in the state of Karnataka in South India. They have also been approached by the northern states of Punjab, Jharkhand and Bihar and are actively involved in a couple of river rejuvenation programmes. Interestingly, they do not believe they are the ideal custodians of this system because they stand to profit and that it should ideally be held by a neutral party.

It is early days though, and only a few areas are geofenced so it is possible that sand exploitation will move to other areas. Another downside to geofencing is that only trucks fitted with a transponder device appear on the radar, so other trucks can enter and leave the geofence without being picked up.[1] To avoid this, the company is urging governments to ensure all trucks that transport sand are colour coded and can be easily identified. But changing the value perception of sand is proving to be an uphill battle. In the grand scheme of things, there are more pressing matters and governments do not yet consider sand important enough to invest the time required to change systems. Sand is classified as a 'minor mineral' in India and therefore warrants less attention than the major minerals, such as iron ore and bauxite. Still, GPS and the IoT offer great promise.

Elsewhere in India, technology is proving to be a much-needed ally. Monitoring of mining areas is a particularly difficult challenge. Not only is it cumbersome but it is also especially dangerous in areas where illegal sand mining is rampant. The Comptroller and Auditor General of India (CAG), the country's supreme audit institution, monitors how various ministries function on the ground and has begun to employ technology to assist with this function. For instance, a 2017 report shows how the CAG found that the PWD in the southern state of Tamil Nadu had failed to verify the geo-coordinates of a mining plan with its environmental clearance during the approval process. Using Google Earth, they were able to map that mining plans had been approved within the boundary of the river whereas environmental clearance had been given for private land adjoining the river. In Figure 21.2, Polygon A indicates the area marked out for quarrying as per geo-coordinates in the approved mining plan. Polygon B indicates area of quarrying as per geo-coordinates in the environmental clearance.

In another instance, the CAG used unmanned aerial vehicles, or drones, to monitor and map a mining area. They found several discrepancies. Failure to comply with instructions had resulted in excess sand being removed and a loss of revenue of INR 21.02 crore (nearly $28 million) to the local exchequer. A drone survey conducted at 5 a.m. showed that sand was being extracted well before the permitted time and that eight excavators were being used when only two were permitted. Sand had been extracted to a depth well over six metres on the riverbed, when the permission was only for a depth of one metre. Excess excavation of sand had resulted in topographical changes in the riverbed, leading to ground water changes and a degradation in the ecology. In short, drone technology proved the inadequate monitoring of sand quarrying operations by the PWD and the District Collectors.[2]

Technology can be enormously helpful in identifying problems, particularly in dangerous situations, but the true solution lies in what happens after these discrepancies are established. On that front, we have miles to go.

21.2 Discrepancies between the approved mining plan (A) and environmental clearance (B)
Source: Google Earth © 2017 Digital Globe

•22•

She is Key

'**A**re you envious of your wife's success?' asks the interviewer. The man at the receiving end of this question smiles and answers, 'I'm not jealous of my wife because she is earning for the family … and the women are very ambitious. They also received a lot of business and training support. If possible, I would also like a little more support for my fish farm too.'[1] This fish farmer was not always in this profession, he used to be a sand miner. He and his wife, like many in the local community, were supported and trained for an alternate livelihood by The Environmental Foundation Limited as part of a project to increase the resilience and adaptation of coastal and riverine communities to the climate crisis and other threats by conserving the ecosystems of the Maha Oya, in Sri Lanka.

The Maha Oya is one of the most important rivers in the country and its associated wetlands play a crucial role in maintaining the socio-economic and ecological fabric of the country. In this project, the men were trained on fish farming while the women opted to become entrepreneurs. The women decided to form a cooperative and called themselves 'Lucky Ladies' – true to their name, they found great success as shoemakers. They were not only trained to make ladies' footwear but also in finance and business management skills. As the orders started to come in, the women gained a higher standing and a voice in the community. When a storm destroyed the fish farm cages, the women were able to support their families. The local ecosystem benefited by being given a chance to recover from the constant assault of sand mining.[2]

Freshwater bodies such as rivers provide critical ecosystem services that society often depends on. People who live in cities often take these ecosystem services for granted but they are fundamental to those who live along the margins of these water bodies in developing countries. They are especially important for the women, who are often tasked with fetching water for the family, caring for sick family members and many other responsibilities that come with the burden of care. During the 2018 World Water Week in Stockholm, Kusum Athukorala, Chair at NetWwater (Network of Women Water Professionals) in Sri Lanka, explained how her organisation got involved in creating awareness about sand mining and its impact.[3] When conducting a gender and water dialogue in a northwestern province of Sri Lanka, they were asked to initiate an advocacy programme to highlight damage due to sand mining. The request came from women who used to have access to drinking water on their doorstep but were now forced to travel up to four kilometres in search of water due to the impact of sand mining.

Sand and gravel allow water to percolate. In effect, they are nature's way of keeping the groundwater table replenished. These materials therefore provide ecosystem services that we often take for granted. Although academic research in many parts of the world is yet to catch up, the lived experiences of communities across the world shows us that sand and gravel plays a critical role in ensuring a region's water security.

Water security in turn underpins food security and liveability in a region. Sand and gravel also provide a critical habitat for wildlife, which disappears when we remove sand from riverbeds, lakes and oceans. For historical reasons, women in general are strongly connected to communities and to nature, so they are the first to feel the impact when ecosystem services are disrupted. This makes it worth targeting women when designing programmes that build resilience against sudden or chronic events that disrupt such services.

There are other reasons for singling out this particular gender. Research has shown that investing in women goes much further in empowering entire communities. A woman who is educated and economically active often puts surplus cash to more productive use. For example, in the Ivory Coast men and women cultivate separate crops and researchers have found that in years when the men's crops have high yields, more money is spent on alcohol and tobacco, whereas when the women's crops have high yields, more is spent on food.[4] Also, lenders of microloans favour women because they are more likely to repay than men.[5] Yet, so many big decisions are still being made without taking into account the impact on women. For instance, when mining projects are on the table, rarely does the impact assessment provide disaggregated data on how poor women, especially from ethnic minority communities, in the affected region stand to be impacted.

When it comes to constructing big-ticket infrastructure such as big dams, there is little evidence that gender-disaggregated data is being collected for the regions where sand and gravel are sourced – or 'borrowed' from if you go by the industry term for these spaces, borrow pits. Big dams require massive amounts of concrete and considering that concrete can be 65–75 per cent aggregates, there is a gaping hole in evidence-based policy making. What we do know is that dams disproportionately affect women among the impacted communities.[6] Women continue to bear an unequal burden before, during and after resettlement, which affects themselves and thereby their entire communities. Readers who would like to delve deeper are recommended to read The World Commission on Dams Report and to explore the work of International Rivers, CGIAR's WLE Greater Mekong, Global Water Initiative – West Africa by The International Institute for Environment and Development (IIED), IUCN, Movimento dos Atingidos por Barragens (MAB) and others.[7]

There is a lot of food for thought in this extract from a 2013 blog by Robin Narcisso, a communications professional who works in the Development Sector at Phnom Penh:

> Currently the dams' projects are designed to include only generic and superficial consultation with the impacted communities. The consultations do not focus on hearing and addressing women's concerns, which is unfortunate since they are the ones suffering the most from it. This should make us wonder whether women in hydropower companies, financial institutions, and the governments of the region have an equal say on how the projects, and the consultations, are designed. Let's take the example of the Xayabury Dam, which is currently being built in Laos by Thai Companies with Thai financing. The construction company, Ch-Karnchang Public Company Limited, has a Board of Directors composed of 12 members, all men. Similarly Krungthai Bank, a Thai public financial institution supporting the dam, has only one woman out of eleven members on the Board of Directors. And the Lao

government? Not surprisingly, the vast majority of high government positions, including the Ministry of Energy and Mines, are occupied by men. Clearly women do not have much influence over decision making in the hydropower business. After realizing this, a set of questions and doubts should naturally follow: What would happen if women equally participated in the design of these projects? Could there be a better understanding that these projects exacerbate gender inequalities? Would they care enough to implement strategies aimed at reducing this issue? Or it would make no difference at all? These are questions that we need to ask.

Let's take a look at mineral sand mining and its impact on women. In Chapter 12, 'Private Gain at Public Expense', we explored how heavy mineral sand mining by multinationals was taking a grave toll on the local people and the environment in Madagascar. But let's explore how some of the women in particular were impacted. Rio Tinto's mineral sand mining operations changed the ecosystem irrevocably as they cleared old-growth forests to make way for mining concessions and built infrastructure to support the export of these minerals. But the women of the region were particularly affected because many of them depended on the ecosystem to support their families. A case in point is the mahampy reed (*Lepironia mucronata*[8]) which has long been the dominant source of income for rural women who harvested the reeds and wove intricate mats and baskets. The sale of these products helped them and their families when rice or manioc were scarce.[9] Mahampy is so important to the communities that for centuries, it has been 'the only species used by the Antanosy to wrap deceased ancestors before they are placed in a tomb'. It is woven into the very language as 'ampy' means 'complete' and is a symbol of solidarity and togetherness.[10] Yet when the mining infrastructure was put in place, it destroyed all the wetlands where the reed grew. Women who had lost access to reeds for weaving mentioned that compensation had been dealt with by local authorities and that they had been excluded from the process.[11] The poorest of the poor, particularly farmers who had to work during the day, were also excluded from decision-making processes.

Rio Tinto/QMM paid for training sessions to teach the women how to harvest mahampy sustainably and how to weave mats.[12] But these were '"training" and education of activities local people have been doing for centuries – but can no longer carry out due to the environmental impacts of the mine'.[13] Communities reported that 'vast reserves' of mahampy 'had been destroyed by Rio Tinto/QMM or made inaccessible'.[14] Despite knowing of the importance of mahampy to the communities, they actively planted invasive species 'kininy bonaky' (Niaouli, or *Melaleuca viridiflora*) that interfered with the growth of mahampy.[15] Women have reported that 'it now takes them as many as six or seven foraging trips, instead of one, to collect enough reeds to weave a mat that sells for less than $3, as the wetlands around Mandena have been mined one by one.'[16] They are now scratching around for other activities that bring them a fraction of what they once made.

There is a need to look at gender-disaggregated data not only in mining-affected communities but also within mining, particularly artisanal mining. Women typically play quite a large role in artisanal mining for industrial minerals such as metals.[17] Approximately 30 per cent of the world's artisanal miners are women, but the actual rate of participation may be significantly higher when part-time work is considered.[18] Women's involvement in mining is often rendered invisible due to 'inequitable power relations and their outcomes' and 'the gender division of labour'.[19] They are not always identified as 'miners' since they are often involved in transporting and processing materials, as opposed to digging. They often work part-time due to their domestic responsibilities. They also take on ancillary roles such as cooks, food vendors, water transporters and providers of other goods and services and are rarely compensated enough or considered adequately in policy, even though these roles are critical to the mining.[20]

Women and girls in artisanal and small mining are also more vulnerable to sexual and gender based violence (SGBV).

> SGBV is actually comprised of multiple forms of physical, social and psychological forms of violence on the basis of gender. In addition to rape and physical violence (e.g. beatings), SGBV further includes sexual harassment, acts of intimidation or humiliation, discrimination or denial of opportunities, exploitation, confinement, neglect and early marriage, among others.[21]

It is distressing to read such reports. Education can be transformational in empowering women.[22] However, the odds remain stacked against them as nearly two-thirds of the illiterate (an estimated 781 million people) are women. What is even sadder is that, as per UN Statistics from as recently as 2015, this proportion has remained unchanged for two decades.[23] Such facts are rarely taken into account when authorities design systems. For example, rampant sand mining in countries such as Vietnam and Cambodia has caused extensive damage to communities living along riverbanks. Many houses have collapsed into the rivers, taking with them hard-earned life savings and, in some cases, infrastructure such as roads.

In September 2019, PBS Newshour featured an interview that documented how the Cambodian government believed it had adequate systems to combat illegal sand mining by putting in place a 24-hour hotline that operated seven days a week. However, a female villager told the reporter that she couldn't read or write and didn't really know how these things worked and the village chief never visited to see what was happening to the houses.[24] Sadly, her story is echoed in many parts of the world.

Women are still more likely than men to live in poverty in both poor and affluent societies and economists have a term for this, 'feminisation of poverty'.[25] Across the world, women consistently earn less than men and are concentrated in the lowest-paid and least secure forms of work.[26] Gender inequality in the economy is said to cost women in developing countries an obscene $9 trillion a year – more than the GDP of the UK, France and Germany combined.[27] Inequality is endemic, not just in societies eking out an existence but also among relatively well off and educated communities in the developed world. For instance, the profession of architecture is still largely male-dominated. Even though we are well into the twenty-first century, a 2017 survey of the world's 100 largest architecture firms by online design magazine Dezeen found that just three of the world's 100 biggest architecture firms were headed by women and only two had management teams that were more than 50 per cent female. In essence, women occupy just ten per cent of the highest-ranking jobs at the world's leading architecture firms, while 16 firms have no women at all in senior positions.[28] These are striking statistics. The top guns making big decisions in designing our world are predominantly male. It is also disconcerting that, despite rigorous campaigning for equality in the profession, the number of women in architecture in the UK actually dropped by a staggering 10.3 per cent in 2019.[29] If the annual women in architecture surveys across the world are anything to go by, even in this strata of society, disparity is commonplace in basic things such as salary, treatment at work and care-giving duties. Would things have been different if there were more women involved in decision making in all spheres of life?

The World Economic Forum's (WEF) Global Gender Gap Index in 2018 paints a stark picture at the global level.[30] Whether it is political and economic leadership or access to financial assets and services, half the world is sorely under-represented. Just 17 out of 149 countries assessed had women as heads of state. A paltry 18 per cent of ministers and 24 per cent of parliamentarians globally were women. Even though we are almost a quarter of the way into the twenty-first century, women spend, on average, twice as much time on housework and other unpaid activities than men in the 29 countries for which data is available. Gender gaps appear to be deeply ingrained, even in skill sets such as AI, a critical in-demand skill set of the future, where 78 per cent of AI professionals are male. If it were not so tragic, it would be funny to read that they predict that the overall global gender gap will close in 108 years across the 106 countries covered since the first edition of the report.[31] We're talking well over a century!

The good news is that many of these industries have recognised this problem, at least in theory. There are several initiatives being run to correct this imbalance, many being led by women, and they are being supported by men who recognise the injustice. At the highest level, the UN has adopted gender equality as a key goal, Sustainable Development Goal 5 (SDG5), to achieve truly sustainable development.[32] Progress has been painfully slow. *Invisible Women: Exposing data bias in a world designed for men* by Caroline Criado-Perez lays out a pretty compelling case of how far we have to go in general. But as awareness increases, let us hope we see many more women leaders and role models from ethnic minority communities in all spheres of life. As idealistic as it may be, I still hope to see a world where equity is a non-issue.

•23•

Through the Eyes of Faith

It is mind-boggling, the schism we've created between sheer respect for nature embedded in our culture and the way we live in reality. The Mahseer a protected species, found in the River Cauvery is dying due to lack of Oxygen. It is considered to be the first incarnation of Lord Vishnu, Matsya Avatar: and this is where the greatness of our culture lay; we connected our Gods to nature, worshipped it and lived in tandem with it. India understood that this great network of human, animals, plants, non-human and all needed space to survive together because we are inextricably linked. We cared. No more. Now we only pontificate and glorify in our words and in our minds, and pick up arms against the slightest perception of disrespect, all while we systematically destroy that which we worship.

Devika Devaiah, Trustee, Save River Cauvery

Devika and her colleagues are on a mission to save River Cauvery in South India from wanton destruction by human activities.[1] To them, the river is more than the waters that flow in it, more than the sediments transported in it and much more than the energy embedded in it. The River Cauvery is a mother, the source of all life, the source of well-being. She has an intrinsic cultural and spiritual value that goes beyond mere economics. The River Cauvery and her tributaries are being threatened by reckless sand mining and other development projects that are endangering the ecological integrity of the region where the river is born.

Meanwhile, in the northern part of the country, a similar fight is being waged to save Maa Ganga (Mother Goddess Ganga), a river that has been granted personhood in law and is considered the holiest river in the country but whose ground-reality falls far short of this exalted status. The fight is being spearheaded by a group of ascetics who live in Matri Sadan, an ashram (hermitage) on the banks of the same river.[2] Matri Sadan is in the state of Uttarakhand in Haridwar, a place of pilgrimage for many devout Hindus. The ashram has been in the news for several years, albeit for unfortunate reasons. It is headed by a seer named Swami Shivanand Saraswati, who claims to have received divine guidance to take up the cause of River Ganga and its destruction due to human activities.

According to Hindu mythology, when celestial deity Ganga was asked to come down to Earth, she initially refused. She feared that humans were too greedy and they would destroy her. She could only be persuaded when she was promised that the saints would protect her. But the Goddess was much too powerful for the Earth. The only way the Earth could sustain her life-giving energy was by allowing her to flow through Lord Shiva's dreadlocks – the sand, gravel and rocks on the bed of the river. Swami Shivanand and his disciples see themselves in this light and they feel honour-bound to protect Maa Ganga against the avarice and corruption around them.

They call themselves 'saints' and they define their organisation as 'a divine organisation which fights against corruption and preserves environment'. It might seem strange that they call themselves saints, but English is a foreign language to them and the words are simply used as a substitute for *sadhu* or *sannyasi* (ascetic), while their 'divine organisation' refers to their religious status. They are fighting for a free-flowing, clean Ganga in which rock quarrying and sand mining is completely banned. It's a tall ask though. The entire development of the region is reliant on the rocks and sand quarried from the bed of the river. Without these materials, all construction would come to a grinding halt. Thousands of livelihoods depend on this activity, but millions more are imperilled due to the destruction it causes. Their chosen mode of protest is the Satyagraha, translated as 'Truth Force'.

Satyagraha was made famous by Mahatma Gandhi, who employed it during India's independence struggle as a key part of his non-violent resistance to British colonial rule. In simplistic terms, it is a hunger strike, but the ascetics believe it is much more than that. They are convinced it sharpens their resolve and moral stance against the destruction of their beloved mother. They say they are willing to sacrifice their mortal bodies in her defence. They have already lost three people in this fight, but they refuse to back down.

The last person who died in this protest made national headlines. He used to be a professor of engineering in one of the country's most prestigious science institutions, IIT Kanpur. He also taught at UC Berkeley for a brief while. His given name was GD Agarwal but when he decided to renounce the material world and pursue a spiritual path, he became known as Swami Gyan Swaroop Sanand or Swami Sanand in short. Swami Sanand fasted for a whole 111 days before he died on 11

October 2018.[3] He had written three open letters to the national government demanding a complete cessation of mining in the rivers, a halt to the construction of dams that impeded the flow of the river and a stop to polluting the river. He received no response while he was alive. But the Prime Minister did tweet his condolences after the swami's demise.

A few days later, a 26-year old ascetic named Swami Aatmabodhananda took on the mantle. He is a computer science graduate from the southern state of Kerala who abandoned his roots when he felt called to pursue a spiritual path. He stopped his intake of normal food and adopted a fruit-and-water-only diet in preparation for the time when he will begin a complete abstinence from normal food. He broke his fast 194 days later after "assurances" from the Director-General of the National Mission for Clean Ganga that laws banning sand mining on certain stretches of the Ganga would henceforth be enforced.[4]

Swami Shivanand runs the modest ashram with a fierce and uncompromising attitude. He appears unfazed as he tackles politicians, bureaucrats, doctors and journalists who come to negotiate with him to stop the protests. He strongly believes that one of his disciples, Swami Nigmananda Saraswati, was murdered in the hospital. As a former professor of chemistry from Kolkotta (former name Calcutta), Swami Shivanand appears comfortable talking about organophosphate poisoning and other topics that come up during the investigation of his disciple's death. A subsequent inquiry by the Central Bureau of Investigation (CBI), does not support his claim but the ascetics have decided to appeal the decision. He and his team are deeply suspicious of the authorities and they believe the sand mining mafia has complete sway over the region and enough political clout to influence such matters. They have learnt to use technology to their advantage though, even if in an amateur manner. They regularly videorecord conversations and interviews and have recently started broadcasting on Facebook live. All of this content is in the native tongue, Hindi, but the documentary 'Satyagraha – Truth Force' is in English.[5] This interesting portrayal of the sorry state of affairs was made by Australian film maker Lisa Harney. Despite years of incessant mining, there had been no EIA until one was demanded by Swami Shivanand. When an EIA was eventually carried out, it stated that the rocks being harvested from the riverbed were only those that were replenished during the monsoon season. This is in sharp contrast to what actually happens on the ground where mining has weakened the riverbed considerably. In 2013, Uttarakhand faced devastating floods when many lives were lost and the economy came to a standstill. Seven years later, little had changed.

Another community in South India has taken up Satyagraha to protest against sand mining. That same community from Alappad, Kerala, that we spoke about in Chapter 8, 'The Dark Side of Development'. This time the entire community rallied together and, women and children included, they are on 'an indefinite relay Satyagraha'. In other words, they are taking turns to go on hunger strike to persuade the authorities to pay heed to their demands. The protest started in early November 2018 and received support from local film actors, their fan clubs and even from Keralites abroad. The movement has effectively used not just hashtags and beautifully designed posters to but also great symbolism. People from many other districts of Kerala have come forward to support the cause. Each of the representatives who visited the seat of the protests brought with them a fistful of sand from their own territory – a beautiful symbol of unity and strength despite the diversity of the grains in the mix. One year after the movement began, hundreds of people gathered to form a human chain and stand in the ocean as a symbol of solidarity.[6] Three thousand people, including women and children, had participated in the relay hunger strike over a whole year. Only time will tell if their means of protest is as powerful in modern times as it was 70 years ago, when it catalysed an entire nation to come together and change world history.

•24•

The Final Answer Lies in the Sandpit

Chapter 12, 'Private Gain at Public Expense', discussed how the people of Madagascar were struggling to get their voices heard in the new gold-rush for heavy mineral sands. Madagascar ranked 152/180 on the Corruption Perceptions Index by Transparency International in 2018. Weak governance is a factor in monitoring and managing the impacts of extractives on fragile settings, and institutional failures can seriously impede local citizens' ability to hold mining companies to account. But there is reason to hope for a better future.

In August 2019, following extensive engagement with mining giant Rio Tinto, Andrew Lees Trust (ALT UK) and Publish What You Pay (PWYP UK) worked with Publiez Ce Que Vous Payez, Madagascar (PCQVP Madagascar) to send a public letter and briefing to Malagasy ministers raising urgent concerns about extractive industry governance in the country. In addition to Malagasy civil society co-signatories, many PWYP member organisations and others from around the world co-signed the letter as supporting organisations.

PWYP UK is a coalition of 30 UK-based NGOs working for a more transparent and accountable extractive sector. It is a member of the UK Extractive Industries Transparency Initiative (UK EITI) Civil Society Network (CSN). Together, the coalition monitors reporting of annual payments made to governments by more than 90 UK-incorporated and London Stock Exchange-listed extractive companies under the mandatory transparency requirements and engages with the UK government and companies to improve the quality of these disclosures. Their work includes analysing payments disclosed under UK law, raising awareness in-country about payments to governments, catalysing public participation in natural resource governance and holding governments and companies to account. They undertake dialogue and advocacy with politicians, officials, companies and civil society allies, with a vision for a well-implemented global extractive transparency standard.[1]

The letter sent to Malagasy ministers was supported by a detailed briefing, 'Mining risks involving the environmental regulator in Madagascar: urgent need for remedy' – both recommended reading. The letter and the briefing highlight how gaps in implementing government policy allow operating companies to pay for assessments/evaluations of their operations by the regulator without due transparency, public participation or accountability provisions. The letter called for the responsible Malagasy ministers to urgently convene a round-table dialogue at the highest level and to include affected communities and civil society to address these gaps. Their key recommendation is that 'The objective must be that all recent and future studies, data and reports produced by [the Malagasy regulator] the ONE for, and paid for by, operating companies are made fully accessible and available, including permanent and free-to-access online publication, for thorough and transparent public scrutiny'.[2]

There is tremendous potential if this recommendation becomes standard operating procedure across all mining initiatives. As the letter points out, 'Rio Tinto is one of the world's largest mining companies and therefore likely to influence the expanding sector in Madagascar. This case therefore demands urgent attention.'[3] It remains to be seen what action the government will eventually take but the action by PCQVP in Madagascar is an important step towards demanding change.

The demand for change is growing louder and stronger each day as our young people remind us of what's at stake and as people-powered movements keep growing in strength. In November 2019, the world's biggest public bank announced its decision to stop funding fossil fuels.[4] 'Divestment', which was a fringe notion only a few years ago, has now become 'material' to the fossil fuel industry. Could divestment also be an answer to sand mining? At this point, we have more questions than answers. But what we do know is that business cannot continue as usual.

In fact, we need to get better at asking questions. Just as I was finishing this book, there was a flurry of excitement in the media because a company backed by Bill Gates had announced a breakthrough for the energy industry and a major step towards solving the climate crisis. California-based Heliogen created 'the world's first technology that can commercially replace fuels with carbon-free, ultra-high temperature heat from the sun'. AI and mirrors concentrate solar energy to produce temperatures above $1,000^{0}C$ on a commercial scale. The use of solar energy in heavy industries such as cement, steel, mining and petrochemicals had been almost non-existent because solar technologies couldn't produce those temperatures. So, this technology is truly exciting and we could very well be on the cusp of change. The CEO of Heliogen said, 'If we go to a cement company and say we'll give you green heat, no CO_2, but we'll also save you money, then it becomes a no-brainer'.[5] But few realise that sand could prove to be the limitation.

Chapter 7, 'In Pursuit of the Holy Grail', questioned the blind pursuit of energy policies for a carbon-free future at the expense of everything else. This is where the rubber meets the road. In terms of technology, we have the ability to produce 'carbon-free' fuel. Let's assume the heavy industries will ignore all their sunk capital and switch to this technology tomorrow, we would still have a problem that isn't widely recognised, as yet. As you have seen, the world faces a looming sand crisis. Where would the sand for the concrete, glass, steel and aluminium industry expansion come from? At what cost? If current trends are anything to go by, we have a lot of work ahead to raise awareness of this issue.

'Bright is the New Black: New York Roofs Go Cool'[6]

With 68 per cent of the world's population expected to live in cities by 2050, the Urban Heat Island phenomenon has been getting a lot of attention in both the popular press and the scientific community.[7] The theory is that dark surfaces absorb heat, while light surfaces reflect heat back. The City of New York has painted more than 9.2 million square feet of rooftop white in the past nine years while Los Angeles has been spending $40,000 per mile to paint streets with white reflective paint.[8]

Painting a town white has been seen as a simple, yet radical way to make up for lost glaciers, to combat the climate crisis and to protect the health of its citizens.[9] There is plenty of evidence that this does work to reduce local temperatures significantly in the summer.[10] But some have urged caution about unknown impacts of this soft geo-engineering solution.[11] Yet others have dismissed it because urban areas form only a minuscule part of the Earth's surface.[12]

I argue that we need to go further and ask deeper questions. What gives the paint or roofing membranes that bright reflective sheen? Yes, it is likely that much, if not all, of it comes from titanium dioxide.[13] After all, this bright white pigment alone is an industry valued at about $15.76 billion in 2018.[14] It has become a fundamental part of the supply chain for industries as varied as construction, tech and garments, and it accounts for two-thirds of the pigments produced in the world.[15] Where is it being sourced from? Under what conditions? Who is held accountable? Who benefits? How? For how long? What is the true cost of this white glow? Is it equitable? Is it truly sustainable? Can 40 years of white paint make up for the loss of species that have evolved over millions of years?[16] Can the prosperity that minerals bring to some economies justify thousands of malnourished children, poisoned waterways and the loss of coastal security and traditional livelihoods for millions?

In Chapter 13, 'White in a New Light', we examined the European Commission's journey to regulate the titanium dioxide industry. On 18 February 2020, the European Parliament 'rejected a political group's request to object to the proposed classification of titanium dioxide ... as a category 2 carcinogen', which put to rest a three-year gridlock over classification and labelling.[17] Parliament passed a regulation that entered into force after 20 days. A harmonised classification system across the EU will be enforced from 1 October 2021 to ensure that end-users take adequate precautions to protect their health.[18]

The new regulation on labels applies only to mixtures containing 1% or more of titanium dioxide. For solid mixtures, labels now need to state 'Warning! Hazardous respirable dust may be formed when used. Do not breathe dust.'[19] For liquids containing titanium dioxide particles with an aerodynamic diameter less than or equal to 10 μm, labels have to explicitly state, 'Warning! Hazardous respirable droplets may be formed when sprayed. Do not breathe spray or mist.'

Many in the industry dispute the regulation because they argue that the risks are based on a dust hazard that is 'not specific to titanium dioxide'.[20] They have legitimate concerns over the wide-ranging impacts and knock-on effects for a wide variety of industries. But it has been a long battle to get some parts of the industry to behave responsibly. In 1998, the European Commission had to take Germany to the European Court of Justice 'for failure to introduce all the necessary legislation to comply with a European Union (EU) Directive dealing with waste caused by the titanium dioxide industry'.[21] Many scientists have called for a critical review of the public health regulations on titanium dioxide and its use in food. Readers who are keen to delve deeper are particularly urged to read Jovanovic (2015) and the other references listed for Figure 13.2 . Our health and well-being are intrinsically tied to that of people in distant corners of the world and to their ecosystems. This classification is a welcome move considering that scant attention is paid to how and where titanium dioxide is sourced or to the cumulative impact from mining feedstocks, production and use (particularly cumulative exposure) on the health of people and ecosystems around the world. But it is not to be taken for granted and the story is far from over. The industry has decided to take legal action against the classification of titanium dioxide. On 13 March 2020, it submitted an action to the General Court of the European Union requesting the classification's annulment.[22] We will have wait and see how these developments play out in Europe over the next two to three years. They are sure to have wide-reaching ramifications on the health and well-being of communities and ecosystems around the world.

As these events were unfolding in Europe, another story was being written in the United States. In Chapter 12, 'Private Gain at Public Expense', we heard about a sand mining company that had taken the local county government all the way to the Minnesota Supreme Court for passing a ban against frac sand mining out of concern for the environmental and health impacts of the activities. On 11 March 2020, the Minnesota Supreme Court upheld Winona County's ban on the mining and processing of frac sand. The long-awaited decision gave hope to local communities but the company continues to believe that the county has acted beyond its authority and that the regulation goes too far.[23] On 8 October 2020, the company announced that it had filed for a review with the U.S. Supreme Court.[24]

Will this saga end here? Once again, we have more questions than answers.

It is important for us to know that although problems related to sand mining have been reported in over 70 countries, there are currently no international conventions that regulate the extraction, use and trade of sand from land-based quarries or from rivers or lakes.[25] What is certain is that scientists do not mince words when they say: 'Time is running out for sand'[26] and 'We believe that the international community needs to develop a global strategy for sand governance, along with global and regional sand budgets.'[27] As far as decision-makers are concerned, sand is a non-renewable resource. The more we extract, the more impoverished a world we leave behind for future generations. The true costs of sand mining are currently externalised on to the environment and society. This is a great opportunity to reverse the trend of increased resource extraction established at the turn of the 21st century. As mentioned in Chapter 1, it's not sustainable to carry on consuming at our current rate – in just 13 years we consumed 30 per cent of all the natural resources we've used in the last 120 years.

Before we implement solutions, we need to make sure they are framed with a long-term view in mind. Can crushed rock be promoted as a solution to the sand crisis if there are few systems in place to monitor and evaluate what is also a non-renewable resource?

What about other non-renewable resources? Limestone ecosystems such as karst caves and towers that have taken millions of years to form are rapidly disappearing because of our seemingly insatiable hunger for cement.[28] How can we avoid this? Without addressing fundamental questions like these, we risk clutching at straws.

It is very tempting to believe in conspiracy theories. But could the real reason we find ourselves in this predicament be what psychologists call 'inattentional blindness'? Our goal orientation and selective attention is having a bigger impact than we realise.[29] When we're completely focused on specific tasks, we may not notice significant events, even when they're staring at us in the face. Perhaps it is too much of a segue to say that overworked people trying to meet deadlines or revenue targets, to pay their mortgages, to attend to childcare while balancing a career, are less likely to notice something that is unexpected. But there is merit in exploring this further because research suggests that inattentional blindness has a significant but unrecognised influence on society. It influences accidents in the construction industry or on roads, it results in higher mortality in hospital settings, and may be the cause of gender disparity in our workplaces.[30] Could it also be the cause for society's blind addiction to sand? Could it be why we fail to see other solutions, even obvious ones?

Sand plays an important role in our lives. Building sand castles and playing in the sand is the epitome of childhood. Even professionals such as software developers use the term 'sandbox' to talk about a testing environment where one is free to play around and experiment. Psychologists and therapists use sandplay as a non-rational, non-verbal way to foster creativity or even to address trauma in children or adults. In general, summers have become synonymous with the beach and many people have special memories associated with sand. As one walks along a beach, with the ocean on one side and land on the other, this humble material, which is both solid and fluid, allows us to let go, relax and have fun. Sand has become so much a part of our lexicon that we fail to notice it. In the English language, we use idioms like a line in the sand, the sands of time, bury one's head in sand, and many more without stopping to think how much it influences our thoughts. We cannot continue to ignore this problem and hope it will go away or sort itself out.

I'm often asked, 'What can I do as an individual?' Plenty. It starts with talking about this topic in casual conversations (you can download a discussion guide from our website). Ask people if they know there are different kinds of sand and that not all kinds of sand can be used as a resource. If you know any architects, designers, landscape architects, environmentalists, teachers, geologists, biologists, chemists, sustainability professionals, surfing enthusiasts and anyone who loves this planet, ask them if they have heard about this topic and what we can do about it. If they remain sceptical, ask them to watch *Sand Wars* and direct them to the social media feed of SandStories.org where scores of people across the world share their lived experiences and how sand mining affects them. Ask them to read Vince Beiser's *The World in a Grain* – and this book if you think it might speak to them.

If you are a journalist, please explore whether sand mining is occurring in your own backyard and be very aware of how the story gets framed. If you work in the architecture, engineering or construction sectors or allied industries, you have an incredibly important role to play in leading us to better solutions. If you are an economist or you work in the finance industry, we need you to adopt a radically different approach, especially with funding projects like dams. If you are an investor, please invest in alternatives to sand rather than exploiting the scarcer kinds of sand. If you are a researcher, try your best to publish open access. So much of the information we need to solve this crisis is hiding behind incredibly expensive pay walls that are beyond the reach of most people.

As a human society, we have come far and we've achieved truly remarkable things. We can certainly provide homes for people and meet other needs without wrecking this precious planet. It calls for collective imagination and the political will to put in place a circular economy. It calls for much greater awareness about the role sand plays in our lives and what we stand to lose if we continue to extract sand indiscriminately. I hate doom and gloom literature as much as anybody and I have tried to provide examples of projects that are making a difference in their communities and people who are taking a stand and following a bold vision. There are so many more that I couldn't write about in the limited amount of time and resources I had at my disposal.

Architects Declare, Structural Engineers Declare and so many other movements are now creating a radical vision of what's possible – let them inspire us. Let's move from what *is* to what *if?*[31] Let's imagine how our beautiful world would look if things turn out okay in the end. How would our world look if we recognise the magnificence and majesty of Mother Nature and let her lead us to a better future?

Acknowledgements

This book was made possible by the generous sponsorship from several people who supported my crowdfunding appeal on Publishizer. My sincere thanks to each of you.

I am hugely indebted to Claire Barnes, Jitendra Sindhwani, Sandra Fernandes, Sharmila Antao, Vishal MFP, Cyril Abreo, Praveen Dsouza OFM, Padmaja Vaswani, Michelle Bauer, and Kenda Cunningham. I'm so grateful for your faith in this project and in me. I couldn't have done this without you. Thanks a million. Special thanks go to Vicky Pereira, Kristel Anbu, P.S. Lourdenadhan, Laura Fantinello, Judit Kerenyi, Eugenie Munakarmi, Allison Hunter, Martine Willox, Yara Willox, Uma Maheshwari Shukla, Rohini Nilekani, Kiki Patsch, Donald Freeman, Colette Stewart, Bibiana Cristòfol Amat, Anusuyamma M., Anand Rudolph Pledger, Aaron Fishbone, Shekar Dattatri, Marta Dorca Serra, Ben Freund, Adeniyi Asiyanbi, Charles Fattouche and Patrick Mueller. You made this book happen. Thank you.

Thank you to Ana Osuna Orozco for your insightful comments on the initial version of the book proposal and to Lee Constantine from Publishizer for convincing me to jump in before I was ready.

A special shout out to Dr. Kiki Patsch who helped me structure the book more effectively and offered me much encouragement and advice.

Thank you to Dhritiraj Sengupta, Riverwatch and Corporate Europe Observatory for permission to use your illustrations.

I'm grateful to Alison Shakspeare from Shakspeare Editorial for taking the time to understand my project. Thank you for your patience, your attention to detail and your kind words of encouragement while working with me to make this book a success.

Thank you to Ella Orr from Much More Social for taking care of social media for me while I focused on the writing and the editing.

Thanks also to Charlotte Webster for your assistance with bringing order to chaos.

Thank you to all the interviewees for generously sharing their time and expertise.

I'd also like to thank Stephen Eades, David Levy, Ray Drabble, Yvonne Orengo, Anselmo Fariña Melián, Ted Auch, Jakob Villioth and Patrick Barry for their helpful comments and inputs.

I'd like to acknowledge the many experts I met at the UNEP Expert Round Table in Geneva and at World Water Week in Stockholm. I found the discussions insightful.

A big thanks to Michelle Bauer and Laura Neocleous for skilfully bringing my ideas to fruition for the book cover image. Thanks also go to Laura Fearn for some of the complex illustrations. Paolo, your creative skills and your ready willingness to help each time I was stuck were simply a godsend. Thank you!

I'd like to thank Bethan Harris, Joey Clifton and all the wonderful women from the Escape community. Being part of this sisterhood has given me much strength and courage.

I am sad that my friend Hicran Cimen Ozdemir passed on so early in life. I am grateful to have shared your gentle, beautiful presence Hicran and especially for your support for this project. You will be missed.

Last but not least, Michelle Bauer and Martine Willox, I'm ever so grateful that you checked in on me during the whole process. I loved the surprise visit pre-lockdown!

References

Chapter 1

1   Driven to Extraction: Can Sand Mining be Sustainable? by Oli Brown and Pascal Peduzzi [WWW Document], 2019. Hoffmann Centre for Sustainable Resource Economy. URL https://hoffmanncentre.chathamhouse.org/article/driven-to-extraction-can-sand-mining-be-sustainable/ (accessed 4.5.20)

2   Van Lancker, V., Francken, F., Kint, L., Terseleer, N., Van Den Eynde, D., Hademenos, V., Missiaen, T., De Mol, R., De Tré, G., Appleton, R., Van Heteren, S., Van Maanen, P.-P., Stafleu, J., Stam, J., Degrendele, K., Roche, M., 2019. Transnational and Integrated Long-term Marine Exploitation Strategies (TILES) (Final Report). Belgian Science Policy, BRAIN-be, Belgian Research Action through Interdisciplinary Networks, Brussels; Bendixen, M., Best, J., Hackney, C., Iversen, L.L., 2019. 'Time is running out for sand'. *Nature* 571, 29–31. doi.org/10.1038/d41586-019-02042-4

3   UNEP 2019. Sand and sustainability: Finding new solutions for environmental governance of global sand resources. GRID-Geneva, United Nations Environment Programme, Geneva, Switzerland

4   Wentworth's grain size distribution for sediments (Source: US Geologival Survey)

Millimeters (mm)	Micrometers (μm)	Wentworth size class	
4096		Boulder	Gravel
256			
64		Cobble	
4		Pebble	
2.00		Granule	
1.00		Very Coarse Sand	Sand
0.50	500	Coarse Sand	
0.25	250	Medium Sand	
0.125	125	Fine Sand	
0.0625	63	Very Fine Sand	
0.0310	31	Coarse Silt	Silt
0.0156	15.6	Medium Silt	
0.0078	7.8	Fine Silt	
0.0039	3.9	Very Fine Silt	
0.00006	0.06	Clay	Mud

Chapter 2

1   The Cries of London: as they are daily exhibited in the streets; with an epigram in verse adapted to each. Embellished with forty-eight elegant characteristic engravings. To which is prefixed, a poetical description of the metropolis., Tenth edition. ed, 1804. J. Harris, Successor to E. Newberry, London. Available at: www.soundsurvey.org.uk/index.php/history/street_cries/brit2/635/3399

2   Available in digital format courtesy of Ian Rawes, www.soundsurvey.org.uk

3   Sucholeiki, R., 2015. The Sand Art Bottles of Andrew Clemens. McFarland

4   Smil, V., 2013. Making the Modern World: Materials and Dematerialization. Wiley

5   Watts, J., 2019. 'Concrete: the most destructive material on Earth'. The Guardian

6   Sandpainted kitchen floor, black and white photography, about 1900-1920, Drenthe, Netherlands, 1900. Available at: https://commons.wikimedia.org/wiki/File:Zandtapijt_in_Drentse_keuken.jpg

7   Krausmann, F., Gingrich, S., Eisenmenger, N., Erb, K., Haberl, H.H., Fischer-Kowalski, M., 2009. Growth in global materials use, GDP and population during the 20th century. Ecological Economics 68, 2696–2705. https://doi.org/10.1016/j.ecolecon.2009.05.007

8   Joy, K.J., Paranjape, S., Gujja, B., Goud, V., Vispute, S., 2018. Water Conflicts in India: A Million Revolts in the Making. Routledge

9   Samean, L., Willemyns, A., 2016. Minister faces music on sand. The Phnom Penh Post

10 Krausmann et al, 2009. Growth in global materials use

11 Kosmatka, S.H., Kerkhoff, B., Panarese, W.C., 2003. Design and Control of Concrete Mixtures, 14th ed. Portland Cement Association, Skokie, Illinois, USA

12 UNEP 2019. Sand and sustainability: Finding new solutions for environmental governance of global sand resources. GRID-Geneva, United Nations Environment Programme, Geneva, Switzerland

13 Moore, D., n.d. Raw Material Preparation [WWW Document]. Cement Kilns. URL https://www.cementkilns.co.uk/ck_rmp.html (accessed 27.3.20); Das, K.B., 1987. Cement Industry of India. APH Publishing

14 How Cement and Concrete Are Made [WWW Document], n.d. Rediscover Conrete. URL http://rediscoverconcrete.com/en/sustainability/how-cement-concrete-are-made.html (accessed 27.3.20)

15 Cement & Concrete Basics FAQs [WWW Document], n.d. Portland Cement Association. URL https://www.cement.org/cement-concrete-applications/cement-and-concrete-basics-faqs (accessed 27.3.20)

16 USGS, 2014. Cement Statistics and Information. U.S. Geological Survey, Reston, Virginia

17 USGS, 2020. Cement Statistics and Information. U.S. Geological Survey, Reston, Virginia

18 UNEP, 2014. Sand, rarer than one thinks

19 Balbo, L., 2013. Architectural Pornography: Saudi Arabia's Kingdom Tower. Green Prophet

20 PricewaterhouseCoopers, n.d. Global Construction 2030: a global forecast for the construction industry to 2030
21 Ibid
22 Ibid
23 Ibid
24 Randall Schaetzl, n.d. Sand and Gravel Mining for Aggregate. Michigan State University
25 Flying sand to the desert.-93 [WWW Document], n.d. Lufthansa Cargo. URL https://lufthansa-cargo.com/cargo-diaries-details/-/asset_publisher/H8t9hOen2LPD/content/flying-sand-to-the-desert-93 (accessed 8.5.20)
26 Rayasam, R., 2016. Even desert city Dubai imports its sand. This is why. BBC Capital
27 Dubai BOUGHT SAND! (for Meydan Racecourse, home to the Dubai World Cup), 2014. FillyGirl. URL http://fillygirl.com/dubai-bought-sand-for-meydan-racecourse-home-to-the-dubai-world-cup/ (accessed 8.5.20)
28 Martin, N., 2003. Sheikh to import 3,000 tons of sand from Lancashire. The Telegraph; Malm, S., 2014. German firm land ultimate deal... selling sand to sheiks of desert-locked Dubai. Daily Mail; Dubai BOUGHT SAND!, 2014
29 Bailey, C., 2009. Where's the beach? Seeking the origins of Waikiki sand. Hawaii Magazine
30 Goodfellow, M., 2015. The 5 best urban beaches around the world. The Independent
31 Stan, C., 2015. The Best Urban Beaches in Europe! Travel for Senses. URL https://www.travelforsenses.com/the-best-urban-beaches-in-europe/ (accessed 28.3.20)
32 Singapore's first urban beach to pop up at Marina Bay, 2015. Wild Singapore News. URL https://wildsingaporenews.blogspot.com/2015/05/singapores-first-urban-beach-to-pop-up.html (accessed 8.5.20)
33 Game-changing solutions from LafargeHolcim [WWW Document], n.d. Agg-Net. URL https://www.agg-net.com/news/game-changing-solutions-from-lafargeholcim (accessed 28.3.20)
34 Ibid Swiss franc to US dollar conversion on 1 December 2019: $1 = CHF 1.00017
35 Schandl, H., Krausmann, F., 2017. The 20th century saw a 23-fold increase in natural resources used for building. The Conversation. URL https://theconversation.com/the-20th-century-saw-a-23-fold-increase-in-natural-resources-used-for-building-73057 (accessed 28.3.20)
36 Krausmann, F., Lauk, C., Haas, W., Wiedenhofer, D., 2018. From resource extraction to outflows of wastes and emissions: The socioeconomic metabolism of the global economy, 1900–2015. Global Environmental Change 52, 131–140. https://doi.org/10.1016/j.gloenvcha.2018.07.003
37 Ibid

Chapter 3

1   House, J.E., House, K.A., 2016. Chapter 12 – Silicon, Germanium, Tin, and Lead, in: House, J.E., House, K.A. (Eds.), Descriptive Inorganic Chem-

istry (Third Edition). Academic Press, Boston, pp. 177–196. https://doi.
org/10.1016/B978-0-12-804697-5.00012-9

2   Re-thinking the life cycle of architectural glass - Arup [WWW Document],
    n.d. URL https://www.arup.com/en/perspectives/publications/research/section/
    re-thinking-the-life-cycle-of-architectural-glass (accessed 6.5.20)

3   Kenward, M., 1972. Reflections on glass research. New Scientist 55, 426–428

4   Nascimento, M.L.F., 2014. Brief history of the flat glass patent – Sixty
    years of the float process. World Patent Information 38, 50–56. https://doi.
    org/10.1016/j.wpi.2014.04.006

5   Kenward, 1972. Reflections on glass research

6   Nascimento, 2014, 'Brief history'

7   Sir Alastair Pilkington, n.d., www.pilkington.com/global/about/education/
    sir-alastair-pilkington (accessed 5.4.20)

8   Re-thinking the life cycle of architectural glass – Arup

9   Corning Introduces Gorilla Glass 6 with Improved Durability for Next-Gen-
    eration Mobile Devices [WWW Document], 2018. Corning. URL https://
    www.corning.com/emea/en/about-us/news-events/news-releases/2018/07/
    corning-introduces-corning-gorilla-glass-6-delivering-improved-durabili-
    ty-for-next-generation-mobile-devices.html (accessed 28.3.20)

10 Hawkes, D., 2018. The Window in British Architecture. VILLUM Window
    Collection

11 Bulgin, 2018. 9 Uses of Fiber Optic Cables [WWW Document]. Design
    Spark. URL https://www.rs-online.com/designspark/9-uses-of-fiber-optic-ca-
    bles (accessed 28.3.20)

12 Ibid; Routley, N., 2017. MAPPED: The world's network of undersea cables.
    Business Insider. URL https://www.businessinsider.com/map-the-worlds-net-
    work-of-undersea-cables-2017-8?r=US&IR=T (accessed 28.3.20)

13 Nat and Friends, 2016. A Journey to the Bottom of the Internet. YouTube

14 Fiber Optic Cable [WWW Document], n.d. Corning. URL https://www.
    corning.com/emea/en/products/communication-networks/products/fiber-op-
    tic-cable.html (accessed 28.3.20); Corning, 2013. Fiber 101. YouTube

15 Research and Markets, 2019. Global Flat Glass Market Size, Share &
    Trends Analysis, 2018-2019 & 2025F [WWW Document]. Globe-
    Newswire News Room. URL http://www.globenewswire.com/news-re-
    lease/2019/12/12/1960027/0/en/Global-Flat-Glass-Market-Size-Share-
    Trends-Analysis-2018-2019-2025F.html (accessed 28.3.20)

16 Specialty Glass Market Segment, Size, Share, Global Trends, 2025 | MRFR
    [WWW Document], 2020. URL https://www.marketresearchfuture.com/
    reports/specialty-glass-market-8430 (accessed 28.3.20)

17 Research and Markets, 2019. Global Flat Glass Market Size.

Chapter 4

1   The three common forms of TiO_2 are rutile, anatase and brookite. Rutile is the
    most stable. Anatase and brookite are stable at normal temperatures but slowly
    convert to rutile when heated above 550^0C and 750^0C, respectively (Royal

Society of Chemistry and the Wolfson Foundation, 2015. TiO$_2$: Manufacture of Titanium Dioxide). The rutile form is more popular due to its higher stability and slightly better whitening abilities, while the anatase form is softer (Robinson, P., 2010. Titanium dioxide. Chemistry World)

2   Davis, C.Q., 2013. What the BLEEP is candy corn? Scienceline. URL http://scienceline.org/2013/10/what-the-bleep-is-candy-corn/ (accessed 8.5.20)

3   Phillips, L.G., Barbano, D.M., 1997. The Influence of Fat Substitutes Based on Protein and Titanium Dioxide on the Sensory Properties of Lowfat Milks 1. Journal of Dairy Science 80, 2726–2731. https://doi.org/10.3168/jds.S0022-0302(97)76234-9

4   Schonbrun, Z., 2018. The Quest for the Next Billion-Dollar Color. Bloomberg Businessweek; Grand View Research, 2019. Titanium Dioxide (TiO$_2$) Market Size, Share & Trends Analysis Report by Application (Paints & Coatings, Plastics, Pulp & Paper, Cosmetics), By Region (North America, Europe, APAC, MEA, CSA), And Segment Forecasts, 2019–2025

5   ICIS, 2010. Titanium Dioxide (TiO$_2$) Uses and Market Data [WWW Document]. URL https://www.icis.com/explore/resources/news/2007/11/07/9076546/titanium-dioxide-tio2-uses-and-market-data/ (accessed 6.5.20)

6   USGS, 2014. Mineral Commodity Summaries, Titanium and Titanium Dioxide. U.S. Geological Survey, Reston, Virginia

7   ICIS, 2010

8   Alcoa, n.d. Alcoa's Reynobond® with EcoCleanTM, Powered by HydrotectTM [WWW Document]. URL https://altechpanel.com/Prods/EcoClean_Brochure.pdf (accessed 06.05.20)

9   Robinson, P., 2010. Titanium dioxide. Chemistry World

10 Self-cleaning glass – How does it work? [WWW Document], 2015. Pilkington. URL https://www.pilkington.com/en-gb/uk/householders/types-of-glass/self-cleaning-glass/how-does-it-work (accessed 7.5.20)

11 Robinson, 2010. Titanium dioxide

12 Fujishima, A., Hashimoto, K., Watanabe, T., 1999. TiO$_2$ Photocatalysis Fundaments and Applications. BKC, Inc., Chiyoda-ku, Tokyo

13 ICIS, 2010

14 RSC (Royal Society of Chemistry) and the Wolfson Foundation, 2015. TiO$_2$: Manufacture of Titanium Dioxide

15 Vela, N., Pérez-Lucas, G., Fenoll, J., Navarro, S., 2017. Recent Overview on the Abatement of Pesticide Residues in Water by Photocatalytic Treatment Using TiO$_2$, in: Janus, M., Application of Titanium Dioxide. IntechOpen. DOI: 10.5772/intechopen.68802

16 NASA grants West Virginia University $100,000 for 3D printed titanium oxide foam research aboard ISS [WWW Document], 2017. 3D Printing Industry. URL https://3dprintingindustry.com/news/nasa-grants-west-virginia-university-100000-3d-printed-titanium-oxide-foam-research-aboard-iss-118011/ (accessed 06.05.20)

17 Rising demand for lightweight vehicles in automobile industry drive the titanium dioxide market [WWW Document], 2020. Benzinga. URL https://www.benzinga.com/pressreleases/20/01/ab15214528/rising-demand-for-light-

weight-vehicles-in-automobile-industry-drive-the-titanium-dioxide-market (accessed 29.3.20)

18 Robinson, 2010. Titanium dioxide
19 ICIS, 2010. Titanium Dioxide (TiO$_2$) Uses and Market Data. https://www.icis.com/explore/resources/news/2007/11/07/9076546/titanium-dioxide-tio2-uses-and-market-data/ (accessed 6.5.20)

Chapter 5

1   Cryer, P., n.d. Waterglass for preserving eggs [WWW Document]. 1900s. URL https://www.1900s.org.uk/1940s50s-preserving-eggs.htm (accessed 29.3.20)
2   Environ Molds, 2018. Sodium Silicate || Water Glass: (Uses from Industrial to Daily Life). YouTube
3   Silicates: applications for every sector [WWW Document], n.d. Silmaco. URL http://www.silmaco.com/applications (accessed 29.3.20)
4   Environ Molds, 2018
5   Knott, P., 1986. A Study of the Flow Performance of a Sodium Silicate Furnace. Aston University, Birmingham
6   Anti-Caking Agents [WWW Document], n.d. Understanding Food Additives. URL http://understandingfoodadditives.org.uk/pages/Ch2p7-1.htm (accessed 29.3.20)
7   Jeans & sandblasting [WWW Document], n.d. Shop Ethical! URL http://www.ethical.org.au/3.4.2/get-informed/issues/jeans-sandblasting/ (accessed 29.3.20)
8   Ship cleaning [WWW Document], n.d. Conjet AB. URL http://conjet.com/method/ship-cleaning/ (accessed 29.3.20)
9   Glass Wool Insulation | Glass Wool Rolls | Glass Wool Slabs [WWW Document], n.d. URL https://www.insulationshop.co/glass_and_mineral_wool_insulation/glass_wool_insulation.html (accessed 11.5.20)
10 A radome is a dome or other structure protecting radar equipment, especially on the outer surface of an aircraft. (Stephen L. Sass, 2013. The Substance of Civilization: Materials and Human History from the Stone Age to the Age of Silicon. Skyhorse Publishing)
11 Fiberglass Benefits [WWW Document], n.d. Fiber-Tech, Inc. URL http://www.fiber-techinc.com/capabilities/extras/fiberglass-benefits/ (accessed 7.5.20)
12 Andersen, N., 2011. Fiberglass Manufacturing How Fiberglass Is Made. YouTube
13 Gardiner, G., 2009. The making of glass fiber [WWW Document]. Composites World. URL http://www.compositesworld.com/articles/the-making-of-glass-fiber (accessed 7.5.20)
14 Fiberglass [WWW Document], n.d. How Products are Made. URL http://www.madehow.com/Volume-2/Fiberglass.html (accessed 7.5.20)
15 In sand casting a hollow mould is made of bonded sand using a wooden pattern in the shape of the desired component. Hollow sections can be introduced by using sand cores in the mould cavity. The pattern is removed and molten metal is poured into the cavity. Once the metal has solidified, the sand mould and any cores are removed. The pattern can be reused and the sand

recycled. Sand Casting [WWW Document], 2014. MetalTek. URL https://www.metaltek.com/capabilities/processes/metal-casting/sand-casting (accessed 7.5.20)

16 Srinivasan, K., Siddharth, C.S.K., Kaarthic, L.V.A., Thenarasu, M., 2018. Evaluation of Mechanical Properties, Economic and Environmental Benefits of Partially Replacing Silica Sand with Biomass Ash for Aluminium Casting. Materials Today: Proceedings, International Conference on Materials Manufacturing and Modelling, ICMMM – 2017, 9 – 11, March 2017 5, 12984–12992. https://doi.org/10.1016/j.matpr.2018.02.283

17 Casting Applications [WWW Document], n.d. The Metal Casting. URL http://www.themetalcasting.com/ (accessed 29.3.20)

18 Ramana Rao, T.V., 2007. Metal Casting: Principles and Practice. New Age International

19 Cain, F., 2009. What is the Temperature of Lava? Universe Today. URL https://www.universetoday.com/27891/temperature-of-lava/ (accessed 29.3.20)

20 Natural and synthetic molding sand and Properties of molding sand, n.d. Mechanical Engineering. URL http://mechanicalinventions.blogspot.co.uk/2012/12/natural-and-synthetic-molding-sand-and.html (accessed 29.3.20)

21 Ramana Rao, 2007

22 Natural and synthetic molding sand, n.d.

23 Ibid

24 Ramana Rao, 2007

25 Ibid; Natural and synthetic molding sand, n.d.

26 Ramana Rao, 2007

27 Sand Casting, n.d. The Library of Manufacturing. URL http://thelibraryof-manufacturing.com/metalcasting_sand.html (accessed 29.3.20)

28 Sand Casting, n.d. CustomPart.net. URL http://www.custompartnet.com/wu/SandCasting (accessed 29.3.20)

29 Carlstedt, T., 2014. Sand Casting vs. Investment Casting. CPM Industries. URL http://info.cpm-industries.com/blog/bid/178170/Sand-Casting-vs-In-vestment-Casting (accessed 29.3.20)

30 Ibid

31 Transport: automobile, aerospace, railways and shipping; Heavy Equipment: construction, farming and mining; Machine Tools: machining, casting, plastics moulding, forging, extrusion and forming; Plant Machinery: chemical, petro-leum, paper, sugar, textile, steel and thermal plants; Defence: vehicles, artillery, munitions, storage and supporting equipment; Electrical Equipment Machines: motors, generators, pumps and compressors; Hardware: plumbing industry pipes, joints, valves and fittings; Household: appliances, kitchen and gardening equipment, furniture and fittings; Art Objects: sculptures, idols, furniture, lampstands and decorative items

32 Casting Applications [WWW Document], n.d. The Metal Casting. URL http://www.themetalcasting.com/ (accessed 29.3.20)

Chapter 6

1 Land reclamation is a term also used for the restoration of former industrial sites. However, in this book I only use the term to refer to the creation of new land either adjoining land masses or as separate islands

2 ten Wolde, H., 2008. Dutch seek islands to combat rising sea threat. Reuters; Savodnik, P., 2013. Azerbaijan Is Rich. Now It Wants to Be Famous. The New York Times

3 Bashir, M., 2009. Lebanon: Cedar Island – A Controversial Construction. Global Voices. URL https://globalvoices.org/2009/02/05/lebanon-cedar-island-a-controversial-construction/ (accessed 30.03.20); Marcus Fairs, 2007. Federation Island by Erick van Egeraat [WWW Document]. Dezeen. URL http://www.dezeen.com/2007/09/24/federation-island-by-erick-van-egeraat/ (accessed 30.03.20)

4 Urquhart, C., 2011. Israel may build artificial island off Gaza Strip coast. The Guardian; Baker, L., 2017. A new island in the Mediterranean...just off Gaza. Reuters; Guinto, J., 2014. China Builds Artificial Islands in South China Sea. Bloomberg Businessweek

5 Schwartz, M., 2006. Encyclopedia of Coastal Science. Springer Science & Business Media; Construction began in 1987 and the airport opened in 1994 (Kansai and Kobe International Airport (Osaka Bay, Japan) [WWW Document], 2000. Earth Watching Project. URL https://earth.esa.int/web/earth-watching/latest-event/-/article/kansai-and-kobe-international-airport-osaka-bay-japan- (accessed 29.3.20)

6 TheLOCATION100, 2011. World's biggest ever construction – Kansai man-made island airport. YouTube; Kansai and Kobe International Airport (Osaka Bay, Japan) [WWW Document], 2000. Earth Watching Project. URL https://earth.esa.int/web/earth-watching/latest-event/-/article/kansai-and-kobe-international-airport-osaka-bay-japan- (accessed 29.3.20)

7 TheLOCATION100, 2011. World's biggest ever construction; Kansai and Kobe International Airport, 2000; Friedman, M., n.d. The Inflation Calculator [WWW Document]. URL https://westegg.com/inflation/infl.cgi (accessed 30.3.20); Lutz, A., 2012. The 15 Most Expensive Megaprojects In Modern History. Business Insider

8 Kansai and Kobe International Airport, 2000

9 Mola, R., 2018. The Airport Is Sinking [WWW Document]. Air & Space Magazine. URL https://www.airspacemag.com/flight-today/how-to-save-a-sinking-airport-180968985/ (accessed 16.10.20)

10 Condition of the Settlement [WWW Document], n.d. Kansai International Airport Land Company, ltd. URL http://www.kiac.co.jp/en/tech/sink/sink3/ (accessed 29.3.20)

11 Sweeney, C., 2010. Airports and Architecture – The World's 18 Strangest Airports. Popular Mechanics. URL https://www.popularmechanics.com/technology/design/g255/4346192/ (accessed 29.3.20)

12 problogic, 2015. Amazing offshore commercial airports. Panethos. URL https://panethos.wordpress.com/2015/09/25/amazing-offshore-commercial-airports/ (accessed 29.3.20)

13 World's largest offshore airport under construction in Dalian, n.d. China Daily

14 Royal Haskoning DHV wins tender to examine viability of Israeli offshore airport construction [WWW Document], 2019. CAPA. URL https://centreforaviation.com/news/royal-haskoning-dhv-wins-tender-to-examine-viability-of-israeli-offshore-airport-construction-892433 (accessed 29.3.20); Another offshore airport proposal; now its Israel's turn, 2018. Blue Swan Daily. URL https://blueswandaily.com/another-offshore-airport-proposal-now-its-israels-turn/ (accessed 29.3.20); Wainer, D., Benmeleh, Y., 2018. Israel's $10 Billion Island Project Sparks European Interest. Bloomberg

15 Battle, L., 2014. Why property developers are gambling on the future of Macau. Financial Times

16 Macau land area grows by over 1/3 since 1999, 2019. Macau News. URL https://macaunews.mo/macau-land-area-grows-by-over-1-3-since-1999/ (accessed 7.5.20)

17 Macao builds a new frontier with ambitious reclamation [WWW Document], 2015. Macauhub. URL http://www.macauhub.com.mo/en/2015/04/24/macao-builds-a-new-frontier-with-ambitious-reclamation/ (accessed 7.5.20)

18 Shepard, W., 2015. "The gift from the sea": through land reclamation, China keeps growing and growing. CityMetric. www.citymetric.com/skylines/gift-sea-through-land-reclamation-china-keeps-growing-and-growing-1350 (accessed 7.5.20)

19 Yang, H., 2012. Gift of land from the sea. China Daily Europe

20 National Beach Nourishment Database [WWW Document], n.d. URL https://coast.noaa.gov/digitalcoast/tools/beach-nourishment.html (accessed 7.5.20)

21 Cai, F., Dean, R.G., Liu, J., 2011. Beach Nourishment in China: Status and Prospects. Coastal Engineering Proceedings 1. https://doi.org/10.9753/icce.v32.management.31; Hanson, H., Brampton, A., Capobianco, M., Dette, H.H., Hamm, L., Laustrup, C., Lechuga, A., Spanhoff, R., 2002. Beach nourishment projects, practices, and objectives—a European overview. Coastal Engineering, Shore Nourishment in Europe 47, 81–111. https://doi.org/10.1016/S0378-3839(02)00122-9

22 Miller, J., 2019. Beach replenishment's future: 'it's just not feasible to protect the whole coast.' The Daily Times

Chapter 7

1 Favors, Z., Wang, W., Bay, H.H., Mutlu, Z., Ahmed, K., Liu, C., Ozkan, M., Ozkan, C.S., 2014. Scalable Synthesis of Nano-Silicon from Beach Sand for Long Cycle Life Li-ion Batteries. Scientific Reports 4. https://doi.org/10.1038/srep05623

2 Nealon, S., 2014. Sand-based lithium ion batteries that outperform standard by three times. Phys.org. URL http://phys.org/news/2014-07-sand-based-lithium-ion-batteries-outperform.html (accessed 7.5.20)

3 Woodward, A., 2019. China could restrict its export of rare-earth metals as a trade-war tactic. Here's what they are and why they're so crucial. Business Insider; Holmes, F., 2019. Australia May Be The Saving Grace For The Rare Earth Metals Market. Forbes

4   Koerth-Baker, M., 2010. 4 Rare Earth Elements That Will Only Get More Important. Popular Mechanics. URL http://www.popularmechanics.com/technology/engineering/news/important-rare-earth-elements (accessed 7.5.20)

5   Gorman, S., 2009. As hybrid cars gobble rare metals, shortage looms. Reuters

6   Monazite (REE) [WWW Document], n.d. National Museums Scotland. URL https://www.nms.ac.uk/explore-our-collections/resources/from-minerals-to-your-mobile/minerals/monazite/ (accessed 7.5.20)

7   Carmichael Coal ("Adani") Mine Cases in Queensland courts [WWW Document], n.d. Environmental Law Australia. URL http://envlaw.com.au/carmichael-coal-mine-case/ (accessed 30.3.20); Stop Adani Wrecking Our Reef [WWW Document], n.d. Fight For Our Reef. URL https://www.marineconservation.org.au/stop-adani-wrecking-our-reef/ (accessed 20.3.20)

8   Leahy, S., 2019. This is the world's most destructive oil operation—and it's growing. National Geographic. URL https://www.nationalgeographic.co.uk/environment/2019/04/worlds-most-destructive-oil-operation-and-its-growing (accessed 30.3.20)

9   Athabasca oil sands, 2016. Wikipedia

10 Personal communication with Dr. Ted Auch, Fracktracker Alliance, Sep 2020

11 U.S. Silica sees sand demand piling up as fracking goes super-sized. Reuters, 2014

12 Vikas Proppant & Granite completes shipping for proppant aggregating Rs 455 cr, 2020. Business Standard

13 EJOLT, 2017. Resistance to fracking projects, Algeria | EJAtlas. Environmental Justice Atlas. https://ejatlas.org/conflict/resistance-to-fracking-projects-in-algeria (accessed 6.5.20)

14 Aulich et al., 1984, describe two methods to prepare high-purity silica from a low-cost starting material for solar-grade silicon production. In the first process, abundantly available quartz sand is purified by fusing it with glass-forming oxides to form a melt from which thin glass fibres are drawn. Subsequent treatment of the fibres with hot hydrochloric acid (HCl) leads to an ion exchange whereby all non-siliceous oxides are removed from the glass network, leaving an insoluble matrix of high-purity silica (Aulich, H.A., Eisenrith, K.-H., Urbach, H.-P., 1984. 'New methods to prepare high-purity silica'. J Mater Sci 19, 1710–1717. doi.org/10.1007/BF00563069); This video seems to depict sand as the starting material. Dr. Eric Rüland, 2013. Solar Module Manufacturing, n.d. www.youtube.com/watch?v=5Sgmp1aUjnA (accessed 6.5.20)

15 Marchal, J., McDonnell, P., Sun, K., J. Krug, D., Laine, R., 2015. A Low Cost, Low Energy Route to Solar Grade Silicon from Rice Hull Ash (RHA), a Sustainable Source. Green Chem. 17. https://doi.org/10.1039/C5GC00622H

16 Aulich et al., 1984

17 Robinson, P. 2010. Titanium dioxide. Chemistry World; Tata Steel and Dyesol produce world's largest dye sensitised photovoltaic module [WWW Document], 2011. Tata Steel. URL https://www.tatasteeleurope.com/en/news/news/2011/2011_dsc (accessed 7.5.20)

Chapter 8

1   Watts, J., 2019. Jagendra Singh: the Indian journalist burned to death.
    The Guardian; Suchitra, M., 2015. Sand mafia attacks journalists again.
    DownToEarth; Guégan, M., Schilis-Gallego, C., 2019. Sand Mafias Silence
    Journalists in India. Daily Maverick; Chaudhary, S., 2019. Journalists Killed
    for Exposing the Illegal Sand Mining Nexus. The Citizen; Sampathkumar, M.,
    2018. Three journalists killed in 24 hours highlights India press freedom prob-
    lem, watchdog groups warn. The Independent; Salopek, P., 2019. Inside the
    deadly world of India's sand mining mafia. National Geographic. URL https://
    www.nationalgeographic.com/environment/2019/06/inside-india-sand-min-
    ing-mafia/ (accessed 31.03.20); 2 activists killed in Gambia in protests against
    sand mining, 2018. AP News; Watts, J., 2018. Almost four environmental
    defenders a week killed in 2017. The Guardian; Beiser, V., 2017. He who
    controls the sand: the mining "mafias" killing each other to build cities. The
    Guardian; Moodley, P., 2019. The race to the bottom: We need fundamental
    change. Natural Justice. URL https://naturaljustice.org/the-race-to-the-bot-
    tom-we-need-fundamental-change/ (accessed 31.03.20); Illegal Sand Mining
    Violence 2018: at least 28 People died across India, 2019. SANDRP. URL
    https://sandrp.in/2019/02/28/illegal-sand-mining-violence-2018-at-least-28-
    people-died-across-india/ (accessed 31.03.20); Reforma, 2019. Environmental
    activist who fought illegal mining murdered in Chiapas. Mexico News Daily;
    Naveen, P., 2018. Forest officer crushed to death by mining mafia in Madhya
    Pradesh. The Times of India; Deep, D., 2016. Forest guard killed while chasing
    sand mafia in Gwalior. The Times of India; Chauhan, C., 2012. In scarred
    country. Hindustan Times; Attackers kill police officer over sand trade, 2017.
    Daily Nation; 50,000 sign petition for murdered anti-mining activist, 2015.
    The Jakarta Post; Reforma, 2019. Environmental activist who fought illegal
    mining murdered in Chiapas. Mexico News Daily; Wild Coast anti-mining
    leader murdered [WWW Document], 2016. Fin24. URL https://www.fin24.
    com/Companies/Mining/wild-coast-anti-mining-leader-murdered-20160323
    (accessed 7.5.20)
2   Rege, A., 2015. Not biting the dust: using a tripartite model of organized crime
    to examine India's Sand Mafia. International Journal of Comparative and
    Applied Criminal Justice 40, 101–121. https://doi.org/10.1080/01924036.2015
    .1082486

Chapter 9

1   Adapted from Maderspacher, F., 2007. 'Bye Baiji?' Current Biology 17, R783–
    R784. https://doi.org/10.1016/j.cub.2007.08.055
2   Chen, Y., Guo, C., Ye, S., Cheng, F., Zhang, H., Lizhu Wang, L., Hughes,
    R.M., 2017. Construction: limit China's sand mining [WWW Document].
    Nature. https://doi.org/10.1038/550457c

3   Choi, C.Q., 2007. Dolphin Species Goes Extinct Due to Humans. Live Science. URL https://www.livescience.com/1760-dolphin-species-extinct-due-humans.html (accessed 7.5.20)

4   Stanfield, M., 2017. Deicide on the Long River: The Story of the Baiji. Remembrance Day For Lost Species. URL https://www.lostspeciesday.org/?p=724 (accessed 7.5.20)

5   Erftemeijer, P.L.A., Riegl, B., Hoeksema, B.W., Todd, P.A., 2012. Environmental impacts of dredging and other sediment disturbances on corals: A review. Marine Pollution Bulletin 64, 1737–1765. https://doi.org/10.1016/j.marpolbul.2012.05.008

6   Cunning, R., Silverstein, R.N., Barnes, B.B., Baker, A.C., 2019. Extensive coral mortality and critical habitat loss following dredging and their association with remotely-sensed sediment plumes. Marine Pollution Bulletin 145, 185–199. https://doi.org/10.1016/j.marpolbul.2019.05.027

7   Phua, C., van den Akker, S., Baretta, M., van Dalfsen, J., n.d. Ecological Effects of Sand Extraction in the North Sea

8   Larson, C., 2018. Asia's hunger for sand takes a toll on endangered species. Science 359, 964–965. https://doi.org/10.1126/science.359.6379.964

9   Chun, Z., 2015. Rapid decline of China's wetlands threatens mass extinction for rare birds. China Dialogue. URL https://www.chinadialogue.net/article/show/single/en/8253-Rapid-decline-of-China-s-wetlands-threatens-mass-extinction-for-rare-birds (accessed 7.5.20)

10 This is relevant because aggregate used in the construction industry consists of sand and gravel. (Mulhollem, J., 2013. Research shows river dredging reduced fish numbers, diversity. PennState News)

11 Ibid

12 Cerema, 2015. Human health risk assessment guidance for dredging and disposal at sea of marine and estuarine sediments; Banergee, P., 2017. The Dangers of Dredging Jamuna. Resilience. URL https://www.resilience.org/stories/2017-07-19/the-dangers-of-dredging-jamuna/ (accessed 31.3.20)

13 Palmer, T.A., Montagna, P.A., Nairn, R.B., 2008. The Effects of a Dredge Excavation Pit on Benthic Macrofauna in Offshore Louisiana. Environmental Management 41, 573–583. https://doi.org/10.1007/s00267-007-9063-5

14 Photo of turtle on Maldives airport runway goes viral, 2019. *Maldives Independent*

15 Muka, S., 2015. Beach Nourishment: Environmental Questions. Through the Aquarium Glass. URL https://throughaquariumglass.blogspot.com/2015/06/beach-nourishment-environmental.html (accessed 31.3.20)

16 Milton, S.L., Schulman, A.A., Lutz, P.L., 1997. The Effect of Beach Nourishment with Aragonite versus Silicate Sand on Beach Temperature and Loggerhead Sea Turtle Nesting Success. Journal of Coastal Research 13, 904–915

17 Peterson, C.H., Bishop, M.J., 2005. Assessing the Environmental Impacts of Beach Nourishment. BioScience 55, 887–896. https://doi.org/10.1641/0006-3568(2005)055[0887:ATEIOB]2.0.CO;2

18 Ceballos, G., Ehrlich, P.R., Barnosky, A.D., García, A., Pringle, R.M., Palmer, T.M., 2015. Accelerated modern human–induced species losses: Entering the sixth mass extinction. Science Advances 1, e1400253. https://doi.org/10.1126/sciadv.1400253

19   He, F., Zarfl, C., Bremerich, V., David, J.N.W., Hogan, Z., Kalinkat, G., Tock-
     ner, K., Jähnig, S.C., 2019. The global decline of freshwater megafauna. Global
     Change Biology 25, 3883–3892. https://doi.org/10.1111/gcb.14753
20   Pollock, F.J., Lamb, J.B., Field, S.N., Heron, S.F., Schaffelke, B., Shedrawi, G.,
     Bourne, D.G., Willis, B.L., 2014. Sediment and Turbidity Associated with
     Offshore Dredging Increase Coral Disease Prevalence on Nearby Reefs. PLOS
     ONE 9, e102498. https://doi.org/10.1371/journal.pone.0102498
21   WWF (2020) Living Planet Report 2020 - Bending the curve of biodiversity
     loss. Almond, R.E.A., Grooten M. and Petersen, T. (Eds). WWF, Gland,
     Switzerland
22   Tollefson, J., 2019. Humans are driving one million species to extinction.
     Nature 569, 171–171. https://doi.org/10.1038/d41586-019-01448-4
23   British Geological Survey, 2018. Humans overtake nature as the biggest con-
     tributors to landscape evolution [WWW Document]. URL http://www.bgs.
     ac.uk/news/docs/PressRelease_Anthropocene.pdf
24   How Cement Is Made [WWW Document], n.d. Portland Cement Associa-
     tion. URL http://www.cement.org/cement-concrete-basics/how-cement-is-
     made (accessed 31.3.20)
25   Rice [WWW Document], 2019. United States Department of Agriculture.
     URL https://www.ers.usda.gov/topics/crops/rice/ (accessed 31.3.20)
26   Nijhuis, M., 2015. Harnessing the Mekong or Killing It? National Geographic
     News
27   Anthony, E.J., Brunier, G., Besset, M., Goichot, M., Dussouillez, P., Nguyen,
     V.L., 2015. Linking rapid erosion of the Mekong River delta to human activi-
     ties. Scientific Reports 5, 14745. https://doi.org/10.1038/srep14745
28   Schwarz, U., Vienna, F., 2015. Hydropower Projects in Protected Areas on the
     Balkans: Summary
29   Ezcurra, E., Barrios, E., Ezcurra, P., Ezcurra, A., Vanderplank, S., Vidal, O.,
     Villanueva-Almanza, L., Aburto-Oropeza, O., 2019. A natural experiment
     reveals the impact of hydroelectric dams on the estuaries of tropical rivers.
     Science Advances 5, eaau9875. https://doi.org/10.1126/sciadv.aau9875
30   Welland, M., 2012. Sand: The Never-Ending Story. University of California
     Press, Berkeley
31   Rocha, C.D.L., Conley, D.J., 2017. Silica Stories. Springer International Pub-
     lishing. https://doi.org/10.1007/978-3-319-54054-2
32   Ibid
33   Welland, M., 2012. Sand

Chapter 10

1   'Drop in catch forced 80K fisherfolk to pull out sand in Thane', 2017. Hindu-
     stan Times
2   Karkaria, B., 2014. Mumbai is on the verge of imploding. The Guardian
3   Godbole, S., 2017. What It's Actually Like To Live In A Mumbai Chawl.
     Homegrown. URL https://homegrown.co.in/article/801844/what-its-actually-
     like-to-live-in-a-mumbai-chawl (accessed 31.3.20)

4   Jog, S., 2015. Realty players import sand from Indonesia, Philippines. Business Standard India

5   Cooper, K.M., 2005. Cumulative effects of marine aggregate extraction in an area east of the Isle of Wight – a fishing industry perspective. (126), Science Series Technical Report. CEFAS, Lowestoft

6   Drabble, R., 2012. Monitoring of East Channel dredge areas benthic fish population and its implications. Marine Pollution Bulletin 64, 363–372. https://doi.org/10.1016/j.marpolbul.2011.10.035

7   Henderson, P.A., 2003. A Review of Marine Dredging Effects on Fish. Technical Report for London Gateway Harbour Empowerment Order; Miro and Royal Haskoning, 2005. Marine Aggregate Environmental Impact Assessment: Approaching Good Practice. in Drabble, R., 2014. Response to Mark Russell (BMAPA) letter. Marine Pollution Bulletin 86, 595–596. https://doi.org/10.1016/j.marpolbul.2014.07.025

8   Lees, P.G., Kenny, A., Pearson, R., 1992. The condition of benthic fauna in suction dredger outwash: initial findings. Annex submitted to the report of the ICES working group on the effects of extraction of marine sediments on fisheries

9   Kim, T., Grigalunas, T., 2009. Simulating Direct and Indirect Damages to Commercial Fisheries from Marine Sand Mining: A Case Study in Korea. Environmental Management 44, 566–578. https://doi.org/10.1007/s00267-009-9339-z

10 Pereira, K. and Rathnayake, R. 2013. Curbing Illegal Sand Mining in Sri Lanka. Water Integrity Network, Berlin; Women on hunger strike over illegal sand mining, 2016. The Times of India; Marion Thibault, 2016. Grain drain, Laos' sand mining damaging the Mekong. https://phys.org/news/2016-07-grain-laos-sand-mekong.html (accessed 4.5.20); de Sam Lazaro, F., 2019. In Cambodia, sand mining is big business — but it comes at a price. PBS News Hour; Skylar Lindsay, 2020. How sand mining puts Southeast Asia's farmers at risk. ASEAN Today. https://www.aseantoday.com/2020/05/how-sand-mining-puts-southeast-asias-farmers-at-risk/; Robert Sowatei Adjei, 2010. Effects Of Action Aid Ghana Land Reclamation Programme On Food Production In The Ga West Municipality Of The Greater Accra Region, Ghana. University Of Cape Coast; Protect the Paardeberg Coalition, n.d. Sand Mining Archives. Join Protect The Paardeberg. https://protectthepaardeberg.org/category/sand-mining/ (accessed 4.5.20); Farmers' sand-frac nightmare, 2012. Salon. https://www.salon.com/2012/05/21/farmers_sand_frac_nightmare/ (accessed 4.5.20)

11 Annoh-Dompreh, F., 2014. Sand winning, a threat to economic productivity (Working Paper). Parliament of Ghana; Annoh Dompreh, F., 2017. Report of the adhoc committee to investigate the effects of sand winning in the country (Working Paper). Parliament of Ghana

12 United Nations, n.d. Goal 14: Conserve and sustainably use the oceans, seas and marine resources. United Nations Sustainable Development. https://www.un.org/sustainabledevelopment/oceans/ (accessed 4.5.20)

Chapter 11

1   Lundqvist, A., Bauer, R., 2017. Trouble in paradise: the Canary Island beach accused of illegally importing sand. The Guardian.; Protests in Palma de Mallorca against sand imports, 2017. Western Sahara Resource Watch. URL https://www.wsrw.org/a246x3896 (accessed 4.5.20); Cortés, A., 2017. Una red de activistas acusó de 'expolio' en 2008 al proveedor de la arena del Sáhara. Diario de Mallorca.; Paz, I. O., 2017. Protesta en Gran Canaria contra el expolio de la arena saharaui. elDiario.; Paz, I. O, 2017. La importación de arena saharaui, un expolio que pasa desapercibido. elDiario

2   Protesta en el puerto de Palmade Mallorca contra el expolio de arena procedente de la ciudad ocupada de El Aaiún, 2017. Sahara Press Service; Europa Press, 2017. El buque con arena del Sáhara no atracará en Palma esta noche. El Mundo; María Aguiló, J., 2017. Autorizada la desestiba de un cargamento de arena del Sáhara en el Puerto de Palma. ABC España; Protests in Palma de Mallorca against sand imports, 2017. Western Sahara Resource Watch. URL https://www.wsrw.org/a246x3896 (accessed 4.5.20); Cortés, A., 2017. Protesta en el puerto: "¡Esta arena es ilegal!" Diario de Mallorca

3   Protests in Palma de Mallorca against sand imports, 2017; Cortés, A., 2017. Una red de activistas acusó de "expolio" en 2008 al proveedor de la arena del Sáhara. Diario de Mallorca

4   Anfi Group, 2015. Anfi Tauro Beach. Vimeo. URL https://vimeo.com/134090552

5   Paz, I.O., 2016. Arena saharaui para remodelar una playa en el sur de Gran Canaria. El Diario

6   Anfi Group, 2015. Anfi Tauro Beach. Vimeo

7   Lundqvist, A., Bauer, R., 2017. Trouble in paradise: the Canary Island beach accused of illegally importing sand. The Guardian

8   Playa Las Teresitas, n.d. Bitacora de los Desembarcos de Arena Saharaui en Canarias. URL https://arenasaharaui.noblogs.org/playa-las-teresitas/ (accessed 1.4.20)

9   The dirty sand of Canary Islands' beaches, 2011. Western Sahara Resource Watch. URL https://wsrw.org/a204x2103 (accessed 31.3.20)

10 Hilary, J., 2006. The betrayal of a forgotten people. The Guardian

11 Lundqvist & Bauer, 2017

12 The dirty sand of Canary Islands' beaches, 2011

13 Paz, I. O, 2017. La importación de arena saharaui, un expolio que pasa desapercibido. elDiario

14 EU Court protects Western Sahara from EU-Morocco trade deal, 2016. Western Sahara Resource Watch. URL https://www.wsrw.org/a105x3695 (accessed 1.4.20); Koester, S., 2018. EU top court: EU-Morocco fishing deal valid as long as not applied to Western Sahara. Reuters

15 Cortés, A., 2017. Una red de activistas acusó de "expolio" en 2008 al proveedor de la arena del Sáhara. Diario de Mallorca

16 The dirty sand of Canary Islands' beaches, 2011

17 This beach has been shipped from an occupied country, 2008. Western Sahara Resource Watch. URL https://wsrw.org/a128x783 (accessed 1.4.20); Madeira

steals another beach, 2008. Western Sahara Resource Watch. URL https://wsrw.org/a128x997 (accessed 1.4.20)

18 Franke, M., 2014. When one country's land gain is another country's land loss: The social, ecological and economic dimensions of sand extraction in the context of world-systems analysis exemplified by Singapore's sand imports (No. 36/2014), IPE Working Papers. Berlin School of Economics and Law, Institute for International Political Economy (IPE)

19 Shifting Sand: how Singapore's demand for Cambodian sand threatens ecosystems and undermines good governance, 2010. Global Witness, London. Lino Moser, Gabriela Schär, 2013. ARCHITECTURE-OF-TERRITORY-HS12_Construction-of-Territory-Singapores-Expansion-into-the-Sea.pdf. ETH Zurich

20 Comaroff, J., 2014. Built on Sand: Singapore and the New State of Risk. Harvard Design Magazine

21 Ibid

22 Chris Milton, 2010. The Sand Smugglers. Foreign Policy

23 Electronics Industry in Singapore [WWW Document], n.d. EDB Singapore. URL https://www.edb.gov.sg/en/our-industries/electronics.html (accessed 31.3.20)

24 Global Witness: Singapore's statement on sand report leaves major concerns unaddressed, n.d. Global Witness. https://www.globalwitness.org/en/archive/global-witness-singapores-statement-sand-report-leaves-major-concerns-un-addressed/ (accessed 4.5.20)

25 Malaysian government to prohibit export of 4 species of fish, shrimp from Jan 1 to Feb 28, 2018. The Straits Times

26 Comaroff, 2014

27 Mahtani, S., 2018. A would-be city in the Malaysian jungle is caught in a growing rift between China and its neighbors. The Washington Post; Ourbis, S., Shaw, A., 2017. Malaysia's Forest City and the Damage Don. The Diplomat

28 Forest City Johor – Home [WWW Document], n.d. URL http://www.forestcityjohor.info/home/4591457883 (accessed 1.4.20)

29 Reuters, 2018. Mahathir bans foreigners from buying Forest City residential units in Malaysia. South China Morning Post

30 Ungku, F., Latiff, R., 2019. Exclusive: In blow to Singapore's expansion, Malaysia bans sea sand exports. Reuters

31 Erickson, A.S., Bond, K., 2015. Dredging Under the Radar: China Expands South Sea Foothold

32 The figure of $5.3 trillion is often quoted in this context, but this article explains why that may be an overestimate: Center for Strategic & International Studies, n.d. How much trade transits the South China Sea? ChinaPower. URL https://chinapower.csis.org/much-trade-transits-south-china-sea/#easy-footnote-bottom-1 (accessed 1.4.20)

33 Li, M., 2018. UNCLOS and the South China Sea Disputes. Juris

34 Bale, R., 2016. One of the World's Biggest Fisheries Is on The Verge of Collapse. National Geographic News

35 Greer, A., 2016. The South China Sea Is Really a Fishery Dispute. The Diplomat

36 Bale, 2016

37 Tiezzi, S., 2016. South China Sea Ruling: China Caused 'Irreparable Harm' to Environment. The Diplomat

38 Bale, 2016

39 Hongzhou, Z., 2015. China's Fishing Industry: Current Status, Government Policies, and Future Prospects. Presented at the China as a Maritime Power Conference, Arlington, VA. www.cna.org/cna_files/pdf/China-Fishing-Industry.pdf

40 Permanent Court of Arbitration, 2016. The Republic of the Philippines v. The People's Republic of China – Press Release

41 United Nations, 1982. United Nations Convention on the Law of the Sea, Article 12, p.66

42 Mori, S., 2017. Thinking About Long-Term Strategy in the South China Sea. Asia Maritime Transparency Initiative. URL https://amti.csis.org/long-term-strategy-scs/ (accessed 1.4.20)

43 Chen, L., 2018. Chinese tourists hold flag-raising ceremony on disputed island in South China Sea. South China Morning Post; Li, A., 2013. Outcry after Chinese tourists pictured hunting rare sea creatures in disputed Paracel Islands. South China Morning Post; Hunt, K., 2015. Satellite images suggest China "building third airstrip" in South China Sea. CNN; China installs weapons on disputed Spratly islands – report, 2016. DW

44 Rauhala, E., 2016. China puts new weapons on South China Sea islands, report says. The Washington Post; BBC News, 2018. South China Sea: "Leave immediately and keep far off" – BBC News. YouTube

45 Watkins, D., 2015. What China Has Been Building in the South China Sea. The New York Times

46 Erickson, A.S., Bond, K., 2015. Dredging Under the Radar: China Expands South Sea Foothold

47 What is China's "magic island-making" ship?, 2017. BBC News

48 The US and China dredging markets are closed to competition from outside. China has very recently begun exporting complete mid-size dredging vessels. However, it has banned the export of technology and plans, akin to European counterparts (FACTBOX-The world's biggest dredging companies, 2010. Reuters)

49 Erickson & Bond, 2015

50 Rabobank, 2013. Dredging: Profit margins expected to remain fairly healthy until 2018, p.6

51 DEME Orders World's Largest Cutter Suction Dredger from Royal IHC, 2017. Dredging Today. URL https://www.dredgingtoday.com/2017/03/01/deme-orders-worlds-largest-cutter-suction-dredger-from-royal-ihc/ (accessed 31.3.20)

52 Hazekamp, N., ten Kate, G., Wiertsema, W., Wilde-Ramsing, J., 2016. Dredging in the Dark. SOMO and Both ENDS

53 Rabobank Publishes Outlook for Dredging Sector, 2013. Dredging Today. URL https://www.dredgingtoday.com/2013/09/09/rabobank-publishes-outlook-for-dredging-sector/ (accessed 1.4.20)

54 EuDA – About EuDA [WWW Document], n.d. URL https://european dredging.eu/ (accessed 1.4.20)

55 Boskalis Awarded Changfang and Xidao Offshore Wind Farm Project in Taiwan and Announces New Bokalift 2 Crane Vessel [WWW Document], 2019. Boskalis Westminster. URL https://westminster.boskalis.com/about-us/news/news-detail/boskalis-awarded-changfang-and-xidao-offshore-wind-farm-project-in-taiwan-and-announces-new-bokalift.html (accessed 1.4.20); Boskalis to cut more than 600 jobs, drops 24 vessels, 2016. Offshore

56 Hazekamp, N., ten Kate, G., Wiertsema, W., Wilde-Ramsing, J., 2016. Human rights a blind spot in the dredging sector – Dredging in the Dark Summary. SOMO and Both ENDS; Hazekamp, N., ten Kate, G., Wiertsema, W., Wilde-Ramsing, J., 2016. Dredging in the Dark. SOMO and Both ENDS; Both ENDS: Fishermen in Indonesia file a complaint against the Dutch Export Credit Agency Atradius DSB [WWW Document], 2019. Both ENDS. URL https://www.bothends.org/en/Whats-new/News/Fishermen-in-Indonesia-file-a-complaint-against-the-Dutch-Export-Credit-Agency-Atradius-DSB/ (accessed 1.4.20); ALP hid $30k MUA-brokered election gift, 2016. The Australian; Van Oord involved in Luanda building plan that involved human rights abuses: Trouw, 2020. Dutch News; Freedberg, S.P., Alecci, S., Fitzgibbon, W., Dalby, D., Reuter, D., 2020. How Africa's Richest Woman Exploited Family Ties, Shell Companies And Inside Deals To Build An Empire. International Consortium of Investigative Journalists; Kuijpers, K., Kleinnijenhuis, J., 2020. Duizenden families in Angola verjaagd voor project van Nederlandse bedrijven. Trouw; Intermediate Court of Mauritius, 2013. Police v Boskalis International bv and anor; Defi Media Group, 2013. Contract in Port: Boskalis Pleads Guilty in Giving Rs 3 Million to Siddick Chady. Business Mega. URL https://business.mega.mu/2013/05/23/contract-port-boskalis-pleads-guilty-giving-rs-3-million-siddick-chady/ (accessed 1.4.20); Boskalis fined for corrupt payments, 2013. Dutch News; lexpress.mu, 2012. Boskalis Accused of Trying to Bribe Officials in South America Also. Business Mega. URL https://business.mega.mu/2012/06/18/boskalis-accused-trying-bribe-officials-south-america-also/ (accessed 1.4.20); Anti-corruption watchdog warns against no-bid contracts, 2019. Maldives Independent; Mojeed, M., 2017. Jonathan's Aide, Three Other Ex-Nigerian Officials Named In $20million Bribery Scandal In Switzerland. Sahara Reporters; Belford, A., Rasheed, Z., 2018. How Paradise Was Carved Up And Sold. Organized Crime and Corruption Reporting Project. URL https://www.occrp.org/en/paradiseleased/how-paradise-was-carved-up-and-sold (accessed 1.4.20); Belgian dredging company under investigation for bribery in Russia, 2019. Willkie Compliance. URL https://complianceconcourse.willkie.com/articles/news-alerts-2019-10-october-20191029-belgian-dredging-company-under (accessed 1.4.20); How NPA Awarded Dredging Contract To Firm "Convicted Of $20bn Bribery Scandal In Switzerland," 2018. Sahara Reporters; Belgian dredging giant involved In #Ukraine corruption scandal, 2016. EU Reporter

57 Gates, B. and M., 2019. We didn't see this coming [WWW Document]. gatesnotes.com. URL https://www.gatesnotes.com/2019-Annual-Letter (accessed 20.09.20)

Chapter 12

1   Eko Atlantic, 2009. Eko Atlantic Inside Story. YouTube
2   Ibukun, Y., Mongalvy, S., Sguazzin, A., 2018. Dream of a Lagos Champs-Élysées Banks on Nigerian Recovery. Bloomberg
3   Ibid; Koran, L., 2016. Questions about Clinton ties to foreign businessmen brothers. CNN
4   Lukacs, M., 2014. New, privatized African city heralds climate apartheid. The Guardian
5   Eko Atlantic, 2009
6   Eko Atlantic, 2019. Business Insider talks to Ronald Chagoury Jr, Vice Chairman, Eko Atlantic City. YouTube
7   Heinrich Böll Stiftung, Environmental Law Research Institute, Community Conservation and Development Initiatives, 2012. Eko Atlantic: The Dream of a New Model City Struggling with Transparency, Good Governance and Negative Environmental Impacts
8   Ajibade, I., 2013. Climate Change And Human Rights: A Case Study Of Vulnerability And Adaptation In Coastal Communities In Lagos, Nigeria. The University of Western Ontario, London, Ontario, Canada, p.158
9   Aradeon, D., 2012. Eko Lagos City – and the new Eko Atlantic City: A case study in development issues, p.4
10 Harbinson, R., 2007. Development recast? A review of the impact of the Rio Tinto ilmenite mine in Southern Madagascar. Panos London for Friends of the Earth, London
11 Scherz, M.D., 2019. Meet the mini frogs of Madagascar – the new species we've discovered. The Conversation. https://theconversation.com/meet-the-mini-frogs-of-madagascar-the-new-species-weve-discovered-113946 (accessed 4.3.20)
12 Madagascar [WWW Document], n.d. World Food Programme. URL https://www.wfp.org/countries/madagascar (accessed 4.3.20)
13 Harbinson, 2007
14 Ibid
15 Orengo, Y., 2014. Andrew Lees – 20 years after his last mission to Madagascar. Ecologist. URL https://theecologist.org/2014/dec/31/andrew-lees-20-years-after-his-last-mission-madagascar (accessed 4.3.20)
16 Madagascar forces free 200 Rio Tinto hostages, 2013. The Telegraph
17 Curtis, M., 2016. The New Colonialism – Britain's scramble for Africa's energy and mineral resources. War on Want, London
18 Gerety, R.M., 2019. The Ecologists and the Mine. Scientific American
19 Ibid
20 Ibid
21 Orengo, Y., 2017. Tall tales and tailings – the truth about Rio Tinto's rare earth mine in Madagascar. Ecologist. URL https://theecologist.org/2017/apr/03/tall-tales-and-tailings-truth-about-rio-tintos-rare-earth-mine-madagascar (accessed 4.3.20)
22 Gerety, R.M., 2019
23 Ibid

24   Ingram, J.C., Whittaker, R.J., Dawson, T.P., 2005. Tree Structure and Diversity in Human-Impacted Littoral Forests, Madagascar. Environmental Management 35, 779–798. https://doi.org/10.1007/s00267-004-0079-9; Virah-Sawmy, M., 2009. Ecosystem management in Madagascar during global change. Conservation Letters 2, 163–170. https://doi.org/10.1111/j.1755-263X.2009.00066.x; Virah-Sawmy, M., Ebeling, J., 2010. The difficult road toward real-world engagement: conservation science and mining in southern Madagascar. Conservation Letters 3, 288–289. https://doi.org/10.1111/j.1755-263X.2010.00126.x; Sarrasin, B., 2006. Économie politique du développement minier à Madagascar: l'analyse du projet QMM à Tolagnaro (Fort-Dauphin). Vertigo 7. https://doi.org/10.4000/vertigo.240; Kraemer, A., 2012. Whose forests, whose voices? Mining and community- based nature conservation in southeastern Madagascar. Madagascar Conservation & Development 7, 87-96–96. https://doi.org/10.4314/mcd.v7i2S.5; Harbinson, R., 2007. Development recast? A review of the impact of the Rio Tinto ilmenite mine in Southern Madagascar. Panos London for Friends of the Earth, London; Huff, A., Orengo, Y., Ferguson, B., 2018. State-Corporate Alliances and Spaces for Resistance on the Extractive Frontier in Southeastern Madagascar, in: Authoritarian Populism and the Rural World. Presented at the ERPI 2018 International Conference – Authoritarian Populism and the Rural World, The Hague, Netherlands; Huff, A., Orengo, Y., 2020. Resource warfare, pacification and the spectacle of 'green' development: Logics of violence in engineering extraction in southern Madagascar. Political Geography 81, 102195. https://doi.org/10.1016/j.polgeo.2020.102195
25   VU Faculteit der Sociale Wetenschappen, n.d. Using and Losing the Forest: Reflections from Madagascar. YouTube; CICADA, 2018. Presentation by Caroline Seagle at the CICADA Conference in Bishoftu, 08-11-2018. YouTube; Caroline Seagle [WWW Document], n.d. Indian Ocean World Centre. URL https://indianoceanworldcentre.com/people/phd-students/caroline-seagle/ (accessed 4.3.20)
26   Seagle, C., 2012. Inverting the impacts: Mining, conservation and sustainability claims near the Rio Tinto/QMM ilmenite mine in Southeast Madagascar. The Journal of Peasant Studies 39, 447–477. https://doi.org/10.1080/03066150.2012.671769
27   Huff, A., Orengo, Y., Ferguson, B., 2018. 'State-Corporate Alliances and Spaces for Resistance on the Extractive Frontier in Southeastern Madagascar', in: Authoritarian Populism and the Rural World. Presented at the ERPI 2018 International Conference – Authoritarian Populism and the Rural World, The Hague, Netherlands
28   Virah-Sawmy, M., 2014. Does 'offsetting' work to make up for habitat lost to mining? The Conversation. URL https://theconversation.com/does-offsetting-work-to-make-up-for-habitat-lost-to-mining-27699 (accessed 4.3.20); Huff, A., Orengo, Y., 2020. Resource warfare, pacification and the spectacle of 'green' development: Logics of violence in engineering extraction in southern Madagascar. Political Geography 81, 102195. https://doi.org/10.1016/j.polgeo.2020.102195
29   Ibid; Gerety, R.M., 2009. Mining and biodiversity offsets in Madagascar: Conservation or 'Conservation Opportunities?' Mongabay Environmental

News. URL https://news.mongabay.com/2009/08/mining-and-biodiver-sity-offsets-in-madagascar-conservation-or-conservation-opportunities/ (accessed 12.5.19); Kill, J., Franchi, G., 2016. Rio Tinto's biodiversity offset in Madagascar. World Rainforest Movement and Re:Common

30 Kill, J., Franchi, G., 2016. Rio Tinto's biodiversity offset in Madagascar. World Rainforest Movement and Re:Common; Ratcliffe, R., 2017. UK blocks Madagascar farmer who says mining firm ousted him from land. The Guardian

31 Yvonne Orengo, 2020. The true cost of Rio Tinto dividends. The Ecologist. https://theecologist.org/2020/apr/07/true-cost-rio-tinto-dividends (accessed 4.5.20)

32 A Ten-Year Program to Combat Chronic Malnutrition in Madagascar [WWW Document], 2018. The World Bank. URL https://www.worldbank.org/en/news/feature/2018/03/08/a-ten-year-program-to-combat-chronic-malnutrition-in-madagascar (accessed 4.3.20)

33 Kill, J., Franchi, G., 2016

34 Andrew Lees Trust, Panos London, 2009. Voices of change: Oral testimony of the Antanosy people

35 Ingram, J.C., Whittaker, R.J., Dawson, T.P., 2005. Tree Structure and Diversity in Human-Impacted Littoral Forests, Madagascar. Environmental Management 35, 779–798. https://doi.org/10.1007/s00267-004-0079-9

36 Seagle, C., 2012. Inverting the impacts: Mining, conservation and sustainability claims near the Rio Tinto/QMM ilmenite mine in Southeast Madagascar. The Journal of Peasant Studies 39, 447–477. https://doi.org/10.1080/03066150.2012.671769

37 Ibid

38 Andrianasolo, R.C., 2019. Nanaitra ahy ity reportage ity ka zaraiko. Facebook

39 A Ten-Year Program to Combat Chronic Malnutrition in Madagascar [WWW Document], 2018. The World Bank. URL https://www.worldbank.org/en/news/feature/2018/03/08/a-ten-year-program-to-combat-chronic-malnutrition-in-madagascar (accessed 4.3.20)

40 Rio Tinto's biodiversity offset in Madagascar: How culture and religion are used to enforce restrictions, 2016. World Rainforest Movement. URL https://wrm.org.uy/articles-from-the-wrm-bulletin/section2/rio-tintos-biodiversity-offset-in-madagascar-how-culture-and-religion-are-used-to-enforce-restrictions/ (accessed 4.3.20)

41 Orengo, Y., 2014. Andrew Lees – 20 years after his last mission to Madagascar. Ecologist. URL https://theecologist.org/2014/dec/31/andrew-lees-20-years-after-his-last-mission-madagascar (accessed 4.3.20); Huff, A., Orengo, Y., Ferguson, B., 2018. State-Corporate Alliances and Spaces for Resistance on the Extractive Frontier in Southeastern Madagascar, in: Authoritarian Populism and the Rural World. Presented at the ERPI 2018 International Conference – Authoritarian Populism and the Rural World, The Hague, Netherlands

42 Rio Tinto threatens to exit Madagascar after CEO is trapped by protesters, 2013. The Telegraph; Hatcher, J., 2013. The White Stuff: Mining Giant Rio Tinto Unearths Unrest in Madagascar. Time

43 Rio Tinto threatens to exit Madagascar, 2013

44 Madagascar forces free 200 Rio Tinto hostages, 2013. The Telegraph; Douguet, V., 2013. Madagascar: Local protests against Rio Tinto. EJOLT. URL http://

www.ejolt.org/2013/01/madagascar-local-protests-against-rio-tinto/ (accessed 4.3.20)

45 CRAAD-OI (Centre de Recherches et d'Appui pour les Alternatives de Développement – Océan Indien), TANY (Collectif pour la défense des terres malgaches), 2018. The legitimate fight of communities surrounding QMM-Rio Tinto's mining project to claim compensation for their land is repressed again

46 Seagle, C., 2012. Inverting the impacts: Mining, conservation and sustainability claims near the Rio Tinto/QMM ilmenite mine in Southeast Madagascar. The Journal of Peasant Studies 39, 447–477. https://doi.org/10.1080/03066150. 2012.671769; Kraemer, A., 2012. Whose forests, whose voices? Mining and community- based nature conservation in southeastern Madagascar. Madagascar Conservation & Development 7, 87-96–96. https://doi.org/10.4314/ mcd.v7i2S.5; Huff, A., Orengo, Y., Ferguson, B., 2018. State-Corporate Alliances and Spaces for Resistance on the Extractive Frontier in Southeastern Madagascar, in: Authoritarian Populism and the Rural World. Presented at the ERPI 2018 International Conference – Authoritarian Populism and the Rural World, The Hague, Netherlands; Orengo, Y., 2018. Rio Tinto: the long road to transparency. Ecologist. URL https://theecologist.org/2018/nov/22/ rio-tinto-long-road-transparency (accessed 4.3.20)

47 Ratcliffe, R., 2017. UK blocks Madagascar farmer who says mining firm ousted him from land. The Guardian

48 The Andrew Lees Trust, 2019. QMM's encroachment onto the lake bed – comparing satellite images: 2009 and 2016

49 ALT UK focuses on food security, natural resource management and commu- nications for development, with an emphasis on strengthening the capabilities of local communities and civil society to lead local development. See www. andrewleestrust.org/. The trust was set up in memory of the renowned envi- ronmental campaigner Andrew Lees who died trying to save Madagascar's rare coastal forests from the Rio Tinto mine. He succumbed to heatstroke while filming the Petriky forest. He had documented what the locals thought about the proposed mine. He found that villagers had no idea about how the mine would change their world forever and was concerned for them and their environment. As I write this, twenty-five years after his death, his fears really don't seem that far-fetched

50 Orengo, Y., 2018. Rio Tinto: the long road to transparency. Ecologist. URL https://theecologist.org/2018/nov/22/rio-tinto-long-road-transparency (ac- cessed 4.3.20)

51 Orengo, Y., 2019. Rio Tinto 'admits buffer breach.' Ecologist. URL https:// theecologist.org/2019/apr/09/rio-tinto-admits-buffer-breach (accessed 4.3.20); Orengo, Y., Emerman, S.H., 2018. Fears of radionuclide-enriched water pollution as Madagascar mining breaches legal limits. Ecologist. URL https://theecologist.org/2018/sep/03/fears-radionuclide-enriched-water-pollu- tion-madagascar-mining-breaches-legal-limits (accessed 4.3.20)

52 CEM Projet Taratra –Publiez Ce Que Vous Payez Madagascar, 28 Au- gust2019. Letter-from-civil-society-to-Malagasy-Government-Ministers- August 2019 [WWW Document]. URL https://www.pwyp.org/wp-content/ uploads/2015/03/Letter-from-civil-society-to-Malagasy-Government-Min- isters-August2019.pdf (accessed 4.3.20); Publiez Ce Que Vous Payez Mad-

agascar, Andrew Lees Trust UK, Publish What You Pay UK, 2019. Briefing Paper – Mining risks involving the environmental regulator in madagascar: urgent need for remedy [WWW Document]. URL https://www.pwyp.org/wp-content/uploads/2015/03/Mining-Risks-Involving-the-Environmental-Regulator-in-Madagasar.pdf

53 Ingestion pathways are ways in which people could be exposed to radioactive substances via contaminated drinking water or food or by accidentally eating contaminated soil present on food or their hands (Swanson, S., 2019. Review Of The Release Of Radioactive Material From The Rio Tinto/Qmm Mine Madagascar); Water around Rio Tinto's Madagascar mine is high in lead, uranium – study, 2019. Reuters

54 Orengo, 2019

55 Carver, E., 2019. Madagascar mine ignites protests, community division. Mongabay Environmental News. URL https://news.mongabay.com/2019/07/madagascar-mine-ignites-protests-community-division/ (accessed 4.3.20)

56 Orengo, Y., 2017. Tall tales and tailings – the truth about Rio Tinto's rare earth mine in Madagascar. Ecologist. URL https://theecologist.org/2017/apr/03/tall-tales-and-tailings-truth-about-rio-tintos-rare-earth-mine-madagascar (accessed 4.3.20)

57 Proactive, 2019. Base Resources' Tim Carstens hails 'world-class' Toliara Project. YouTube

58 Huff, A., 2017. Black sands, green plans and vernacular (in)securities in the contested margins of south-western Madagascar. Peacebuilding 5, 153–169. https://doi.org/10.1080/21647259.2016.1277012

59 CRAAD-OI Madagascar [WWW Document], n.d. Facebook. URL https://www.facebook.com/pg/craadoi/posts/ (accessed 4.3.20)

60 Carver, E., 2019. Madagascar mine ignites protests, community division. Mongabay Environmental News. URL https://news.mongabay.com/2019/07/madagascar-mine-ignites-protests-community-division/ (accessed 4.3.20)

61 Blac-Pamard, C., 2009. The Mikea Forest Under Threat (southwest Madagascar): How public policy leads to conflicting territories. Field Actions Science Reports 3; Venart, L., 2015. Ranobe: Madagascar's Forgotten Forest. Lemur Conservation Network. URL http://www.lemurconservationnetwork.org/ranobe-madagascars-forgotten-forest/ (accessed 4.3.20); Raharinirina, V., 2019. Toliara sand mining for metals, Ranobe, Madagascar [WWW Document]. Environmental Justice Atlas. URL https://ejatlas.org/conflict/wtr-ranobe-forest-mining-madagascar (accessed 8.3.19); Huff, A., 2017. Black sands, green plans and vernacular (in)securities in the contested margins of south-western Madagascar. Peacebuilding 5, 153–169. https://doi.org/10.1080/21647259.2016.127701

62 Huff, 2017

63 Personal communication with an expert from the UNEP round table organised as per Chatham House rules

64 Orengo, Y., 2019. Rio Tinto retreats from sensitive zone in Madagascar. Ecologist. URL https://theecologist.org/2019/mar/08/rio-tinto-retreats-sensitive-zone-madagascar (accessed 4.3.20); Gerety, R.M., 2019. The Ecologists and the Mine. Scientific American

65 USGS, 2020. Mineral Commodity Summaries 2020 Sand and Gravel (Industrial). U.S. Geological Survey, Reston, VA

66 Webinar: Frac Sand Mining - Fracking's Hidden Connection to America's Breadbasket, 2017. Halt the Harm Network webinar series

67 Malone, S., Kelso, M., Auch, T., Edelstein, K., Ferrar, K., Jalbert, K., 2015. Data inconsistencies from states with unconventional oil and gas activity. Journal of Environmental Science and Health, Part A 50, 501–510. https://doi.org/10.10 80/10934529.2015.992678

68 Concerned Health Professionals of New York, Physicians for Social Responsibility, 2019. Compendium of Scientific, Medical, and Media Findings Demonstrating Risks and Harms of Fracking (Unconventional Gas and Oil Extraction) Sixth Edition

69 Shafto, J., 2019. Proppant providers struggle for pricing power as producers look to local sand. S&P Global Market Intelligence. URL https://www.spglobal.com/marketintelligence/en/news-insights/trending/Ix8bxL_oXNiisg_Gd4-efg2 (accessed 4.3.20)

70 King, H.M., n.d. What is Frac Sand? [WWW Document]. Geology.com. URL https://geology.com/articles/frac-sand/ (accessed 4.3.20)

71 Beans, L., 2014. Groups Call for Ban on Frac-Sand Mining in Wisconsin. EcoWatch. URL https://www.ecowatch.com/groups-call-for-ban-on-frac-sand-mining-in-wisconsin-1881850979.html (accessed 4.3.20)

72 Auch, T., 2020. Trends in Proposed State Legislation to Weaken Environmental Regulations. FracTracker Alliance. URL https://www.fractracker.org/2020/07/trends-in-proposed-state-legislation-to-weaken-environmental-regulations/ (accessed 18.09.20)

73 Wisconsin Network for Peace and Justice, n.d. Resolution Opposing Frac Sand Mining Industry and Environmental Degradation

74 Personal communication with Dr. Ted Auch, FracTracker Alliance, Sep 2020

Chapter 13

1 Health effects due to titanium nanoparticles in food and toothpaste cannot be excluded, 2016. National Institute for Public Health and the Environment. URL https://www.rivm.nl/en/news/health-effects-due-to-titanium-nanoparticles-in-food-and-toothpaste-cannot-be-excluded (accessed 4.3.20)

2 Neslen, A., 2019. EU to opt against health warning for suspected carcinogen. The Guardian; Toxic lobbying: the titanium dioxide label debate continues, 2019. Corporate Europe Observatory. URL https://corporateeurope.org/en/2019/06/toxic-lobbying-titanium-dioxide-label-debate-continues (accessed 4.3.20)

3 REACH committee convenes over cancer classification and labelling of titanium dioxide, 2019. ChemSec. URL https://chemsec.org/reach-committee-convenes-over-cancer-classification-and-labelling-of-titanium-dioxide/ (accessed 4.3.20)

4 Baskut Tuncak, 2019. Letter from the Special Rapporteur on the implications for human rights of the environmentally sound management and disposal of hazardous substances and wastes

5   Titanium minerals – brighter long term future despite current woes, 2016. Roskill. URL https://roskill.com/news/titanium-minerals-brighter-long-term-future/ (accessed 4.3.20)

6   The older sulfate route since the 1920s and the newer chloride route since the late 1950s (Chloride TiO_2 better than sulfate?, 2002. European Coatings. URL http://www.european-coatings.com/Editorial-archive/Chloride-TiO2-better-than-sulfate (accessed 4.3.20))

7   Lane, D.A., 1991. Pollution Caused by Waste From the Titanium Dioxide Industry: Directive 89/428. Boston College International and Comparative Law Review 14, 11

8   Mergers: Commission approves Tronox's acquisition of Cristal, subject to conditions, 2018. European Commission. URL http://europa.eu/rapid/press-release_IP-18-4361_en.htm (accessed 4.3.20)

9   Cristal fined £3m for Paul Doyley's chemical blast death, 2016. BBC News

10   Miami Chemical, 2017. China "EPA" Crackdown Shuts Down Tens of Thousands of Factories…with No End in Sight

11   How to kill a fjord, 2017. WeDive. URL http://www.wedive.no/2017/03/04/how-to-kill-a-fjord/ (accessed 4.3.20)

12   Nordic Mining's threat to a fertile fjord, n.d. Earthworks. URL https://earthworks.org/stories/vevring/ (accessed 4.3.20)

13   Milne, R., 2016. Norway: Environmental hero or hypocrite? Financial Times; Nordic Mining's threat to a fertile fjord, n.d. Earthworks. URL https://earthworks.org/stories/vevring/ (accessed 4.3.20)

14   Fjordaksjonen [WWW Document], n.d. URL http://fjordaksjonen.org/ (accessed 4.3.20)

15   Nordic Mining's threat to a fertile fjord, n.d. Earthworks. URL https://earthworks.org/stories/vevring/ (accessed 4.3.20)

16   Visual Culture and Public Health Posters – Environmental Health – Lead Poisoning, 2011. U.S. National Library of Medicine. URL https://www.nlm.nih.gov/exhibition/visualculture/lead.html#01 (accessed 4.3.20)

Chapter 14

1   Kumar, H., Gettleman, J., Yasir, S., 2019. How Do You Save a Million People From a Cyclone? Ask a Poor State in India. The New York Times

2   Griggs, G.B., 2017. Coasts in crisis: a global challenge. University of California Press, Oakland, California

3   A renowned sand miner has been caught on camera boasting about how he managed to persuade the authorities to 'fall in line'

4   Sandhya Ravishankar, 2018. The Lede Exclusive : US, German governments lobby for lifting of ban on illegal beach sand mining. The Lede. https://thelede.co.in/lede-exclusive-us-german-governments-lobby-lifting-ban-illegal-beach-sand-mining/ (accessed 5.4.20)

5   Sandhya Ravishankar, 2017. Thirty Years of Official Collusion Helped Tamil Nadu's Beach Miners Break the Law. The Wire. https://thewire.in/environment/30-years-of-governments-colluding-with-miners-have-de-

stroyed-tamil-nadus-beaches (accessed 5.4.20); Sandhya Ravishankar, 2019. Vast Amounts of Illegally Mined Atomic Mineral Found in Tamil Nadu. The Wire. https://thewire.in/business/illegal-sand-mining-monazite-tamil-nadu (accessed 5.4.20)

6   Sandhya Ravishankar, 2017. The Countdown Begins For Tamil Nadu's Beach Sand Mining Cartel. The Wire. https://thewire.in/environment/countdown-begins-tamil-nadus-beach-sand-mining-cartel (accessed 6.5.20)

7   Ravishankar, S., 2020. Rs 5800 Crore Dues: More Irregularities In Beach Sand Mining [WWW Document]. The Lede. URL https://www.thelede.in/governance/2020/10/15/rs-5800-crore-dues-more-irregularities-in-beach-sand-mining (accessed 14.10.20)

8   NDTV, 2013. Tamil Nadu bureaucrat shunted for crackdown on illegal sand mining. Tamil Nadu, India; Tuticorin District Collector Ashish Kumar transferred, 2013. Deccan Herald

9   Woodward, A., 2019. China could restrict its export of rare-earth metals as a trade-war tactic. Here's what they are and why they're so crucial. Business Insider

10 Heavy Minerals, n.d. Sandatlas. URL http://www.sandatlas.org/heavy-minerals/ (accessed 4.3.20)

11 Callaghan, R.M., Curry, K.C., 2018. 2016 Minerals Yearbook – Garnet, Industrial. U.S. Geological Survey

12 Callaghan & Curry, 2018

13 Zircon [WWW Document], n.d. LKAB Minerals. URL https://www.lkab-minerals.com/en/products/zircon/ (accessed 4.5.20)

14 Desai, P., 2009. FACTBOX-Nuclear industry and zirconium. Reuters

15 Monazite (REE) [WWW Document], n.d. National Museums Scotland. URL https://www.nms.ac.uk/explore-our-collections/resources/from-minerals-to-your-mobile/minerals/monazite/ (accessed 4.5.20)

16 Gwinnett, G., 2019. Medallion Resources set to assess potential locations for a monazite rare-earth processing plant. Proactive. URL https://www.proactiveinvestors.co.uk/companies/news/223596/medallion-resources-set-to-assess-potential-locations-for--a-monazite-rare-earth-processing-plant-223596.html (accessed 4.5.20); LMEWEEK-Rio Tinto throws its weight behind Africa as mining central, 2017. Reuters

17 Tomio Shida, 2019. History offers lessons in escaping China's rare-earth dominance. Nikkei Asian Review

18 ICIS, 2007. Titanium Dioxide (TiO2) Uses and Market Data. https://www.icis.com/explore/resources/news/2007/11/07/9076546/titanium-dioxide-tio2-uses-and-market-data/ (accessed 6.4.20)

19 Desai, 2009

20 Boyer, R.R., 1995. Titanium for aerospace: Rationale and applications. Advanced Performance Materials 2, 349–368 from Bodunrin, M.O., 2019. South Africa is one step closer to processed titanium alloys. Phys.org. URL https://phys.org/news/2019-11-south-africa-closer-titanium-alloys.html (accessed 4.5.20)

21 Thorium, 2017. World Nuclear Association. URL https://www.world-nuclear.org/information-library/current-and-future-generation/thorium.aspx (accessed 4.5.20)

22 Ibid
23 No plans to stop Alappad mining: E P Jayarajan, 2019. The New Indian
    Express
24 John, H., 2018. Villages vanish in this coastal district of Kerala as they succumb
    to sand mining. Mongabay. URL https://india.mongabay.com/2018/10/villag-
    es-vanish-in-this-coastal-district-of-kerala-as-they-succumb-to-sand-mining/
    (accessed 4.5.20)
25 Ramesh, M., 2019. 'Save Alappad, Stop Mining': Angry Residents Plead
    Kerala Govt. The Quint
26 As an aside, it is interesting and saddening to note that in July 2019, without
    following a proper consultation process, the Government of India rushed
    through an RTI Amendment Bill that radically alters the autonomy of the in-
    stitution and could significantly impact transparency and accountability (Sinha,
    R., 2019. Explainer: The Right to Information (Amendment) Bill, 2019. PRS
    Legislative Research. URL https://www.prsindia.org/theprsblog/explain-
    er-right-information-amendment-bill-2019 (accessed 4.5.20); Bhatnagar, G.V.,
    2019. 'RTI Bill Shrouded in Secrecy, How Will it Enhance Transparency?' Ask
    Former CICs. The Wire; India: International Focus [WWW Document], n.d.
    The Constitution Unit UCL. URL https://www.ucl.ac.uk/constitution-unit/re-
    search/research-archive/foi-archive/international-focus/india (accessed 4.5.20))
27 Plan Budget [WWW Document], n.d. National Disaster Management
    Authority, Government of India. URL https://ndma.gov.in/en/about-ndma/
    budget/plan-budget/69-citizens-corner/ (accessed 4.5.20)
28 SandStories.org. www.sandstories.org/blog/2020/5/27/a-conversation-with-
    joanna-thomson-trustee-of-the-goodwin-sands-conservation-trust (accessed
    29.5.20)
29 Gowen, P., 2010. House of Commons Crown Estate Inquiry, input from
    MARINET. Marinet. URL http://www.marinet.org.uk/campaign-article/
    house-of-commons-crown-estate-inquiry-input-from-marinet?page_num-
    ber_0=3 (accessed 4.5.20)
30 Frans Uelman, 2017. IADC Webinar: Dredging Equipment – Its evolution,
    capabilities and importance for maritime infrastructural works
31 World's most powerful Cutter Suction Dredger 'Spartacus' set to join DEME
    fleet [WWW Document], n.d. DEME Group. URL https://www2.deme-
    group.com/ecoterres/news/worlds-most-powerful-cutter-suction-dredger-
    spartacus-set-join-deme-fleet (accessed 4.5.20)
32 Marine Aggregates [WWW Document], n.d. Tarmac. URL http://www.
    tarmac.com/marine/ (accessed 4.5.20)
33 Media Release: Nature's Dangerous Decline 'Unprecedented'; Species Extinc-
    tion Rates 'Accelerating,' n.d. IPBES. URL https://ipbes.net/news/Media-Re-
    lease-Global-Assessment (accessed 4.5.20)
34 The exact number has been questioned by some scientists. For the purpose and
    intent of this book, it is important to focus on the fact that life on Earth is an
    interconnected web and disrupting this web has grave consequences that are
    best avoided. Nonetheless, if you are keen on following the scientific dialogue,
    you can read the response of the authors at Purvis, A., Butchart, S.H.M.,
    Brondízio, E.S., Settele, J., Díaz, S., 2019. No inflation of threatened species.
    Science 365, 767–767. https://doi.org/10.1126/science.aaz0312

300

Chapter 15

1   Can the circular economy transform the world's number one consumer of raw materials? [WWW Document], 2016. World Economic Forum. URL https://www.weforum.org/agenda/2016/05/can-the-circular-economy-transform-the-world-s-number-one-consumer-of-raw-materials/ (accessed 4.5.20)

2   Re-thinking the life cycle of architectural glass – Arup, n.d. https://www.arup.com/en/perspectives/publications/research/section/re-thinking-the-life-cycle-of-architectural-glass (accessed 6.5.20)

3   Ibid

4   Main glass sectors [WWW Document], n.d. Glass Alliance Europe. URL https://www.glassallianceeurope.eu/en/main-glass-sectors (accessed 4.5.20)

5   The circular economy and the promise of glass in concrete, 2016. Ellen MacArthur Foundation

6   FEVE (The European Container Glass Federation), 2019. Container glass recycling in Europe

7   What is Cradle to Cradle Certified™? [WWW Document], n.d. Cradle to Cradle Products Innovation Institure. URL https://www.c2ccertified.org/get-certified/product-certification (accessed 4.5.20)

8   Kamilli, R.J., Kimball, B.E., Carlin Jr., J.F., 2017. Tin (USGS Numbered Series No. 1802- S), Tin, Professional Paper. U.S. Geological Survey, Reston, VA. https://doi.org/10.3133/pp1802S. Note: Currently, at least half of the world's tin comes from Southeast Asia where there are plenty of stories of devastation and destruction due to tin mining. Solder for electronics accounts for the largest global share of tin use. Float glass production represents the sixth-largest global use for refined tin

9   Nascimento, M.L.F., 2014. Brief history of the flat glass patent – Sixty years of the float process. World Patent Information 38, 50–56. https://doi.org/10.1016/j.wpi.2014.04.006

10 Sand becomes "increasingly scarce and expensive", 2017. Dezeen. https://www.dezeen.com/2017/10/11/sand-crisis-scarce-expensive-threatening-glassmaking-construction-atelier-nl-dutch-design-week/ (accessed 8.5.20)

11 Circular Driven Economy Symposium 2018 [WWW Document], n.d. Circular Driven Economy. URL https://www.cdeglobal.com/us/events/circular-driven-economy-symposium-2018 (accessed 4.5.20)

12 Notes taken during Mark Tomlinson's speech at the Circular Driven Economy Symposium 2018

13 Recycled materials: Ready-to-use concrete born again from rubble from Parisian heritage projects [WWW Document], 2018. LafargeHolcim.com. URL https://www.lafargeholcim.com/lafargeholcim-recycling-aggneo (accessed 4.5.20)

14 LafargeHolcim's aggneo® circular economy solutions breathe new life into heritage sites in Paris, 2017. LafargeHolcim.com. https://www.lafargeholcim. com/aggneo-circular-economy-project-paris (accessed 5.14.20)

15 European Environment Agency, 2020. Construction and demolition waste: challenges and opportunities in a circular economy (Briefing). URL https:// www.eea.europa.eu/themes/waste/waste-management/construction-and-dem-olition-waste-challenges (accessed 4.5.20)

16 Stadt Zürich erhält den ersten Preis für nachhaltiges Bauen – Stadt Zürich [WWW Document], 2019. URL https://www.stadt-zuerich.ch/hbd/de/ index/ueber_das_departement/medien/medienmitteilungen/2019/septem-ber/190925a.html (accessed 4.5.20)

17 A low carbon, circular economy approach to concrete procurement – City of Zurich (Switzerland) (No. 88), 2019, GPP in Practice. European Commission

18 Ibid

19 Stadt Zürich, 2019

20 Ibid CEM III is slower to get to full strength than OPC. It is not suitable for building a 30-storey apartment block because it adds to the wait time before each floor is built. It is most suitable for use when a source of slag sand is within easy reach

21 A low carbon, circular economy approach, 2019

22 Ibid

23 Ibid

Chapter 16

1 New Horizon: Demolition with a Mission [WWW Document], n.d. New Horizon. URL https://newhorizon.nl/ (accessed 4.5.20)

2 PWC, 2018. Top bouwondernemingen in Nederland: Een performance-meting

3 The Making of Circl: The Story of a 'Circular' Pavilion in Amsterdam's Zuidas District [WWW Document], n.d. Circl. URL https://circl.nl/themakingof/en/ (accessed 4.5.20)

4 Ibid

5 SBE19 Brussels – BAMB-CIRCPATH 'Buildings as Material Banks – A Pathway For A Circular Future,' 2019. IOP Conference Series: Earth and Environmental Science, Brussels, Belgium. https://doi.org/10.1088/1755-1315/225/1/012006

6 Smeets, A., Wang, K., Drewniok, M.P., 2019. Can Material Passports lower financial barriers for structural steel re-use?, in: SBE19 Brussels – BAMB-CIRCPATH

7 Sonter, L.J., Herrera, D., Barrett, D.J., Galford, G.L., Moran, C.J., Soares-Filho, B.S., 2017. Mining drives extensive deforestation in the Brazilian Amazon. Nature Communications 8. https://doi.org/10.1038/ s41467-017-00557-w; University of Vermont, 2017. New Amazon threat? Deforestation from mining: Surprising amount of rainforest loss occurs on – and off – mining leases. ScienceDaily. URL https://www.sciencedaily.com/ releases/2017/10/171018090212.htm (accessed 4.5.20)

8   Srinivasan, K., Siddharth, C.S.K., Kaarthic, L.V.A., Thenarasu, M., 2018. Evaluation of Mechanical Properties, Economic and Environmental Benefits of Partially Replacing Silica Sand with Biomass Ash for Aluminium Casting. Materials Today: Proceedings, International Conference on Materials Manufacturing and Modelling, ICMMM – 2017, 9 – 11, March 2017 5, 12984–12992. https://doi.org/10.1016/j.matpr.2018.02.283

9   Smeets, A., Wang, K., Drewniok, M.P., 2019. Can Material Passports lower financial barriers for structural steel re-use?, in: SBE19 Brussels – BAMB-CIRCPATH

10   Wang, K., de Regel, S., Debacker, W., Michiels, J., Vanderheyden, J., 2019. Why invest in a reversible building design?, in: SBE19 Brussels – BAMB-CIRC-PATH

11   Ibid

12   Summary of BAMB Final event SBE19 BRUSSELS – BAMB-CIRCPATH [WWW Document], 2019. BAMB. URL https://www.bamb2020.eu/post/summary-bamb-final-event/ (accessed 7.5.20)

13   UK Architects Declare Climate and Biodiversity Emergency [WWW Document], n.d. URL https://www.architectsdeclare.com/ (accessed 4.5.20)

14   Hurst, W., 2019. Introducing RetroFirst: a new AJ campaign championing reuse in the built environment. Architects Journal. URL https://www.architectsjournal.co.uk/news/introducing-retrofirst-a-new-aj-campaign-championing-reuse-in-the-built-environment/10044359.article (accessed 4.5.20)

Chapter 17

1   UNEP 2019. Sand and sustainability: Finding new solutions for environmental governance of global sand resources. GRID-Geneva, United Nations Environment Programme, Geneva, Switzerland

2   Fantina, R., 2016. From Banned Crayons To Concrete, Gaza Struggles To Rebuild After A Decade Of Israeli Blockade. MPN News; Israel's new Gaza restrictions, 2010. Al Jazeera; Gaza Up Close, 2019. Gisha – Legal Center for Freedom of Movement. URL https://features.gisha.org/gaza-up-close/ (accessed 4.5.20); World Leaders: Lift the Gaza Blockade [WWW Document], 2016. Avaaz. URL https://secure.avaaz.org/campaign/en/gaza_blockade_aida/ (accessed 4.5.20); Where's the housing boom?, 2015. Gisha – Legal Center for Freedom of Movement. URL https://features.gisha.org/wheres-the-housing-boom/ (accessed 4.5.20); Hall, R., 2016. Lebanon doesn't want Syrian refugees getting too comfortable, even in winter. PRI

3   BIOHM: The Future of Home [WWW Document], n.d. BIOHM. URL https://www.biohm.co.uk/ (accessed 4.5.20)

4   Mushroom mycelium makes ingenius insulation, 2018. The Secret Story of Stuff: Materials of the Modern Age. BBC Four

5   Initial test results show Thermal Conductivity = 0.024W/m.K and VOC Rating = A+, is the highest possible rating (BIOHM: Join the Revolution [WWW Document], n.d. BIOHM. URL https://www.biohm.co.uk/so/6eM__cFpF?cid=35e15651-aa08-4c11-b685-acf41b1d4c3a#/main (accessed 4.5.20))

6   Manufacturing with fungi [WWW Document], n.d. Onion Collective. URL
     https://www.onioncollective.co.uk/industry-for-watchet (accessed 4.5.20)
7   Triagomy [WWW Document], n.d. BIOHM. URL https://www.biohm.co.uk/
     triagomy (accessed 4.5.20)
8   Ibid
9   Brundtland Commission, 1987. Report of the World Commission on Environ-
     ment and Development: Our Common Future
10   BIOHM: A multi award-winning research and development led company
     that allows nature to lead innovation. Pre-register for exclusive early access to
     our crowd-funding campaign. [WWW Document], n.d. Seedrs. URL https://
     biohm.seedrs.com/ (accessed 4.5.20)
11   Goulding, J.S., Rahimian, F.P. (Eds.), 2019. Offsite Production and Manufac-
     turing for Innovative Construction: People, Process and Technology. Routledge,
     Abingdon, Oxon/New York, NY
12   Walker, P., Thomson, A., Maskell, D., 2016. 6 – Straw bale construction, in:
     Harries, K.A., Sharma, B. (Eds.), Nonconventional and Vernacular Construc-
     tion Materials. Woodhead Publishing, pp. 127–155. https://doi.org/10.1016/
     B978-0-08-100038-0.00006-8
13   Ibid
14   Ibid; Straw cuts energy bills by 90%, 2013. BRE Centre for Innovative
     Construction Materials, University of Bath. URL https://www.bath.ac.uk/
     announcements/straw-cuts-energy-bills-by-90/ (accessed 4.5.20)
15   King, B., 2006. Design of Straw Bale Buildings: The State of the Art. Green
     Building Press, Carmarthenshire, Wales; Morrison, A., n.d. Help Preserve
     the Oldest Straw Bale Structure in Europe. StrawBale. URL https://www.
     strawbale.com/oldest-europe-sb/ (accessed 4.5.20)
16   Donovan, D., Whitnack, S., Khan, S., Donovan, B., n.d. Seismic performance
     of innovative straw bale wall systems – Project summary. Center for Civil
     Engineering Earthquake Research, University of Nevada Reno. URL https://
     www.unr.edu/cceer/projects/straw-house (accessed 4.5.20); Henry, M., 2012.
     The Original Nebraska Straw Bale Buildings. The Sustainable Home. URL
     http://thesustainablehome.net/the-original-nebraska-straw-bale-buildings/
     (accessed 4.5.20); News – BaleHaus withstands Hurricanes [WWW Doc-
     ument], n.d. Modcell Straw Technology. URL https://www.modcell.com/
     news/balehaus-withstands-hurricanes/ (accessed 4.5.20); California Straw
     Building Association, n.d. Fire-Resistive Strawbale Walls Survive North Bay
     Wildfires; Morrison, A., n.d. Fire Resistance of Straw Bale Walls Outperforms
     Conventional Construction. StrawBale. URL https://www.strawbale.com/
     fire-resistance-of-straw-bale-walls-outperforms-conventional-construction/
     (accessed 4.5.20); King, S., 2013. Straw Bale Fire Test Video EBNet. YouTube
17   Kean, S., 2010. From the Bottom Up. Science 327, 638–639. https://doi.
     org/10.1126/science.327.5966.638
18   PAKSBAB: Pakistan Straw Bale and Appropriate Building [WWW Docu-
     ment], n.d. PAKSBAB. URL http://www.paksbab.org/ (accessed 4.5.20)
19   Straw cuts energy bills by 90%, 2013. BRE Centre for Innovative Construction
     Materials, University of Bath. URL https://www.bath.ac.uk/announcements/
     straw-cuts-energy-bills-by-90/ (accessed 4.5.20)

20 First straw eco homes could cut heating bills by 90 per cent, 2015. BRE Centre for Innovative Construction Materials, University of Bath. URL https://www. bath.ac.uk/announcements/first-straw-eco-homes-could-cut-heating-bills-by-90-per-cent/ (accessed 4.5.20)

21 Ibid

22 Ibid

23 Strawtec Brochure, 2018

24 CNBC TV Report: STRAWTEC Building Solutions with 10 million $ investment in Rwanda, 2015

25 Harvey, F., 2019. Ply in the sky: the new materials to take us beyond concrete. The Guardian

26 HAUT: Realising the tallest wooden residential building in the Netherlands [WWW Document], n.d. ARUP. URL https://www.arup.com/projects/haut (accessed 4.5.20)

27 Architects Climate Action Network launches campaign to save structural timber [WWW Document], 2020. Dezeen. URL https://www.dezeen. com/2020/04/23/architects-climate-action-network-launches-cam-paign-to-save-structural-timber/ (accessed 4.5.20)

28 SmartCrusher bv – Concrete recycling – c2c [WWW Document], n.d. URL https://www.slimbreker.nl/smartcrusher.html (accessed 8.5.20). This recognition is awarded by the Ministry of Infrastructure and Water Management in the Netherlands as part of the drive to make the country 100 per cent circular by 2050. The country is doing a fine job of encouraging innovation

29 Bakker, M., Hu, M., Nusselder, S., Maqbool, A.S., Deen, R., Blake, G., Bouwens, J., Fauzi, R.T., 2015. Closed Loop Economy: Case of Concrete in the Netherlands. Universiteit Leiden and Delft University of Technology

30 SmartCrusher bv – News [WWW Document], n.d. Slimbreker. URL https:// www.slimbreker.nl/news.html#morenews (accessed 4.5.20)

31 Bakker et al, 2015

32 Urban mining of concrete: End-of-life recovery altering the future of cement with Smartcrusher, n.d. Shifting Paradigms. URL https://shiftingparadigms.nl/ projects/smartcrusher/ (accessed 4.5.20)

33 Lehne and Preston, 2018. Making Concrete Change: Innovation in Low-carbon Cement and Concrete. Chatham House, London

34 How Cement and Concrete Are Made [WWW Document], n.d. Rediscover Conrete. URL http://rediscoverconcrete.com/en/sustainability/how-cement-concrete-are-made.html (accessed 27.3.20)

35 Urban mining of concrete: End-of-life recovery altering the future of cement with Smartcrusher, n.d. Shifting Paradigms. URL https://shiftingparadigms.nl/ projects/smartcrusher/ (accessed 4.5.20)

36 Padma, T.V., 2018. Mining and dams exacerbated devastating Kerala floods. Nature 561, 13–14. https://doi.org/10.1038/d41586-018-06145-2; Sand Wars, 2017. Al Jazeera; Fisk, R., 2018. Lebanon's mountains are being wiped from the map – but does anyone care? The Independent; Lebanon activists in uphill battle against illegal quarries, 2019. Arab News; Galupo, R., 2018. 30 held for illegal quarry in Pampanga. The Philippine Star; Haiti – Environment : Towards the total closure of illegal quarries, 2018. Haiti Libre; Illegal quarrying rampant in Nha Trang, 2017. VietNamNet

37 Kaya, T., Hashimoto, M., Pettingell, H., 2009. The Development of Sand Manufacture from Crushed Rock in Japan, Using Advanced VSI Technology; Marinet, 2015. Marine Aggregate Extraction – The Need to Dredge: Fact or Fiction?

38 Natural sand prohibition of export measures is implemented immediately to prevent illegal exports [WWW Document], 2006. General Administration of Customs | Government of China. URL http://www.customs.gov.cn/tab-id/4370/ctl/infodetail/infoid/22975/mid/3758/default.aspx?containersrc=%5B-g%5Dcontainers%2F_default%2Fno+container (accessed 4.5.20)

39 Mainland to Resume Exporting Natural Sand to Hong Kong, Macao – china. org.cn, 2007. Xinhua News Agency; Mainland hopes to resume sand trade with Taiwan, 2007. China Daily

40 Kaya, T., Hashimoto, M., Pettingell, H., 2009. The Development of Sand Manufacture from Crushed Rock in Japan, Using Advanced VSI Technology

41 Pettingell, H., n.d. Sand Supply in South Wales... A New Factor?

42 Marinet, 2015. Marine Aggregate Extraction – The Need to Dredge: Fact or Fiction?

43 Lusty, A., 2008. Sand Industry Leads Revival of Japanese Aggregates. Quarry

44 Pilegis, M., Gardner, D., Lark, R., 2016. An investigation into the use of manufactured sand as a 100% replacement for fine aggregate in concrete. Materials 9. https://doi.org/10.3390/ma9060440

45 Gardner, D., Lark, R., Pilegis, M., 2013. Sand from Surplus Quarry Material (No. QRF_b-SC9086-CF). Cardiff University

46 Pilegis, M., Gardner, D., Lark, R., 2012. Manufactured Sand For a Low Carbon Era. Presented at the 8th International Conference: Concrete in the Low Carbon Era, Dundee, UK

47 Gardner et al, 2013; Marinet, 2015

48 Marinet, 2015

49 UNEP/UNECE, 2016. GEO-6 Assessment for the Pan-European Region (rev. 1). United Nations Environment Programme, Nairobi, Kenya, p.219

50 O.C.O Technology [WWW Document], n.d. O.C.O Technology. URL https://oco.co.uk/technology/ (accessed 4.5.20)

51 Greig, S., 2019. Leaving a lighter aggregate footprint. Aggregates Business Europe 13, 12–15, p.13

52 Lakeside Energy from Waste and O.C.O Technology Sign 10-Year Deal [WWW Document], 2020. O.C.O Technology. URL https://oco.co.uk/lakeside-energy-from-waste-and-o-c-o-technology-sign-10-year-deal/ (accessed 4.5.20)

53 Greig, 2019

54 UNEP/UNECE, 2016. GEO-6 Assessment for the Pan-European Region (rev. 1). United Nations Environment Programme, Nairobi, Kenya, p.219.

Chapter 18

1   Park in the Past is an exciting and innovative heritage and conservation project that aims to create a totally unique heritage attraction and vital community resource [WWW Document], n.d. Park in the Past. URL http://www.parkinthepast.org.uk/ (accessed 4.5.20)

2   Restore Quarries, 2015. Action 1a Report: Mineral Planning and Restoration Approaches in NW Europe, Mineral Site Restoration: Policy into Practice, p. 26 Section D

3   Welcome to HeidelbergCement Group [WWW Document], n.d. Heidelberg-Cement Group. URL https://www.heidelbergcement.com/en (accessed 4.5.20)

4   Enhance biodiversity with your idea – Nature will be the biggest winner! [WWW Document], n.d. The Quarry Life Award. URL https://www.quarrylifeaward.com/ (accessed 4.5.20)

5   The Sand Motor: Introduction [WWW Document], n.d. Zandmotor. URL https://www.dezandmotor.nl/en/the-sand-motor/introduction/ (accessed 4.5.20)

6   Results After Five Years [WWW Document], n.d. Zandmotor. URL https://www.dezandmotor.nl/en/research/results-after-five-years/ (accessed 4.5.20)

7   Hansford, M., 2017. Dutch sand engine comes to Norfolk. New Civil Engineer

8   Ibid

9   Ibid

10 Ibid

11 Driven to Extraction: Can Sand Mining be Sustainable? by Oli Brown and Pascal Peduzzi [WWW Document], 2019. Hoffmann Centre for Sustainable Resource Economy. URL https://hoffmanncentre.chathamhouse.org/article/driven-to-extraction-can-sand-mining-be-sustainable/ (accessed 4.5.20)

12 Parkinson, R.W., Ogurcak, D.E., 2018. Beach nourishment is not a sustainable strategy to mitigate climate change. Estuarine, Coastal and Shelf Science 212, 203–209. https://doi.org/10.1016/j.ecss.2018.07.011

13 Hino, M., Field, C.B., Mach, K.J., 2017. Managed retreat as a response to natural hazard risk. Nature Climate Change 7, 364–370. https://doi.org/10.1038/nclimate3252

14 Crowdfunding: Dam Removal in Europe [WWW Document], n.d. WWF. URL https://crowdfunding.wnf.nl/ (accessed 4.5.20)

15 American Rivers, 2019. 99 Dams Removed to Restore Rivers in 2018

16 Howard, B.C., 2016. River Revives After Largest Dam Removal in U.S. History. National Geographic News

17 Moving Mountains: Elwha River Still Changing Five Years After World's Largest Dam-Removal Project: More than 20 million tons of sediment flushed to the sea, 2018. U.S. Geological Survey. URL https://www.usgs.gov/news/moving-mountains-elwha-river-still-changing-five-years-after-world-s-largest-dam-removal (accessed 4.5.20)

18 Howard, B.C., 2016. River Revives After Largest Dam Removal in U.S. History. National Geographic News

Chapter 19

1   Perlin, J., 1999. From Space to Earth: The Story of Solar Electricity, 1st edition. Routledge, Ann Arbor, MI

2   Xakalashe, B.S., Tangstad, M., 2011. Silicon processing: from quartz to crystalline silicon solar cells, in: Southern African Pyrometallurgy 2011. Presented at the Southern African Institute of Mining and Metallurgy, Johannesburg

3   Marchal, J., McDonnell, P., Sun, K., J. Krug, D., Laine, R., 2015. A Low Cost, Low Energy Route to Solar Grade Silicon from Rice Hull Ash (RHA), a Sustainable Source. Green Chem. 17. https://doi.org/10.1039/C5GC00622H

4   Bose, D.N., Haldar, A.R., Chaudhuri, T.K., 2015. Preparation of polysilicon from rice-husk. Current Science 108, 1214–1216. Prof. Dwarka Bose reports: 'In 1982, the Swiss Government was interested in sizeable funding of our project as it would generate rural employment, but this fell through due to internal politics. The question we always faced from Indian funding agencies was 'Has this been done elsewhere?'' Nothing came of it and despite India's ambitious plans for solar, it does not produce polysilicon within the country (Bose, D., 2014. Further to 'Polysilicon production in India.' Current Science 107, 734). Also read Murthy, H.S.G.K., 2014. Silicon technology in India: a tribute to A. R. Vasudeva Murthy. Current Science 107, 129–135 and Bose, D.N., 2014. Polysilicon production in India. Current Science 107, 20–21

5   PGurus, T., 2016. India needs to invest in Polysilicon manufacturing to meet its energy objectives. PGurus. URL https://www.pgurus.com/india-needs-to-invest-in-polysilicon-manufacturing-to-meet-its-energy-objectives/ (accessed 4.5.20)

6   US Patent Application for Biogenic Silica as a Raw Material to Create High Purity Silicon [WWW Document], 2014. JUSTIA Patents. URL https://patents.justia.com/patent/20150110701 (accessed 4.5.20)

7   Epstein, E., 1994. The anomaly of silicon in plant biology. Proc Natl Acad Sci USA 91, 11–17. https://doi.org/10.1073/pnas.91.1.11

8   Based on an interview with Prof. Laine; Mayaterials Home [WWW Document], n.d. Mayaterials, Inc. URL http://www.mayaterials.com/Home (accessed 4.5.20

9   Global $11.43 BN Specialty Silica Market to 2025 – Rising Demand from Rubber, Food, Healthcare, and Coatings Industries, 2019. GlobeNewswire News Room

10 Phillips, S., 2019. Silica-Enhanced Rubber Compounds and You. LiveAbout. URL https://www.liveabout.com/silica-enhanced-rubber-compounds-3234486 (accessed 4.5.20)

11 Goodyear Reaches Supply Agreements for Rice Husk Ash Silica [WWW Document], 2015. Goodyear Corporate. URL https://corporate.goodyear.com/en-US/media/news/goodyear-reaches-supply-agreements.html (accessed 4.5.20)

12 Global $11.43 BN Specialty Silica Market to 2025

13 Schoelynck, J., Subalusky, A.L., Struyf, E., Dutton, C.L., Unzué-Belmonte, D., Vijver, B.V. de, Post, D.M., Rosi, E.J., Meire, P., Frings, P., 2019. Hippos (Hippopotamus amphibius): The animal silicon pump. Science Advances 5, eaav0395. https://doi.org/10.1126/sciadv.aav0395 from Dasgupta, S., 2019.

Hippos poop a lot of silica, and that's critical for Africa's rivers and lakes. Mongabay. URL https://news.mongabay.com/2019/05/hippos-poop-a-lot-of-silica-and-thats-critical-for-africas-rivers-and-lakes/ (accessed 4.5.20)

14 Ibid

15 McWhan, D., 2012. Sand and Silicon: Science that Changed the World. Oxford University Press, Oxford., p.44; Perry, C.C., 2003. Silicification: The Processes by Which Organisms Capture and Mineralize Silica. Reviews in Mineralogy and Geochemistry 54, 291–327. https://doi.org/10.2113/0540291 (The research on industry v. nature was published in 2003 and lot has changed since then, so it warrants deeper research.); To understand what a gigaton is see Mooney, C., 2015. To truly grasp what we're doing to the planet, you need to understand this gigantic measurement. The Washington Post

16 DeMaster, D.J., 2001. Marine Silica Cycle. Encyclopedia of Ocean Sciences

17 McWhan, D., 2012

18 Armbrust, E.V., 2009. The life of diatoms in the world's oceans. Nature 459, 185–192. https://doi.org/10.1038/nature08057

19 What are Diatoms? - Diatoms of North America [WWW Document], n.d. URL https://diatoms.org/what-are-diatoms (accessed 4.5.20)

20 Armbrust, E.V., 2009

21 DeMaster, D.J., 2001

22 Kudela, R.M., 2008. Silicon: Nitrogen Interactions in the Marine Environment, in: Nitrogen in the Marine Environment. Academic Press, Cambridge, MA, pp. 1589–1626

23 Tréguer, P., Nelson, D.M., Van Bennekom, A.J., DeMaster, D.J., Leynaert, A., Quéguiner, B., 1995. The Silica Balance in the World Ocean: A Reestimate. Science 268, 375–379. https://doi.org/10.1126/science.268.5209.375

24 McWhan, D., 2012. p.46

25 Tréguer, P., Pondaven, P., 2000. Silica control of carbon dioxide. Nature 406, 358–359

26 DeMaster, D.J., 2001.; Kudela, R.M., 2008.; Tréguer, P., Bowler, C., Moriceau, B., Dutkiewicz, S., Gehlen, M., Aumont, O., Bittner, L., Dugdale, R., Finkel, Z., Iudicone, D., Jahn, O., Guidi, L., Lasbleiz, M., Leblanc, K., Levy, M., Pondaven, P., 2018. Influence of diatom diversity on the ocean biological carbon pump. Nature Geoscience 11, 27–37. https://doi.org/10.1038/s41561-017-0028-x

27 Kudela, R.M., 2008; Armbrust, E.V., 2009

28 Armbrust, E.V., 2009

29 Liu, D., Yuan, P., Tian, Q., Liu, H., Deng, L., Song, Y., Zhou, Junming, Losic, D., Zhou, Jieyu, Song, H., Guo, H., Fan, W., 2019. Lake sedimentary biogenic silica from diatoms constitutes a significant global sink for aluminium. Nature Communications 10, 4829. https://doi.org/10.1038/s41467-019-12828-9

30 Dasgupta, S., 2019. Hippos poop a lot of silica, and that's critical for Africa's rivers and lakes. Mongabay. URL https://news.mongabay.com/2019/05/hippos-poop-a-lot-of-silica-and-thats-critical-for-africas-rivers-and-lakes/ (accessed 4.5.20)

31 Tréguer, P., Pondaven, P., 2000.; Tréguer et al., 2018

32 Harrison, K.G., 2000. Role of increased marine silica input on paleo-pCO2 levels. Paleoceanography and Paleoclimatology 15, 292–298. https://doi.org/10.1029/1999PA000427

33 Kudela, R.M., 2008

34 Armbrust, E.V., 2009

35 Ibid

36 McWhan, D., 2012

37 Taylor Maavara, Hans H. Dürr, Philippe Van Cappellen, 2014. Worldwide retention of nutrient silicon by river damming: From sparse data set to global estimate. Global Biogeochemical Cycles 28, 842– 855. https://doi.org/10.1002/2014GB004875; Qiuwen Chen, Wenqing Shi, Jef Huisman, Stephen C Maberly, Jianyun Zhang, Juhua Yu, Yuchen Chen, Daniele Tonina, Qitao Yi, 2020. Hydropower reservoirs on the upper Mekong River modify nutrient bioavailability downstream. National Science Review. Oxford Academic. https://doi.org/10.1093/nsr/nwaa026; De La Rocha, C., Conley, D.J., 2017. Silica Stories. Springer International Publishing. https://doi.org/10.1007/978-3-319-54054-2

38 De La Rocha and Conley, 2017

39 Tréguer, P., Pondaven, P., 2000

40 Kudela, R.M., 2008.; Chen, C., Zhu, J., Beardsley, R.C., Franks, P.J.S., 2003. Physical-biological sources for dense algal blooms near the Changjiang River. Geophysical Research Letters 30. https://doi.org/10.1029/2002GL016391; Humborg, C., Ittekkot, V., Cociasu, A., Bodungen, B. v, 1997. Effect of Danube River dam on Black Sea biogeochemistry and ecosystem structure. Nature 386, 385–388. https://doi.org/10.1038/386385a0

41 Tréguer, P., Pondaven, P., 2000

42 Tréguer et al., 1995

Chapter 20

1 Lanfear, S., 2019. High Seas. Our Planet

2 The MSFD is the first EU legislative instrument related to the protection of marine biodiversity, as it contains the explicit regulatory objective that 'biodiversity is maintained by 2020', as the cornerstone for achieving good environmental status GES (Legislation: the Marine Strategy Framework Directive [WWW Document], n.d. European Commission. URL http://ec.europa.eu/environment/marine/eu-coast-and-marine-policy/marine-strategy-framework-directive/index_en.htm (accessed 4.5.18)). But it is worth noting that laws are only as good as their enforcement. Experts from Marinet say that whilst the MSFD asserts a legal requirement for EU seas to attain 'good environmental status' by 2020 against a range of parameters (descriptors), the reality is that many of the criteria for GES under these descriptors have been diluted or ignored (e.g. one of the criterion for GES which requires every fish and shellfish stock to 'display an age and size profile consistent with a healthy stock'). In other words, every stock should contain adults which are able to live their entire life span. The larger and older a fish is, the more fecund

it is in reproductive terms for the stock as a whole; so, older fish in a stock are vital if an over-fished stock is to regenerate. Although the MSFD has this 'age profile' requirement as one of its GES criteria, in practice, it is largely ignored. Hence EU fish stocks remain in a highly degraded condition, as does the wider ecological structure of the sea in which fish are a key component

3   Marinet also thinks it is important to study the impacts of dredging on smaller organisms that are the building blocks at the base of the whole food chain and ecological structure of the system, that is, the meiofauna (organisms below 1 mm in diameter) and microfauna (organisms below 0.1 mm in diameter)

4   Personal communication with Dr. Keith Cooper. Oct 2019

5   Grab surveys refer to a process where sediments are collected from the seabed at the specified location in order to measure particle size and the kind of animal species that live in them

6   Personal communication with Dr. Keith Cooper. Oct 2019

7   Guerra, F., Grilo, C., Pedroso, N.M., Cabral, H., 2015. Environmental Impact Assessment in the marine environment: A comparison of legal frameworks. Environmental Impact Assessment Review 55, 182–194. https://doi.org/10.1016/j.eiar.2015.08.003; Kaikkonen, L., Venesjärvi, R., Nygård, H., Kuikka, S., 2018. Assessing the impacts of seabed mineral extraction in the deep sea and coastal marine environments: Current methods and recommendations for environmental risk assessment. Marine Pollution Bulletin 135, 1183–1197. https://doi.org/10.1016/j.marpolbul.2018.08.055

8   Ma, D., Fang, Q., Guan, S., 2016. Current legal regime for environmental impact assessment in areas beyond national jurisdiction and its future approaches. Environmental Impact Assessment Review 56, 23–30. https://doi.org/10.1016/j.eiar.2015.08.009. ; Kaikkonen, L., Venesjärvi, R., Nygård, H., Kuikka, S., 2018. Assessing the impacts of seabed mineral extraction in the deep sea and coastal marine environments: Current methods and recommendations for environmental risk assessment. Marine Pollution Bulletin 135, 1183–1197. https://doi.org/10.1016/j.marpolbul.2018.08.05

9   David Levy, 2019. David Levy – We're Listening – A new perspective emerging in marine dredging – Jun 19. URL http://www.marinet.org.uk/david-levy-blog/david-levy-were-listening-a-new-perspective-emerging-in-marine-dredging-jun-19 (accessed 4.3.20)

10 Wright, D., 2014. Conserving the Great Blue. Marinet in association with The ACT! Alliance and The Ecologist

11 The Crown Estate, British Marine Aggregate Producers Association (BMAPA), 2017. Good Practice Guidance – Extraction by Dredging of Aggregates from England's Seabed

12 Marinet, 2014. Tyndal research paper into Offshore Aggregate induced Erosion. Marinet – Marine Conservation For The UK. www.marinet.org.uk/campaign-article/tyndal-research-paper-into-offshore-aggregate-induced-erosion (accessed 6.5.20)

13 Ibid

14 The aggregates levy has been subject to various litigation. Over the years, the use of recycled and secondary aggregate in the UK increased as a proportion of overall aggregate consumption, to reach 30%, while the rest of Europe was

at 10%. However, this growth did plateau. The UK government announced a comprehensive review in 2020

15 The Crown Estate, n.d. The Marine Aggregates Levy Sustainability Fund (MALSF) www.marinedataexchange.co.uk/aggregates-data.aspx (accessed 6.5.20)

16 The Crown Estate, 2019. Marine Data Exchange Report January – June 2019 https://thecrownestate.maps.arcgis.com/apps/MapSeries/index.html?appid=-4c14a168b8564612be8696fc6fc531fa (accessed 6.5.20)

17 The Crown Estate, n.d. Marine aggregate extraction www.marineaggregates. info/index.php/marine-aggregates/marine-aggregate-extraction (accessed 6.5.20)

18 The Crown Estate, n.d. Sustainable aggregates. Marine Aggregates Information Centre. www.marineaggregates.info/index.php/sustainability/sustainable-aggregates (accessed 6.5.20)

Chapter 21

1 Since 1 January 2019, the Government of India does have an official mandate for GPS on all new public/passenger vehicles and also commercial vehicles with national permits

2 Comptroller and Auditor General of India, 2018. Report No.7 of 2017 – Economic Sector Government of Tamil Nadu

Chapter 22

1 Mangroves4theFuture, 2011. The Lucky Ladies of the Maha Oya. YouTube

2 This particular project was a short-term one. It would be great to see longer projects receive funding and support

3 Sand mining's concrete threat to rivers: impacts and potential solutions, n.d. https://www.worldwaterweek.org/event/8001-sand-minings-concrete-threat-to-rivers-impacts-and-potential-solutions (accessed 6.5.20)

4 Bohnet, I., 2016. What Works: Gender Equality by Design. Harvard University Press, Harvard, MA., p.10

5 D'Espallier, B., Guérin, I., Mersland, R., 2011. Women and Repayment in Microfinance. World Development 39, 758–772. https://doi.org/10.1016/j. worlddev.2010.10.008

6 Srinivasan, B., 2001. Social Impacts of Large Dams: Gender, Equity and Distribution Issues. Economic and Political Weekly 36, 4108–4114

7 World Commission on Dams, 2000. Dams and Development: A New Framework for Decision-Making; Aguirre, M., 2011. Commentary: Dams are a Women's Issue. International Rivers. URL https://www.internationalrivers. org/resources/commentary-dams-are-a-women's-issue-1677 (accessed 4.5.20);

Clayton, T., 2013. Greater Mekong River Basin: Women and Dams. WLE Mekong. URL https://wle-mekong.cgiar.org/women-and-dams/ (accessed 4.5.20); Skinner, J., 2016. Women pay heavier price for big dams. International Institute for Environment and Development. URL https://www.iied.org/women-pay-heavier-price-for-big-dams (accessed 4.5.20)

8   Mahampy, n.d. MalagasyWord.org

9   Seagle, C., 2013. Inverting the impacts: Mining, conservation and sustainability claims near the Rio Tinto/QMM ilmenite mine in Southeast Madagascar, in: Green Grabbing: A New Appropriation of Nature. Routledge, Abingdon, Oxon/New York, NY, pp. 211–242., p.227

10 Ibid

11 Ibid

12 Gerety, R.M., 2019. The Ecologists and the Mine. Scientific American; Fairhead, J., Leach, M., Scoones, I. (Eds.), 2013. Green Grabbing: A New Appropriation of Nature. Routledge, Abingdon, Oxon/New York, NY., pp.v, viii, 241, and 211

13 Seagle, 2013

14 Ibid

15 Ibid

16 Ibid

17 Hinton, J., Beinhoff, C., Veiga, M., 2003. Women and Artisanal Mining: Gender Roles and the Road Ahead, in: Hilson, G. (Ed.), The Socio-Economic Impacts of Artisanal and Small-Scale Mining in Developing Countries. Taylor & Francis, pp. 161–203. https://doi.org/10.1201/9780203971284.ch11; Eftimie, A., Heller, K., Strongman, J., Hinton, J., Lahiri-Dutt, K., Mutemeri, N., 2012. Gender Dimensions of Artisanal and Small-Scale Mining: A Rapid Assessment Toolkit. The World Bank

18 Ibid

19 Hinton, J.J., 2011. Gender Differentiated Impacts and Benefits of Artisanal Mining: Engendering Pathways out of Poverty A Case Study in Katwe Kabatooro Town Council, Uganda. The University of British Columbia, Vancouver

20 Eftimie, A., Heller, K., Strongman, J., Hinton, J., Lahiri-Dutt, K., Mutemeri, N., 2012. Gender Dimensions of Artisanal and Small-Scale Mining: A Rapid Assessment Toolkit. The World Bank; Hinton, J.J., 2011. Gender Differentiated Impacts and Benefits of Artisanal Mining: Engendering Pathways out of Poverty A Case Study in Katwe Kabatooro Town Council, Uganda. The University of British Columbia, Vancouver

21 Hinton, J., 2016. The Gender Dimensions of Tin, Tantalum and Tungsten Mining in the Great Lakes Region (No. 25797 – 26). Gender Resource Facility

22 Eftimie, A., Heller, K., Strongman, J., Hinton, J., Lahiri-Dutt, K., Mutemeri, N., 2012. Gender Dimensions of Artisanal and Small-Scale Mining: A Rapid Assessment Toolkit. The World Bank

23 The World's Women 2015 [WWW Document], 2015. United Nations. URL https://unstats.un.org/unsd/gender/chapter8/chapter8.html (accessed 4.5.20)

24 de Sam Lazaro, F., 2019. In Cambodia, sand mining is big business — but it comes at a price. PBS News Hour

25 McLanahan, S.S., Carlson, M.J., 2001. Poverty and Gender in Affluent Nations. International Encyclopedia of the Social & Behavioral Sciences

26 Oxfam, 2017. An Economy That Works for Women: Achieving women's economic empowerment in an increasingly unequal world; UN Women, 2015. Progress of the World's Women 2015-2016: Transforming economies, realizing rights. UN Women, New York, NY

27 Staszewska, K., 2015. Close the gap! The cost of inequality in women's work. ActionAid

28 Fairs, M., 2017. Survey of top architecture firms reveals 'quite shocking' lack of gender diversity at senior levels. De Zeen

29 Murray, C., 2019. By highlighting the problems faced by women in architecture, are we making it worse? De Zeen

30 World Economic Forum, 2018. Global Gender Gap Report 2018. World Economic Forum, Cologny/Geneva, Switzerland

31 Ibid

32 Sustainable Development Goal 5: Achieve gender equality and empower all women and girls [WWW Document], n.d. United Nations. URL https:// sustainabledevelopment.un.org/sdg5 (accessed 7.4.20)

Chapter 23

1 Save River Cauvery | Facebook [WWW Document], n.d. URL https://www. facebook.com/SaveRiverCauvery (accessed 5.4.20)

2 मातृसदन (Matri Sadan) [WWW Document], n.d. मातृसदन (Matri Sadan). URL http://matrisadan.org/ (accessed 5.4.20)

3 Indian activist, 86, dies while fasting for cleaner Ganges, 2018. Reuters

4 Koshy, J., 2019. Swami Atmabodhanand breaks 194-day fast for Ganga after govt. promise. The Hindu

5 Lisa Sabina Harney, 2016. Satyagraha Truth Force Int 2015. English subtitles. YouTube

6 Kerala villagers form human chain to mark 1 year of protests against beach sand mining, 2019. The News Minute

Chapter 24

1 PWYP United Kingdom Coalition [WWW Document], n.d. PWYP. URL https://www.pwyp.org/pwyp_members/united-kingdom/ (accessed 7.4.20)

2 CEM Project Taratra, 2019. Letter from civil society to Malagasy Government Ministers – Concern about the future of the extractive industries in Madagascar

3 Ibid

4 Ambrose, J., Henley, J., 2019. European Investment Bank to phase out fossil fuel financing. The Guardian

5 Egan, M., 2019. Secretive energy startup backed by Bill Gates achieves solar breakthrough. CNN Business

6   Lynch, P., 2012. Bright Is The New Black: New York Roofs Go Cool. NASA. URL https://www.nasa.gov/topics/earth/features/ny-roofs.html (accessed 8.4.20)

7   68% of the world population projected to live in urban areas by 2050, says UN, 2018. UN Department of Economic and Social Affairs. URL https://www.un.org/development/desa/en/news/population/2018-revision-of-world-urbanization-prospects.html (accessed 8.4.20); Akbari, H., Menon, S., Rosenfeld, A., 2009. Global cooling: increasing world-wide urban albedos to offset CO2. Climatic Change 94, 275–286. https://doi.org/10.1007/s10584-008-9515-9; National Research Council, 2015. Climate Intervention: Reflecting Sunlight to Cool Earth. The National Academies Press, Washington, DC

8   Kotecki, P., 2018. New York City has painted over 9.2 million square feet of rooftops white — and it could be a brilliant heat-fighting plan. Business Insider

9   Knight, M., 2010. Can painting mountains restore a glacier? CNN; Collyns, D., 2010. Can painting a mountain restore a glacier? BBC News; Lewis, D., 2017. Cool roofs: beating the midday sun with a slap of white paint. The Guardian; Kotecki, P., 2018. New York City has painted over 9.2 million square feet of rooftops white — and it could be a brilliant heat-fighting plan. Business Insider; Macintyre, H.L., Heaviside, C., 2019. Potential benefits of cool roofs in reducing heat-related mortality during heatwaves in a European city. Environment International 127, 430–441. https://doi.org/10.1016/j.envint.2019.02.065

10 In the City, Bright is the New Black, 2010. NASA Earth Observatory. URL https://earthobservatory.nasa.gov/images/77717/in-the-city-bright-is-the-new-black (accessed 8.4.20)

11 Pearce, F., 2018. Urban Heat: Can White Roofs Help Cool World's Warming Cities? Yale Environment 360; Schiller, B., 2011. Painting Your Roof White Doesn't Work. Fast Company

12 Armstrong, S., 2009. Are you allowed to paint your roof white? The Telegraph

13 Gaffin, S.R., Imhoff, M., Rosenzweig, C., Khanbilvardi, R., Pasqualini, A., Kong, A.Y.Y., Grillo, D., Freed, A., Hillel, D., Hartung, E., 2012. Bright is the new black—multi-year performance of high-albedo roofs in an urban climate. Environmental Research Letters 7; US Patent for Thermoplastic polyolefin membrane with enhanced thermal resistance Patent [WWW Document], 2011. JUSTIA Patents. URL https://patents.justia.com/patent/9920515 (accessed 8.4.20); APOC 247 White Elastomeric Roof Coating Safety Data Sheet, 2014; Carlisle Sure-Flex™ Reinforced Pvc Membrane Technical Data Bulletin, n.d.

14 Grand View Research, 2019. Titanium Dioxide Market Size & Share | TiO2 Industry Report 2019-2025

15 Schonbrun, Z., 2018. The Quest for the Next Billion-Dollar Color. Bloomberg Businessweek

16 Gerety, R.M., 2009. Mining and biodiversity offsets in Madagascar: Conservation or 'Conservation Opportunities?' Mongabay Environmental News. URL https://news.mongabay.com/2009/08/mining-and-biodiversity-offsets-in-madagascar-conservation-or-conservation-opportunities/ (accessed 4.5.20)

17 EU Parliament rejects titanium dioxide objection | Food Packaging Forum www.foodpackagingforum.org/news/eu-parliament-rejects-titanium-dioxide-objection (accessed 7.3.20)

18 Vincentz Network GmbH & Co. KG, 2020. EU publishes official regulation on titanium dioxide. European Coatings. www.european-coatings.com/Markets-companies/Raw-materials-market/EU-publishes-official-regulation-on-titanium-dioxide (accessed 6.4.20)

19 Official Journal of the European Union, 2020. https://eur-lex.europa.eu/legal-content/EN/TXT/PDF/?uri=CELEX:32020R0217&from=EN (accessed 6.4.20)

20 William Reed Business Media Ltd 2020, 2020. European Commission publishes titanium dioxide classification. www.cosmeticsdesign-europe.com/Article/2020/02/19/European-Commission-publishes-titanium-dioxide-classification (accessed 6.4.20)

21 European Commission, 1998. Commission decides to take Germany to European Court of Justice on titanium dioxide https://ec.europa.eu/commission/presscorner/detail/en/IP_98_606 (accessed 6.4.20)

22 Legal action against the classification of titanium dioxide, 2020. TDMA. https://tdma.info/news/legal-action-against-the-classification-of-titanium-dioxide/ (accessed 4.6.20)

23 Minnesota Supreme Court upholds Winona County ban on frac sand mining, 2020. Star Tribune. www.startribune.com/minnesota-supreme-court-upholds-winona-county-ban-on-frac-sand-mining/568701922/ (accessed 6.5.20)

24 Minnesota Sands asks U.S. Supreme Court to review Winona County's silica sand mining ban, 2020. Duluth News Tribune

25 UNE. Many sand mining companies supply a variety of industries. Yet, our legislation, monitoring and education remains fragmented on this topic

26 Bendixen, M., Best, J., Hackney, C., Iversen, L.L., 2019. Time is running out for sand. Nature 571, 29–31. https://doi.org/10.1038/d41586-019-02042-4

27 Torres, A., Liu, J. "Jack," Brandt, J., Lear, K., 2017. The world is facing a global sand crisis. The Conversation. http://theconversation.com/the-world-is-facing-a-global-sand-crisis-83557 (accessed 6.5.20)

28 Limestone habitats | Fauna & Flora International, n.d. www.fauna-flora.org/environments/limestone-habitats (accessed 6.5.20)

29 Légal, J.-B., Chekroun, P., Coiffard, V., Gabarrot, F., 2017. Beware of the gorilla: Effect of goal priming on inattentional blindness. Consciousness and Cognition 55, 165–171. https://doi.org/10.1016/j.concog.2017.08.004

30 Liao, C.-W., Chiang, T.-L., 2016. Reducing occupational injuries attributed to inattentional blindness in the construction industry. Safety Science 89, 129–137. https://doi.org/10.1016/j.ssci.2016.06.010; Hyman Jr, I.E., 2016. Unaware Observers: The Impact of Inattentional Blindness on Walkers, Drivers, and Eyewitnesses. Journal of Applied Research in Memory and Cognition 5, 264–269. https://doi.org/10.1016/j.jarmac.2016.06.011; Jones, A., Johnstone, M.-J., 2017. Inattentional blindness and failures to rescue the deteriorating patient in critical care, emergency and perioperative settings: Four case scenarios. Australian Critical Care 30, 219–223. https://doi.org/10.1016/j.aucc.2016.09.005; Bohnet, I., 2016. What Works: Gender Equality by Design. Harvard University Press, Harvard, MA

31 The Book: From What Is To What If [WWW Document], n.d. Rob Hopkins. URL https://www.robhopkins.net/the-book/ (accessed 8.4.20)

Index

Thank you for reading *Sand Stories: Surprising truths about the global sand crisis and the quest for sustainable solutions*

You can download a discussion guide to spark lively conversations based on *Sand Stories* with friends, colleagues, family or even complete strangers at **www.sandstories.org**

You can also download the list of references by chapter, and those used for the illustrations.

I look forward to welcoming you to the SandStories community of change makers.

Reviews are fundamental to a book's success. You can help this book reach a wider audience by leaving a review on any online platform that you frequent. Thank you ever so much.

Printed in Great Britain
by Amazon

80436071R00202